TERMINAL VELOCITY

This book is dedicated to
the memory of my mother and father

TERMINAL VELOCITY

STEVE DEVEREUX

His own brutal account of action in the Falklands, Northern Ireland and beyond

SMITH GRYPHON
PUBLISHERS

First published in paperback in Great Britain in 1997 by
SMITH GRYPHON LIMITED
12 Bridge Wharf, 156 Caledonian Road
London N1 9UU

First published in hardback in Great Britain by
Smith Gryphon in 1997

A CIP catalogue record for this book is available from the
British Library

ISBN 1 85685 149 4

Designed by Hammond Hammond

Printed and bound in Great Britain by
Caledonia International

CONTENTS

ACKNOWLEDGEMENTS

Special thanks to my brother Clive for all his encouragement and persistence over the years, without whom this book would not have been written; to Steve 'the Marine' Welsh, for his abusive and invigorating attitude; and to Tony Mac from the Guards who enlightened me to the fact that there is a life outside the Paras and the SAS.

I'd also like to thank the team at Smith Gryphon: Robert Smith – especially for his initial faith and continuing enthusiasm; Helen Armitage; Roger Hammond and Roderick Brown.

TERMINAL VELOCITY: (1) The speed of a bullet on impact with a target; (2) The greatest speed attained while freefall parachuting.

Glossary

AA Anti-Aircraft

alley a Parachute Regiment term for a soldier who is smart-looking and warlike in appearance

AOD Automatic Opening Device

arc an area between two points to cover with weapons

APC Armoured Personnel Carrier

Arwen semi-automatic multi-shot gas discharger

ASAP as soon as possible

bag off chat up a girl – successfully

ball bullet (not tracer)

basha sleeping shelter

beaster hard exercise, usually in the gym or running

belt order webbing

bergen military rucksack

binned taken off the course

bivvi bag Gortex sleeping bag cover

black kit anti-terrorist clothing

bomb burst to run very fast; to charge

brick non-Parachute Regiment term for a four-man patrol

Brits British

bug out to escape (from the enemy)

chew the fat talk generally about nothing

chopper any helicopter

civvy civilian

CLC Charge Linear Cutting

CO Commanding Officer

comms communications

CP Command Post

CPO Command Post Operator

craphats any member of the British Armed Forces who does not wear 'the maroon beret'

crow Para recruit

CSM Company Sergeant Major

CTR Close Target Recce

dead fall fallen trees or other foliage

DF Defensive Fire – preprogramming the location of specific targets

diffy deficient, normally used of army issue equipment

dixie washing up

DMS Direct Moulded Sole (footwear)

double tap the action of squeezing the trigger twice in quick succession

DPM Disruptive Pattern Material (camouflage)

DS Directing Staff (instructor)

DZ Drop Zone

FAC Forward Air Controller

Fan short for Pen y Fan, a mountain in the Brecon Beacons

FIBUA Fighting In Built Up Areas

flak vest a vest worn over the uniform to stop bomb secondary fragmentation

FPF Final Protective Fire

FRG Federal Riot Gun

full screw corporal – two stripes

Gemini small inflatable assault boat

green kit Army DPMs

gonk (to) sleep

gop (to) stink

GPMG SF General Purpose Machine Gun (7.62mm) Sustained Fire

grunts soldiers of little or no rank

HAHO High Altitude, High Opening

HALO High Altitude, Low Opening

HE High Explosive

head sheds Higher Command

heads naval term for toilets

Herc C130 Hercules transport aircraft

Hexy Hexamine – a small solid fuel brick used as a firelighter for the one-man stove

HQ Headquarters

IA Immediate Action

IC In Command

IED Improvised Explosive Device

illum illumination

infil to infiltrate

Int intelligence

Int Rep Intelligence Report

jack to give up

JATE Joint Aircraft and Transport Establishment

JNCO Junior Non-Commissioned Officer

ks kilometres

Killing Zone an area of ground where rounds are fired on automatic to cover an area so that nothing survives

Lance Jack Lance Corporal–one stripe

LAW Light Anti-Tank Weapon

LCU Landing Craft Utility

LMG Light Machine Gun

loadie a military aircrew man/woman

loading bay a safe point where weapons are loaded or unloaded

LOE Limit of Exploration

LSL Landing Ship Logistic

LUP Lying Up Position

LVTP 7 armoured personnel carrier

MFC Mortar Fire Controller

MOE Method of Entry

MP5 German Heckler and Koch sub-machine gun (9mm)

M16 5.56mm automatic rifle

M203 5.56mm automatic rifle with 40mm grenade launcher below

M79 40mm grenade launcher

NAAFI Navy Army and Air Force Institute

ND Negligent Discharge of a weapon

net radio network

NI Northern Ireland

non tac not in a tactical environment

OC Officer Commanding

Oerlikon 20mm AA cannon (Swedish)

OP Observation Post

oppo member of the patrol

Ops Operations

pads brat a child of a serviceman, brought up in Army housing – pads

PCAU Parachute Course Administration Unit

P Check to verify a person's identity

PE Plastic Explosives

PIRA Provisional Irish Republican Army

PJI Parachute Jump Instructor

Player a terrorist, e.g. PIRA

PNG Passive Night Goggles

pole bed a raised bed supported between two poles

poncho a small personal

camouflage cover tied at four corners

Prod   Protestant

QOH   Queen's Own Highlanders

QRF   Quick Reaction Force

RAP   Regimental Aid Post

RCD   Radio-Controlled Device

RCIED   Radio-Controlled Improvised Explosive Device

RCT   Royal Corps of Transport

RE   Royal Engineers

Recce   Reconnaissance

REME   Royal Electrical and Mechanical Engineers

REMF   Rear Echelon Mother Fucker

RPG   Rocket Propelled Grenade (Soviet)

R&R   Rest and Recuperation

RSM   Regimental Sergeant Major

RTU'd   Returned to Unit

RUC   Royal Ulster Constabulary

Rupert   nickname for an officer

sangar   fortified lookout post

SAS   Special Air Service

SBS   Special Boat Squadron

Scimitar   Light tank armed with 30mm automatic cannon

Scorpion   Light tank armed with 76mm gun

SD   Suppressed MP5

SF   Special Forces

sit-rep   situation report

slot   to kill

SLR   Self Loading Rifle

Slur   nickname for the SLR

SMG   Submachine Gun

SNCO   Senior Non-Commissioned Officer

sniveller   parachute which opens partially

Snowcat   small tracked vehicle for use in snow

SOPs   Standing Operational Procedures

SQM   Squadron Quarter Master

SSM   Squadron Sergeant Major

stagging   being on guard duties

SUIT   Sight Unit Infantry Trilux, a small telescopic sight for an SLR

sunray   commander

tab   to march with full kit

TAOR   Tactical Area of Responsibility

TAP   Tactical Assault Parachute

TOF   Time of Flight

tom   a 'private' in the Parachute Regiment

TOS   Taken off Strength. Taken off the unit's manning

UDR   Ulster Defence Regiment

UNSC   United Nations Security Council

US   Unserviceable

VCP   Vehicle Check Point

VW   Voluntary Withdrawal

webbing   a series of pouches for holding ammunition and rations attached to a belt and worn around the waist

Wombat   Weapon of Mobility Battalion Anti-Tank

WP   White Phosphorus (or 'warm person') grenade

yoke   top shoulder straps for webbing

2IC   Second in Command

66(LAW)   Light Anti-Tank Weapon

84   84mm anti-tank rocket fired from the shoulder by a two-man team, also known as the 'Charly Gee' or 'Carl Gustav'

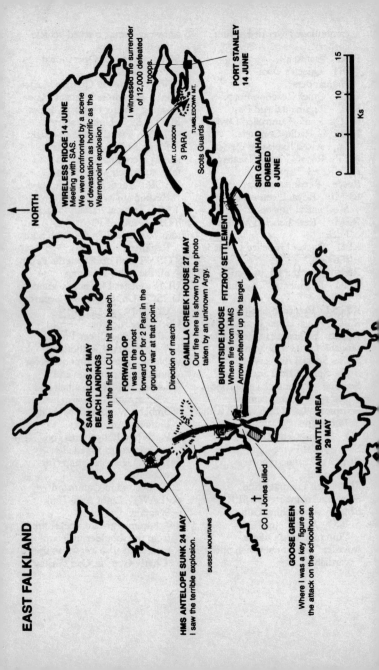

EAST FALKLAND

NORTH

WIRELESS RIDGE 14 JUNE
Meeting with SAS.
We were confronted by a scene
of devastation as horrific as the
Warrenpoint explosion.

I witnessed the surrender
of 12,000 defeated
troops.

PORT STANLEY
14 JUNE

MT. LONGDON
3 PARA
TUMBLEDOWN MT.
Scots Guards

SAN CARLOS 21 MAY
BEACH LANDINGS
I was in the first LCU to hit the beach.

FORWARD OP
I was in the most
forward OP for 2 Para in the
ground war at that point.

Direction of march

CAMILLA CREEK HOUSE 27 MAY
Our fire here is shown by the photo
taken by an unknown Argy.

BURNTSIDE HOUSE
Where fire from HMS
Arrow softened up the target.

FITZROY SETTLEMENT

SIR GALAHAD
BOMBED
8 JUNE

HMS ANTELOPE SUNK 24 MAY
I saw the terrible explosion.

SUSSEX MOUNTAINS

CO H Jones killed

MAIN BATTLE AREA
29 MAY

GOOSE GREEN
Where I was a key figure on
the attack on the schoolhouse.

0   5   10   15
Ks

PREFACE

Goose Green, East Falkland, 28 May 1982

I will do such things –
What they are yet I know not,
but they shall be
the terrors of the earth.

SHAKESPEARE: *KING LEAR*, ACT II SCENE IV

**TIME: 13.27hrs ZULU (Greenwich Mean Time)
SITUATION: Taking casualties from heavy
enemy incoming fire**

I COULDN'T MOVE. To my left I could see nothing. To my right I could just make out an Argy's boot. He looked dead when I went to ground, but he might be wounded or feigning death. There wasn't much room – the dip I had come to rest in was barely enough to cover me. It had cover from view and cover from fire, but for how much longer? The ground around me was being torn up by the Oerlikon cannon which was zeroing in on me. Those 20mm rounds were thudding into the peat, big style. Sods of earth were being thrown all over the place. I was trapped. Concerned about the threat which lay just a few feet from me, I had no choice but to reach for my bayonet, rip it out of its scabbard and snap it on to my rifle. I had to make sure this twat was dead before I could move off. The cannon switched its fire and within a second the ground stopped vibrating, but my relief was short-lived when I turned to the body on my right. He hadn't moved – I could still see the underside of his boots. The gun had found a better target; perhaps they thought they had slotted me. Small arms fire was whipping in over my head every few seconds. I decided to do it. I flipped over onto my back, slowly raised my rifle above my shoulders and, resting the bayonet on the side of the dip, levelled it up as far as I dared. I could at least shoot the sole of the Argy's boot. With my left hand against the forward part of the dip supporting my weapon, I squeezed the trigger with my right. One round hit and went through the boot. The leg kicked up about three feet and fell back. Confirmed! The Argy was now dead for sure. No screams, no nothing.

That threat out of the way, I now turned my attention on regrouping with Buster and Dick. Once again I appeared to be more forward than the rest of the patrols. I had seen both of them go to ground on the left, slightly behind me – five metres away. I wondered if the cannon had zeroed in on them.

'Hey Dick, Buster. Where the fuck are you?'

'Over here to your right. You alright? Some fucker should take those mortars out!'

'Yeah, it would be nice to see one of those fucking Harriers fly over and drop a 1000-pounder on the twats.'

'Those cunts are too busy looking after their carrier. They need their galley intact for their bacon and eggs in the morning.'

I shouted to Buster to see if he could make a dash for the dead ground about 30 metres to our front. We couldn't sit here all day. We had to reorganise ourselves and try to wait for the rest of the blokes to get off the main slope and join us. Only then could we become an effective fighting force – all of us had split up when the Oerlikon let rip.

Buster's ankle was pretty bad even before the attack. He had twisted it whilst tabbing across one of the 'rock runs,' when we left the Observation Post (OP) at Sussex Mountains. He hadn't said much about it, but I could see it was giving him some gyp. I didn't know what their cover was like, but I had only one option if I wanted to move: break cover from the point I had come in at. But if the enemy saw me go to ground in the first place – which they obviously did – the chances of them keeping their aim on that point and waiting for me to move out had to be about 90 per cent. I shouted to Dick, 'What's your cover like?'

'Wet, windy and shallow.'

'Can you both cover me while I make a dash for it?'

'No problems, Devs. Do it on three. OK?' His reply sounded switched on.

There's never a good time to move forward during a battle, especially with absolutely no heavy support weapons. The most we had was the Machine Gun Platoon with the General Purpose Machine Guns on Sustained Fire, but they were back on the high ground. A GPMG on SF was a fantastic weapon. I had seen one totally chew up the gable end of a house, making it collapse. And the gunners were shit-hot at their job. But the GPMG was no match for the Oerlikon.

The small arms fire above me from both directions was ferocious. Because we were so far forward and out of communication with the rest of the platoon, the chances of being shot in the back by our own troops while skirmishing forward were almost as great as being slotted by the Argies. But it was a decision I had made and Dick and Buster were keen to go along with it. None of us was in a position to put rounds down on the enemy. So we had to move. It was our job. The passion and the aggression which we all had for getting on and finishing the job did not come from a loyalty to Queen and country or to the politicians who had sent us here, or from the thought of another power taking over a part of the United Kingdom. The officers might have thought about this Queen and country bollocks, but we blokes didn't. We were doing this for ourselves and for the Regiment.

I got ready to move. My pulse was up, I could feel it pounding all over my body. I pulled the strap tight on my helmet and ripped the magazine off my weapon to check I had enough rounds should I need to fire. I was going to need rounds when I gave covering fire to Dick and Buster for their move. The magazine was almost full. I blew some shit out of the flash hider at the end of the barrel, leaned on one side and pulled my webbing belt as tight as I dared, and checked that all the pouches were done up and that the grenades dangling off the D rings at the top of my yoke were safe. I did this in seconds – it was routine. The last thing I did was adjust the 66mm Light Anti-Tank Weapon (LAW) and the M79 grenade launcher slung over my back into a comfortable position so they wouldn't snag when I made my dash.

There was no let-up in the activity above my head. The hissing of 7.62mm rounds and the sizzling of tracer rounds landing around me hadn't stopped.

'You ready?' I screamed.

'Ready! On three?' Dick yelled back.

'Yeah.'

'One. Two. Three!'

On 'Three' I leapt up and ran as fast as I could towards the dead ground. When the other two saw me go they exposed themselves to give me covering fire. I tried to zigzag as best I could, but the ground in front was cut up badly, full of tufts of grass and soft divots caused by mortar rounds that had exploded an hour before. As I ran I was focusing in on everything in front of me. I didn't care what was happening behind – all I had to do was get to a larger piece of dead ground to secure it for Dick and Buster. Then all three of us had to meet up and sort a battle plan.

I was aware of the dead Argy I had shot through the boot as I broke cover. His head and half the top part of his left shoulder had been blown away and the rest of his torso was peppered with holes. He must have been hit by his own men, probably from the 3.7inch Anti-Aircraft (AA) gun – it couldn't have been from our side. All we had was 7.62mm, which wouldn't have taken his head off.

Now I could see another trench in front of me which hadn't been visible when I was lying down. Much larger than the ones I had previously attacked, it could easily hide the three of us. As I closed in on it I could hear covering fire being put down by Dick and Buster. With five feet to go my legs were suddenly gone from me and I was violently knocked down. Something had hit me on my right side, the force spinning me around and dumping me on my back. I lay facing up at the sky. It was a grey cloudy sort of day, the sort that threatened rain which never came. I was conscious but couldn't hear a thing. I was stunned. A feeling of serenity came over me, then all of a sudden a piercing noise brought me to my senses.

Had I been hit? I couldn't feel anything. I instinctively reached out with both hands for my weapon, but because I was on my back, the 66 light anti-tank weapon, M79 grenade launcher and my webbing beneath me arched my body up so much I couldn't use my hands. I had to turn over onto my stomach. I grabbed my rifle, then became aware of a burning sensation coming from my right thigh. I dropped my right hand down to feel for blood. I didn't dare look down – I had to focus on what was happening in front of me. I *had* to drag myself into the trench and into cover. I brought my hand up. It wasn't wet or bloodstained, but it was throbbing big style. Dick called out; was I alright? I tried to reply but couldn't. The force, whatever it was, had knocked ten tons of shite out of me. I dragged myself towards the trench. Those last few feet felt like a thousand. There was no let-up in the incoming small arms, but luckily it didn't seem directed at me. The Argies couldn't see me because the earth thrown up making the trench had been piled in a bank, giving me an extra six inches in which to hide.

I got to the edge of the trench and fell in. It was deep and part of the wall fell with me as I crashed to the bottom. I fought to get a grip of myself. Semi-conscious, my head screaming with pain, I thought my brain was going to explode. Then the 20mm opened up again and tore up the side of the trench, kicking up large clumps of earth which sprayed down on top of me. Unknown reserves of willpower suddenly brought me back to life. I screamed to Dick that I was alright. He said that they were coming and with that, two bodies came hurtling into the trench, feet first. Buster, followed by Dick.

'Fuck me. What the shite happened to Devs?' Dick looked me over for any visible signs of a wound.

'Dunno. One minute I was up and running, the next I got hit. Dunno what with though.' I looked down to where the pain was coming from on my right thigh and saw that my first magazine pouch had a hole in it. Quickly I flipped open its top and found that an Argy SLR 7.62mm round had penetrated the pouch, travelled through one magazine, and lodged itself in one of the live bullets. That's what had flung me in the air like a sack of shite; that was the cause of the throbbing around my thigh. I was very lucky. I had been hit and it didn't even break the skin. It reminded me of all those old clichéd stories I had heard from men who had been in combat – a life saved because the fatal bullet had been stopped by a cigarette lighter in the top pocket. I now had my own 'good luck' story, but didn't think about it, I just took the good rounds out of the damaged magazine, topped up two mags which I kept down the front of my smock and put the round into my pocket. I was thinking of keeping the mag but it was added weight and surplus to my immediate requirements, so I tossed it up out of the trench.

Our newly found home was quite big. It was L-shaped, both parts ten feet long, and deep enough to stand up in. Duct boards of some kind were fitted around the sides so you could raise yourself up above the height of the trench. It must have been home for a couple of weeks to someone. There was a ton of Argy kit spread all over the place: ammunition boxes, webbing, small US issue rucksacks, personal pieces of kit, such as toothbrushes, books and letters from loved ones back in Argentina. Also, there were two previous tenants around the dogleg of the L, still in their firing positions but slightly slumped back. Buster put two rounds into both of them, for good measure. Best to make sure.

The battle had been raging for a number of hours now and all of us had taken a battering. It was still unclear to us how many blokes had survived the initial onslaught. We had no idea of casualties, dead or wounded, but we knew that there must have been some.

However, my thoughts weren't really in that direction. Though I felt sorry for those who had got caught out in the open and couldn't make it into the relative safety of where we were now, I had to think ahead. How could we make good our forward position? There was no point in moving ahead. What we had to keep going was the momentum of our advance but we couldn't do it without fire support. We needed a few 1000-pounders dropped by the Harriers or support from the Artillery's Howitzer 105s; definitely something more than a couple of hundred men firing 7.62mm.

Having faced the wrath of the Argy 20mm cannons it would have been total madness to advance any further forward at this stage. We had a quick Chinese Parliament to talk over our options. Conclusions? Very limited. We could either press on – certain death, stay put for a bit and see who caught up, or go back. Going back was a non-option. We decided to stay put, keeping an eye out for the rest of the blokes. We reckoned they weren't far behind us and if they were switched on they would have seen us take refuge. Buster kept watch as I tried to sort myself out. My headache had died down a bit but I was still a bit shaken. I half knelt and half stood, trying to take the weight of my webbing off my shoulders by lodging it on the trench wall. I was severely conscious of the pain in my thigh, but there was jack shit I could do about it. I watched Dick prepare a brew. Shaking earth off my rifle, I knelt down beside the burning hexy stove. I wasn't cold but I warmed my hands anyway. The battle still raged above us, but we were safe for the time being.

As I waited for Dick's brew, my attention was drawn to one of those Argy letters. I picked it up and tried to read it. It was in Spanish, from his mother. That was all I could understand, but I guessed at its content. I thought of my mum, dad and two brothers. What would they be doing now? I knew that my younger brother was going off to Spain for a fortnight. It was Friday. Dad always had Friday off. He didn't particularly like London on a Friday. He preferred to leave late on a Thursday, trusting Clive, my older brother, to look after the family business. Suddenly I felt frustrated that I could not pick up the phone and give them a quick call just to let them know things were OK. In Northern Ireland I had hardly ever phoned them – probably because then I was always near a telephone. I thought what a frigging selfish shit I had been ever since I joined up. A wave of emotion swept through me. 'What if?', 'Why?', 'Why didn't I?' filled up my brain. Once again, guilt crept up on me. I sat deep in thought, feeling alone and isolated from all those things that I held dear to me. I sat thinking about what had gone before . . .

PART ONE

CHAPTER ONE

'Aldershot, this is Aldershot.'

I DIDN'T GET a particularly encouraging farewell from my mother when my parents dropped me off at Waterloo Station.

'Good luck, son,' Dad said. Mum was sharper.

'You'll be back, you're not cut out for the Paras, we didn't bring you up like that.'

I responded with a peck on the cheek; not a hug, just a peck. I could see she was concerned but that made me feel embarrassed.

'Give us a call when you get settled,' Dad shouted as he drove away. Mum looked through me and waved gently. I could see tears beginning to fill her eyes. I thought, Shit! I'm only going 40 miles down the road, I'll be back next week.

I turned into the station. What did she mean, I was not cut out for the Paras? I couldn't figure that out. My mother knew nothing about the Army, let alone the Parachute Regiment. But then, at 18, neither did I.

I couldn't wait to leave school. I can remember enjoying learning to play rugby at the age of eight, but as far as anything else went, forget it. Sport was what I really excelled at, I was above average in English, maths and French; in everything else I was pretty poor. I found it hard to concentrate and by 14 I wanted to get out of the classroom and into the real world to see what it had to offer.

I took the exams everyone took but left school before I got the results and still don't know what grades I achieved – if any. Two years of work in the real world led me through a string of jobs, from trainee salesman at London's Spitalfields market to a management position for an oil company running two of their petrol filling sites. It was during this job I bumped into two old school friends quite by accident on the same day, a coincidence which was to have such an effect on my life.

I was on my way to work when I stopped to get a newspaper. Coming out of the shop, I almost bumped into him.

'Er, sorry mate. Alan Berry! Shit, how are you?' I said, amazed.

'I'm very well, Devs. How are you, old boy?'

I hadn't seen him since leaving school over two years before. He said he was in the Army, the Royal Artillery to be exact. He said it with such confidence, as if he was stating the obvious and saying, 'Don't you know this uniform.' But he wasn't in uniform, he was in civvies, almost a Prince Charles lookalike: double vented, single-breasted jacket and matching trousers. He looked really smart, in a dickhead sort of way.

We got chatting. Like me, Alan had been an athlete – in his case, an outstanding one. On one occasion we both attended the annual Three As athletics meet at Crystal Palace. Alan won his preliminary heats easily; I just scraped through mine. In my final I came last, or eighth as I said to myself then. Losing was not a good feeling. That race was to stick with me for some years. Alan, however, won his main race.

As kids we often used to play together at his house. He had some toy soldiers and an old wooden castle, heavily constructed to survive re-enactments of historical sieges.

Unlike me, Alan stayed on at school, and became head boy. He passed all his exams, then went to military college and passed all the exams there. After that he went on to Officer Training at Sandhurst. He passed and was awarded the 'sword of honour' for the best recruit. The perfect gentleman.

We talked briefly about what we had done since school, then parted.

Later that day I saw Dave Letts, another old school friend, in the

3

pub, on leave from the Army – the Royal Green Jackets. Every class in every school has one boy who matures physically faster than everyone else. Dave was ours: first to try cigarettes, first to date girls, first to lose his virginity. Dave was with a mate from the Green Jackets, Sticks. We had a few beers and I told Dave that I had seen Alan, and that he was an officer in the Royal Artillery.

'Fucking Rupert,' he said. His remark went over my head – what did he mean?

The night's conversation with Dave and Sticks never strayed from how many women they would shag if the women were lucky that night, and how good *their* section was, how good *their* Platoon was, *their* Company, *their* Battalion; how good the Green Jackets were, and how fucked up were the other wankers in the British Army. Dave and Sticks were getting pissed because the previous day their platoon had won a match-and-shoot competition against other Companies of Green Jackets. This involved marching in full kit over a distance of ten miles or so to a rifle range, then shooting at targets, usually metal plates eight inches square, called falling plates, which fell when hit. For their efforts they had been granted a long weekend.

I saw Dave over the next few days and generally he spoke about what he thought of the army. I don't know why I interrogated him so much because I was in a good, well paid job. I could go places with that oil company. But in truth, I was bored.

For some reason, at the end of that particular week-end I offered to drive Dave back down to his barracks in Hampshire some hundred or so miles away. Sticks was making his own way back. On the journey I quizzed Dave at length about the army and the Green Jackets.

The Green Jackets were an infantry outfit where the only trade you were taught was killing people, unlike a Corps units such as the Royal Engineers where you also learnt a second trade – surveying, for example.

Though no academic, Dave was not lacking in the brain department. And as, in the 1970s, the attitude towards the military was 'Well, you can't do fuck all else, best join the army,' I was a bit surprised by his choice. But I never asked Dave why he wanted to join the army in the first place. The reason why Dave joined the

4

Green Jackets was because the Army Recruiting Sergeant who interviewed him was a Green Jacket. He said that's what happens when you go into the army recruiting office. You are interviewed by, for example, a Sergeant from the Household Division Guards, and if you seem to be a 'good egg' and you pass your acceptance exams, he will persuade you to join his regiment. Force, I think was the word Dave used. Anyway, he was happy. He was due to be posted to Ireland for six months very soon, and was really looking forward to that. First operational tour.

It was a long drive home, but my old Triumph Herald was as faithful as ever. I had plenty of time to think about what I was going to do and where I wanted to go in life. Quite profound for me, analysing what I wanted to do with my life! By the time I got back to my parents' home it was two in the morning. It was clear to me that I had to do something with my life, otherwise I would be doomed to spend the rest of it in and around south London. The way I saw it, I had two options. One, I would stay in the nice, tidy job that I had and continue to play rugby – I could try to cut it in the club rugby scene, aiming for a cap for England. Two, I could join the Marines, as Dave had suggested to me during our long drive to Hampshire.

When I got up a few hours later I had made my decision. I arrived in work earlier than normal just in time to see the day girl opening up. I told her I was off to my other site some miles away; I would be back in the afternoon, covering myself in case the area manager did a spot-check. Then I drove to Blackheath Navy recruiting office where a Marine Recruiting Sergeant told me about the Marines, gave me a few pamphlets, and advised me to go away and think about it.

I went straight to the pub across the road, ordered a coke and sat down to read what I had been given, just to kill a bit of time. Thirty minutes later I was back.

'That was quick,' the Marine Sergeant said.

I was to report next Monday to sit exams to see if I was a suitable candidate to join the Royal Marine Commandos. I did so with an old rugby mate of mine, Rhino Richards. He was in two minds what to do with himself as well. His father had served with the SAS in the Second World War and he thought, 'Well, Dad's done it and he still talks about it. It can't be a bad life. What the fuck.'

We both passed our initial written exams, scoring well enough to be looked at as POs (Potential Officers). So we went back that afternoon to sit the physical: the odd push up, press up and chin up. Then we waited for the overall results.

We both failed. Rhino failed the physical, which surprised me because he could run the 100 metres in under 12 seconds, and had been pushing weights for years. I failed, not because of the physical – I passed that – but because I had a police record. Complicated story – basically as a teenager I drove a friend's car without insurance, and of course a licence. At that age I was so cocky I thought I was really clever, and that only I knew best.

I didn't feel so clever that day in the recruiting office when my past was dragged up to smack me square between the eyes. Welcome to the real world, I thought. Here I was offering my service to Queen and country, only to be turned down without even being given a fighting chance because of some minor offence committed several years before.

What to do? I had been boasting to my mates that I was joining the Marines and would not be back for a few months. What a wanker, they might think. And what might mum and dad think?

The Marine Sergeant was apologetic; he could sense my disappointment when I asked him if I could come back and try again.

'Sorry laddie, the Royal Marines will not accept anyone with a criminal record. You might try the Paras.'

'What?'

'The Paratroopers, the Army.' He grinned. 'They accept all sorts in that mob.'

I sensed sarcasm in his voice. 'Where are they?' I asked.

'Next door.'

The Paratroopers, I thought. Who the frig are they? Next best? – well, I'll give it a try.

After the initial interrogation about why I wanted to join, I sat and passed all the relevant exams and interviews, and was given a date to report to a place near Birmingham for three days of introduction to the army.

There we did all the usual form filling and more physical tests, were put into squads, did lots of running around, got fed, slept a bit. We were there to be processed into whatever Regiment or Corps we wanted to join or the army thought most useful to them. It was a crap three days, but I passed the three-day period and was given a date to report to the Depot, the Parachute Regiment in Aldershot, in two months' time.

The train journey from London took less than an hour. As the train came to a halt at Aldershot, I heard the station tannoy system playing a recording that every prospective Para recruit who has spent even a day at the Parachute Regiment Depot will tell you is a chilling reminder that you are about to disembark from the sane train of life and freedom is no more: ALDERSHOT, THIS IS ALDERSHOT. ALL CHANGE.

At this point, you have two choices. One, you get off the train and go to the Depot; or two, you get off the train, cross the platform and catch the next train back home. There is of course a third option – go to the nearest pub, have a skinfull, say 'Fuck the army and the Paras' – but that's only for really sad bastards.

Outside the station there was an army coach. It was raining. I mingled with other, dazed blokes, each carrying a holdall or suit-case. Then a soldier wearing a red beret appeared; a Corporal. 'All Para recruits over here,' he shouted. 'This is your transport, and it's leaving right now.'

A few blokes moved towards the coach; I followed. I stood in line and was checked on the coach.

I gave my name. The Corporal ticked me off his list and I went and sat at the rear of the coach. Nobody spoke on the coach, not even the Corporal. As we drew up to the Depot I could see two guards standing to attention by a sentry box. An old aircraft, a Dakota, stood opposite. Another guard came up to the coach, checked the driver's ID card, put his hand up and waved us on. The double barrier was raised just enough for the coach to drive through.

This short ride, less than two miles, was the first and last time I was to be picked up from the station by the Paras. I guess the army has to show some concern for the safety and wellbeing of their newest recruits, just once.

7

There were 20 or so of us, mostly aged about 18, not knowing what the frig we had let ourselves in for, but all volunteers. We were given a brief order – my first order in the Paras.

'This is Depot, the Parachute Regiment, and in this fucking Depot you run at *all* times,' the Corporal said before the coach drew to a halt outside what looked like an office block. 'Follow me,' he shouted and disappeared across what looked like a five-a-side tarmac football pitch towards an office standing on its own.

Everyone clambered off to follow. Suitcases were slung across people's heads, blokes swore at each other as we all piled out and ran towards the Corporal now standing 60 metres away. Being at the back I was one of the last to get out and consequently, one of the last to join the queue outside the office.

'Come on you wankers,' the Corporal shouted at the stragglers.

I ran to catch up but I was the last in the queue. Well, I thought, someone has to be. People were jockeying to get out of the rain. There was a sign alongside the office: 'Recruit Company Office', in a light blue on a maroon background. Now the Corporal walked over to us. He came up to me.

'What's your name, wanker?'

'Devereux.'

'NUMBER?' he bellowed.

Number? I thought.

'NUMBERRR you twat, what's your fucking number? And stand to attention while you're talking to me, you civvy piece of shite.'

I rattled off the eight digit number, cowering back into the rest of the crowd. As he came closer, I could see beads of rain settling on his face – it was pissing down. In his late 20s, he had jet black sideburns and a thick Fu Manchu moustache. I looked down to where the rain was bouncing off the tarmac and on to the paving slabs. There were a few sniggers from the rest of the recruits. Then I looked at the Corporal again. 'Sorry, sorry sir,' I said.

'Don't call me sir, you cunt, I'm not a fucking officer. See these strips? See them?'

'Yes.'

'Well, they are called stripes and two of the fuckers means I'm a

Corporal, got it? One. Two.'

'Yes.'

'Yes fucking what!'

'Yes, Corporal.'

'LOUDER.'

'YES, CORPORAL,' I screamed back.

'And see these, Devereux?' He was pointing to his parachute wings sewn on above his strips. They were what we were here for: to be wearing these wings six months from now.

'YES Corporal.'

'Well, if you don't start switching on from right now, this might be the last time you ever see a set of wings, get me Devereux?'

The sniggers turned into laughs and he went ballistic. When he turned and glared at the rest of the recruits, they turned away like puppies who know they have done something wrong. Then he spun back to face me: 'Devereux, see that fire hose over there?' he said.

It was 20 metres away, on a bright red, two-wheeled carriage. The sort a horse might once have pulled.

'Yes, Corporal.'

'Well, double over there and stand to attention!'

I sped off, but a sharp yank from behind brought me to a sudden halt.

'Devereux, you forgot something.' He turned me around and showed me: my holdall. As I picked it up, the Corporal added:

'Hey Devereux, you know we are fighting a war somewhere? You know that, cockhead?'

'Yes, Corporal. In Ireland, Corporal,' I said.

'This camp is an open camp and your bag could be a bomb planted by the IRA. Start fucking switching on!'

I doubled away over to the fire hose along with my holdall. The Corporal turned back to the others and told them to shut the fuck up, then ordered them to line up against me, facing the office block. Everyone took their luggage with them, everyone got very wet. Then the Corporal bellowed one last order to me.

'Devereux, give me 50. The rest, down and do 20.'

At first I was not sure what he meant but as the kid next to me went down in press-up mode, I instantly followed suit.

The formal processing and form filling took about ten minutes.

9

During that time the rain stopped and the sun appeared and shone brightly: a typical English summer Sunday afternoon. I spoke and joked with some blokes ahead of me but they didn't respond.

Waiting in the queue I had a chance to look around. Around the tarmac area there were five main barrack blocks, of three levels, all joined by a walkway at every level. In the middle of the complex there was a building that looked like the cook house and above that, the NAAFI. There were recruits running all over the place, some in battle dress, some dressed in red T-shirts and navy-blue short trousers. Apart from the ones in PT kit they all wore a camouflage baseball-type cap.

Great, three more to go. The recruits processed before me were doubling away around the far side of the office to a barrack block with the name Ridgeway and Blythe on its side, where a Para was shouting at them to keep up. They would disappear into the block for a few minutes. I would hear screams from another Para inside bollocking someone; 'Get a fucking move on!' They would then come running back, disappear again, then reappear carrying a mattress, pillows and blankets, all the while screamed at by yet another Para. I reckoned that we were to live on the first floor of Ridgeway and Blythe block. I could hear recruits being told to clean windows and lockers.

I studied the routine with a sense of knowing what was to come. I prepared myself for it. Strange, I thought, that earlier bollocking had switched me on.

Two more blokes to go. I could just see the Fu Manchu Corporal through the office window, standing to attention while the Para behind the desk questioned each recruit and made a few squiggles in his book. From behind one of the barrack blocks came more yelling: 'Keep up! You, you little pussy, you're going to be back-squadded if you don't get to the front. NOW.'

I turned to see about 40 recruits, in full battle dress with weapons, carrying each other in a fireman's carry. Covered from head to foot in mud, sweat and, in some cases, blood, they looked absolutely bollocked. There was a lot of screaming, kicking and punching from the training staff in white vests, combat trousers and boots, as the platoon struggled onto the quadrangle. Some staff were also carrying recruits, or offering

10

encouragement to the tail-enders by way of physical abuse.

'Devereux, you're next,' the Corporal said. He had quietly approached me whilst I was looking at this rabble. 'That's 447 platoon, doing P Company build-up.'

I didn't know what that was, but strangely, I wanted some of it.

In the office I was told that I had the rank of Private, that I was to be billeted in Ridgeway and Blythe block and that after the admin clerk was done with me, I was to get a move on. I learnt that the Corporal was Corporal Blake. The admin clerk pointed to where I had seen recruits coming in and out like ants. I filled out forms, signed for my temporary ID card and was told to double away in the direction of another screaming Para waiting at the entrance to the barrack block. I collected my bedding and clothing, signing for it all without really checking it. In the army you sign for everything, and I mean *everything*. I ran back up to the billet and found my name on a bed space. Bummer, I thought: my bed space was right by the door. I'll be the first person the Corporal kicks when he walks in. I dropped my gear down and ran over to the cook house. The doors were locked.

'Hey, Devereux,' shouted the Corporal. 'The entrance is the other side, dickhead.'

He was walking across the square with the other members of our platoon training staff, looking quite relaxed, even human. He pointed to the recruit office; they all laughed loudly. I knew they were talking about me. My cards had been marked within an hour of walking into the Depot.

I ran round to find some of my platoon being given a bollocking by another Sergeant in a red beret, with a red sash across his body.

'Hey you,' he shouted.

'Yes Sergeant,' I shouted back.

'Call me STAFFFFF, Shit-for-brains. I'm a PROVOST Sergeant and therefore you call me STAFFFFF. Had any scoff yet?'

'No, staff.'

'Well fuck off and get some.'

'Yes, STAFF.'

I ran up to the cook house. There was not much left: a plate of

11

chips and shepherd's pie. I sat down on a table with one other chap I knew to be in my platoon. We didn't have much of a conversation: all he really told me was that the Provost Sergeant, 'a right bastard', had caught a couple of our platoon smoking outside the cook house. 'Now they have got to area clean the whole camp.'

'*All* of it?'

'Yeah.'

What a bastard it was to be a smoker, I thought.

I left him and returned to the billet, now alive with bodies, to sort out my new stuff. This was a nightmare for all of us. None of us knew what we had signed for. We were not given a check list but by a process of asking each other we worked out what we had actually signed for. Luckily I was not diffy of anything: some were missing a PT vest, parts of their webbing and so on.

In the army, everything has to be accountable at some stage, but the easiest people to mislead are those who have the least knowledge of the system – raw recruits. Some blokes had signed for equipment that they had not been issued with in the first place. But raw recruits are the least likely to admit a loss or indeed question anyone else's integrity, for fear of being a whinger. You just have to get on with it. We were all fair game when we were totally green.

I watched a bit of TV in the NAAFI, but went to bed early. We were on parade 05.30hrs the next day and rumour had it that there was going to be a run first thing. Anyhow, going downtown was out of bounds to all new recruits.

I was tired, more from apprehension than fatigue. I thought as I drifted to sleep, Great, day one over and done with. Piece of piss.

Next morning broke very early with a corporal kicking the barrack room door open with his boot, screaming, 'Come on you fuckers, get your hands off your dicks, get a shit, shower and shave, downstairs in 20 minutes, Oh yeah, PT kit, white tops.' Most of us made it. Stragglers had their names taken and were told to do 50 press ups. The rest of us were told to do 20.

We were split up into groups. We reckoned that a run was imminent, and rumour had it that it was going to be a beaster. Instead, we were just herded from one store to the next, picking up more uniforms, more webbing and cleaning kit, and the allocation of room jobs. We were given a basic layout of the barracks and told of more do's and don'ts.

We were introduced to our OC – Officer Commanding the Recruit Company, who told us about the Regiment's history, wished us all good luck and left. Then we met the Regimental Sergeant Major recruit company (RSM). His style was different: sharp, abrupt, almost violent. He read us the riot act. If any of us didn't like it, they should fuck off: 'We don't like wasting the army's money on shit people who don't know why they signed up and anyway, the Paras don't accept wankers and since most of you look like wankers you should all fuck off now down the road and sign up with the RCT.' No one moved. We had lost two recruits during the night. For whatever reason they felt their future lay the other side of the Dakota. So we started with a platoon of 42.

The days flew by. We were taught how to make beds, wash and clean everything so it sparkled like new, shave and dress properly, all under a constant barrage of physical and mental abuse from our instructors.

This wasn't callousness, nor was it aimed at any one recruit. If you did well, OK; if you fucked up for whatever reason, be prepared to learn from that mistake and take the punishment with some dignity. The days were split into fitness training, weapon training drill (where we were taught to fire, strip and clean – blindfolded – all the field weapons used by the Regiment), lectures on Regimental history, tactics, and endless room and locker inspections. We were taught to work as a team, that nothing else mattered apart from achieving that most coveted of possessions, the 'Red Beret'. That was our aim, to be a Paratrooper. We were the best and fuck the rest.

I also got to grips with the structure of the Regiment. It was made up of three Battalions, 1, 2 and 3 Para (each of 600 men), which were in turn divided into Rifle Companies. There were five of these: A, B, C, D and HQ. Each Company (except HQ) broke down into three Platoons, which further fragmented into Sections – except Pathfinder Platoons, which had Patrols instead. Intakes, such as the one I was in, were organised into Platoons and numbered sequentially: mine was 449 Platoon, and the one immediately before it, 448 Platoon (obviously). It was a lot to take in, but I soon had the hang of it.

But in every aspect of the Regiment, there was so much to learn. I had never been tested so much in my life, or so I thought at that stage. During those first weeks we lost about 20 blokes: some jacked it in, some were injured, others had to leave. We were down to almost half of our starting number.

I entered the fourth week of Para training on a high. Trying to justify to myself that I was now a part of the Paras was my way of getting through the next five months when, hopefully, I would pass the parachute course and get posted to a Parachute Battalion. If the truth be known, I had only passed two-thirds of the basic infantry training course, which all recruits entering the infantry have to pass before they go on to their relevant Regimental depots for further recruit training.

I spent much of my leave in a pub near my home. There I heard a rumour that there was a party nearby, so a couple of us forced the issue with the guy who mentioned it and eventually we got the address. It turned out to be an old friend of mine, so there was no problem with gatecrashing. There were three of my mates and two other blokes who happened to be in the pub at the time: a Royal Marine and a guy from the Artillery. We had got talking and chewing the fat, things were going well. It had the makings of a great Saturday night. It was, from what I can remember.

On the Monday morning, standing under the cover way back at Depot Para waiting for my squad's turn to get beasted on the drill square, I had a chance to reflect on the weekend's proceedings. It occurred to me that there had been a bit of trouble at the party I'd managed to gatecrash but no way could I remember what it was. The morning began with some serious drill. Fuck me, I thought, 40 minutes of this. I'm fucking dying!

Then a Land Rover drew up alongside the parade square and four RMPs (Royal Military Police) got out. They were met by someone I knew all too well and so did half the Parachute Regiment: 'the Bastard' – the RP (Regimental Policeman). One mean fucker, he was any recruit's worst nightmare. One hour in his nick equalled days spent in a Turkish prison.

As we marched past the gathering from hell, I thought some

14

poor bastard had done something bad with a capital B. Another person had joined them, the OC. We came to a halt. All five headed towards the parade ground. Then the Bastard was pointing with his pace stick towards the squad I was in. My name was called out.

I broke ranks, marched over to the edge of the parade ground and came to attention to where the OC and company were standing. I could not salute, since I was wearing the issue camouflage cap – I had not yet earned the red beret. In these circumstances you have to brace up – to puff out your chest like a bloated chicken, mouth closed. The OC said nothing. In a tone of respect because of the presence of the OC, the Bastard said:

'Private Devereux, these gentlemen would like to speak to you about a murder.'

Before I had time to think, the RMP Sergeant spoke. 'Private Devereux, I am arresting you for murder. Anything you say . . . '

I saw the Bastard smirk. The Parachute Regiment has a long tradition of sorting its own house out and generally deals with incidents against the law in-house. But murder was different. This became apparent just before I was marched away in double time.

A lift in the Land Rover was not on offer. The Bastard's passing order was when, or if, I returned from the RMPs, I was to report to him in person at his jail, whatever the time of day. The thing with the Army is, even if you are innocent, you still get tried twice. An hour later I was to learn what was in store for me for the rest of the day.

I was marched into the main office of RMPs 160 Provost. The Desk Sergeant wasn't doing anything in particular; he pretended to make himself look busy, to show the prisoner – me – that he was in control. I marked time in a rapid fashion; sweat was pouring down my face and was being soaked up by my issue khaki shirt. I smelt disinfectant and heard some prisoner being shouted at from behind me. I thought I might be next. Think! I had to give them something. Playing dumb was not the thing to do right now. What the hell happened on Saturday? Who the fuck had been murdered? Why? How? Then a command came without warning from behind me.

'Prisoner, Prisoner HALT.'

The Desk Sergeant looked me straight in the eyes from across

15

the desk. 'Corporal, what's this sweaty Para doing in my jail?' he said.

'Private Devereux, Sergeant,' the Corporal replied.

'Charge?'

'Murder, Sergeant.'

I felt myself shaking. It was obvious I was scared.

The Sergeant addressed me. The obvious questions: Number? Rank? Name? I was fine on these. Then, 'DOB?' I was stumped. What the hell was DOB?

'Date of birth! What's your fucking date of birth, Private?'

I barked out the relevant numbers.

When he had entered my details down in the book, he mumbled 'Charge – murder' and without looking up, ordered the Corporal to put me into cell three. Then I was double timed out and into it. The door was already open. I was halted with my nose two inches from the far wall of the cell, but the order to about turn and come to the 'at ease' position was not given. Then the door slammed behind me and then I heard the lock drop.

What the *shit* was going on? This was all new to me. But my short experience with the army had at least taught me to obey the words of command from your seniors. No way was I going to break the position I had been left in – that would incur as much wrath as the murder charge. I couldn't see much as I stood facing the wall, just a bed to my left, a chair to my right. I stood there listening to an exchange between an RMP and another prisoner:

'Hey, White, we've got one of your Para mates in the cell next door. You fuckers are all the same, aren't you!'

'Yes, *Corporal*.' White's reply implied, When I get out of here, if I see you downtown I'm going to kick ten tons of shit out of you.

Then the door flew open and before I knew it I was being marched down the corridor where White had been polishing the floors. He was standing to attention as I was marched by, sweating as much as I was. He had his parachute wings up so I reckoned he was from the Battalion.

I was taken to another room where there were three men: a man in a suit, a Para Major and an RMP Major. I was left standing to attention. There were no introductions. None of the niceties of a civilian police station where the interviewing officers have to tell you your rights and introduce themselves to you by rank.

I thought the suit was a civvy policeman, but I was never told. In the army you don't ask questions like 'Why have I been arrested?' You just answer questions.

These came in a logical sequence: 'Where were you on Saturday last?' 'Were you at a party?' 'What was the address?' 'You met with two other service men at that party, did you?' I answered as openly as I could, but naïve answers such as 'I can't remember' or 'I was drunk' seemed to irritate the suit. But I honestly couldn't remember much.

I appealed to the Para major for an explanation of what was going on. He explained that a man had been found stabbed to death down the road from the party I was seen at last Saturday, and that I, along with the Royal Marine and an Artillery guy, was being interviewed in connection with this. I protested that there were many other people at the party – maybe one of them did it. The Major went on. The murdered man was seen in the pub with me plus the Marine and the Artillery soldier, and we were all seen talking to him during the evening. The Major continued: 'So that's the reason why we are all here: you are the prime suspect and if you can't come up with a better story, then you'll have as much chance of joining the Parachute Regiment as a kamikaze pilot picking up his medal.'

That really worried me, so for the next few hours I retraced my steps of that evening.

It had not occurred to me to ask for legal representation. It was not the done thing. All I wanted was to pass the Para training. I was innocent, I knew that; well, at least that's what I believed at the time (and still do), but trying to convince the suit was a problem. The interview become more intense. I was allowed to sit down by this time – I had been standing to attention for over an hour. My leg muscles were burning up yet I still had to keep my composure in front of the Para Major. I wanted to prove to him that although the circumstances of last Saturday pointed in my direction, and I could not explain why, I was totally innocent and I was not going to admit to anything I had not done.

I felt that the Major was batting for me and that became apparent during the end of the afternoon's interview when, after the same old questions from the suit, he stood up and said, 'I think Private Devereux's answered all your questions. It's time to bring this interview to an end.'

But the suit had the last word:

'Major, you know I have the authority to arrest Private Devereux, but at this stage I feel that it is not necessary. In the meantime, however, he remains your responsibility and you must make him available for further interview if the need arises.'

Why was everybody talking about me, not *to* me, I thought. But I was used to it. After all, who the hell was I? Just another number. Still, I felt I had been well looked after by the Major. He had acted like my lawyer. I guess he was looking after one of his flock.

I was escorted to the entrance of 160 Provost. I was free. The RMP behind me said that he had had a call from 'the Bastard' and that I was to report to him ASAP.

I felt the cool air attack the sweat on my shirt, could see the Dakota ahead of me, the marker for the entrance to Depot Para. As I marched towards it my mind wasn't really clear on the day's events, but I cleared my head of the past interrogation. I had one thing on my mind that afternoon: I was going to take the Bastard's punishment and enjoy it. This system was not going to beat me. I spent six hours in his jail being beasted; although I was innocent, this was the Army's way. And, in the end, nobody was actually charged with the murder.

Three weeks later, we had just returned from Basic Wales. This was a two-week test of live firing of platoon weapons, tactics and living out in 'the cuds' and a test for all of us to see if the Paras were really what we wanted. At this stage we were told if you can't hack it, piss off. As I said, some did. This depletion in numbers gave the instructors more time to focus on the rest of us. The first six-week period was coming up – our platoon's first major drill test, called 'passing out', to show to the OC that 449 Platoon had reached the level of drill discipline expected from the Parachute Regiment. If we failed, we would all have to start again from day one. No way did I want a rerun of Basic Wales. An extra incentive was exchanging the camouflage baseball-style hats for the coveted red beret.

Drill was a pain in the arse. I understand the logic behind it but the constant spinning around and stamping down hard was really beginning to take its toll. My heels were almost coming off and it affected the daily runs and assault course sessions which, up until then, I had no problems with.

At about this stage of our training we were boosted back up to 42 by members of what was commonly known as the 'Hitler Youth' – 20 members of Junior Para who had joined the army at 16. Now they were 17 they could join the big boys. This was their chance to get into the Paras. Most of them had fathers, brothers or uncles who had served, or who were still serving, in the Parachute Regiment, and they knew all the tricks of the system. It was good to join forces with them. I got to know Gary Barnes, Barney as he liked to be called, a strong fit guy who appeared to be the big daddy of the 'baby Paras'. More mature than the rest, he knew what he wanted and how to get it out of life. We got on really well, and he sorted my heels out by supplying all sorts of medical tape and spirits to hold them together, which hardened them up.

I passed out along with the rest of the platoon. Great, first hurdle over with and what's more, our first long weekend since day one of the training!

I was now ready for the next stage – Pre-Para Company, known as P Company, halfway through our training. I had learnt a lot over these past weeks. I had got stronger, fitter, more confident, and able to deal with the other recruits around me, and, more importantly, I got to grips with the weapons and tactics training. I can still remember my determination to pass. The feeling I had in my stomach that day has never really left me. It still brings a shiver down my back when I think of what I, personally, achieved in that week. It was no great feat of endurance, but to me it was sheer ecstasy.

The test was simple. It was run over five days, two events per day, one in the morning, one in the afternoon, with no fucking about by the staff between tests. That came later, at night, with the customary barrack room and locker inspections – all part of the test. The Parachute Regiment had run P Company for years. There was no way of skiving, no short cuts, no way to cheat. It was in essence the most beautiful brutal physical and mental discipline ever thought up and the hardest Para physical military test in the world, apart from SAS selection.

On the morning of day one we found ourselves on a short but fierce run in light order: that is, boots, denim trousers and webbing order weighing 25 pounds, plus the SLR (Self Loading Rifle). The run was to take us over a training ground known as Long Valley or 'the tank tracks' – a huge area of rugged open quagmire, used by the military to test tanks. When it rained the track's trenches filled up with water and became a sea of mud. In the summer when the sun had baked the mud dry it became a series of concrete-like ruts up to two feet deep crisscrossing the valley. This area also featured such evocatively named hills as Hospital, Hungry, Miles and Flag Staff. The run was eight miles long. Only our local knowledge of the area was in our favour; it helped in pacing ourselves. In the end, though, trying to do so was pretty mindless; I found I lost more energy in doing that, rather than just switching off and trying to stay somewhere near the front runners. That afternoon was taken up with an indoor assault course test – total endurance and total commitment for a couple of hours.

Day two. We were marched out again to Long Valley carrying our 'logs': eight men strapped to a telegraph pole by rope loop holders around the trunk of the pole. The march out to the start line was hard enough. Then the race, a six-miler, began, a free for all. It started on a wide open expanse of the valley and it was our log's tactic to be the first to the first hill, Hungry Hill, 600 metres ahead. Once you were in front you could keep the pace to your own liking, because thereafter overtaking places along the route were few and far between. But no sooner had we run 400 metres than our two lead men tripped, sending our log head first into a deep rut, which in turn yanked the rest of us with such force that the rope cut severely into our wrists. We were less than a couple of minutes into the race and already we had to change sides of the log because of wrenched wrists.

The pain in my left wrist was excruciating; it was bleeding badly from the rope burns. But I noticed the other logs also had their problems. We were the last to hit Hungry Hill, but during the next 60 minutes we had a series of lucky passes of other logs, and as we came down the last hill we could see a Land Rover 400 metres away on level ground in the distance. Our instructors were in a frenzy. They were shouting and kicking at their respective team logs. (I found out later that the staff had bet on who would be the winning log, and it was not uncommon for large sums of money to change hands.) Our instructor was giving it max support; it was the first time I had heard him call Barney by his nickname. Adrenalin was flowing, pain barriers dealt with. There is no such thing as a pain barrier, I heard myself think. I was muttering, screaming encouragement to my team. This race really mattered to me. I felt good, strong, inspired.

We were off the hill now, about 50 metres behind the lead log. 'CHANGE!' bellowed our instructor.

We downed the log and changed positions for the last time. I screamed at Barney to take the front position with another bloke; I took up the rear. Two blokes fell off on the change over, one just lay exhausted on the ground, the other staggered around trying to catch his breath. The instructor went ape shit, screaming, 'GET BACK ON MY FUCKING LOG, YOU WANKERS!'

Only one of our guys caught up. I shouted to stay with the log but not bind himself on, just to grab the rope and pull, fearing he might collapse on the log and bring us all down. Barney was going at it like the bull of a man he was, swearing at all of us to give it maximum effort.

We caught up the lead log with 200 metres to go. All the instructors were shouting, even the staff from the finishing point ran up to give final screams of encouragement. We were shifting now, really shifting, and passed the lead log yelling, giving one another as much shit as we could think of. Two more men dropped off. That left five of us. I bellowed to Barney that if we just gave it one last spurt we were home and dry. I don't think he heard any of it. I don't think he even knew how many of us were left on the log until he turned around after we passed the finishing post.

After what seemed to be a lifetime but was only seconds we stopped and dropped the log. We were all bent down, doubled over, not looking up, not hearing anything, sweat pissing out of every pore. It was nearing midday at the height of summer – fucking roasting. Then I was snapped out of my daze by the platoon Corporal:

'Well done, lads. Fall in over here, FUCKING MOVE IT!'

The race was not over until every man who had finished the race was with his log standing to attention in front of the OC. But we were there! Five fucking winners! It's a good feeling, winning; nothing like it.

The rest of the logs came in. To complete the course was the test: winning, as far as the staff was concerned, was not so important – unless they won the bet. It was a test to suss out each recruit's ability to work under extreme pressure in the worst environments.

While all of us who had passed were secretly revelling in our achievements, we saw those who did not make it getting a severe bollocking from staff. Medics were on hand to sort out the injured and putting IV drips into two recruits obviously bound for the Cambridge Military Hospital in Aldershot; heat exhaustion, it was rumoured.

Because we had won the race I was ordered up to collect the prized P Company flag from the OC. He gave all of us a quick pep talk, then I marched out, shook hands with him and received the flag.

'Well done Private Devereux, and well done to log three.'

'Thank you sir.'

'Get that wrist sorted by this afternoon, you'll need it for the milling,' the OC added, grinning.

I looked down at my left wrist. For a time I hadn't felt a thing but on seeing it, I felt the pain surge up my arm. There was a band of wet red skin, about four inches wide, around my wrist with a thick strip of raw flesh dangling from the injury. All my knuckle heads were ripped open and were covered in congealed blood and dirt. Shit, that was really hurting, I thought.

'Yes sir,' I said.

Milling is a fight between two men gloved up in a boxing ring, the aim being to punch ten tons of shit out of your opponent. No style was necessary; whether you were orthodox or a southpaw, it didn't matter. The staff would give a thumbs up to whoever they thought had put up the best fight – not based solely on how many times you put your opponent down. I was pitched up against a Geordie lad, a bit of a bully, who I disliked intensely. He was three inches taller than me but I was about two-and-a-half stone heavier.

I also had a lower centre of gravity. Some weeks previously I had a run-in with him in the scoff queue at the cookhouse. We were about to kick off and if it hadn't been for a passing member of staff, we would have fought there and then.

The bell rang out and I charged out on to the mat to meet this wanker, who happened to be Junior Para boxing champion, head on. He was trying to box me with his well proven style, I was using brute force with more brute force. He put me down once through my lack of semi-controlled boxing skills. A slip, I thought. I severely butted him a few times with my head, quite unintentional! The crowd roared with approval. I managed to get a couple of humdinger punches in, which made his eye swell and cut his top lip before the bell.

The end result? A draw. I was happy with that. I had drawn first blood and I still had my good looks. Geordie and I never spoke after that, not one word. He later passed and was posted to 1 Para.

The following day of P Company was just as physical: an eight-miler across the same terrain, this time carrying a purpose-built metal-framed stretcher and railway sleepers to make up the weight. The load was spread between eight of us but in sixteen-man teams. We were all wearing full battle dress, webbing and platoon weapons. Each had a rifle; the old friendly Self Loading Rifle (SLR, affectionately known as 'the Slur') a robust thing of 7.62mm calibre, and the General Purpose Machine Gun (the GPMG), a very reliable and accurate belt- or drum-fed 7.62mm beast. Those who were not on the stretcher had to take turns in carrying the two GPMGs allocated to each team, ahead of the stretcher. It was gruelling.

Another test was the airborne assault course, the 'Trainazium', a rigid structure built of scaffolding poles, cargo nets, planks of wood and telegraph posts; at its highest point it measured well over 40 feet. This was a confidence tester – you had to run around the course showing no hesitation anywhere. If you did, then you were bollocked while the rest of your platoon looked on. If you still refused to go on, the staff would adopt a more delicate tone to get you down without drama or injury.

I think the acceptable annual number of severe injuries on the 'Trainazium' was only half a dozen, and they had been used up by the previous courses. A fractured arm or leg was not deemed too serious: death, however, was.

The most unnerving part was the highest point, the parallel bars, where, once you had climbed the tower you had to balance and straddle your legs across two scaffolding poles about two feet apart and eight feet in length, without using hands. I reached that point too soon. The recruit before me refused it and was cautiously guided down by the staff. As he passed me I said, 'Come on Joe, you've got this far, it's a piece of piss. Don't listen to those wankers down there. Just do it.'

He looked at me, wordless, eyes wide open. Beads of sweat covered his face. He was white. It was as if he had found his own level, found peace of mind. The Paras were definitely not for him. I never saw Joe again.

So the pressure was on. With my chest still heaving up and down from the climb, I took the pigeon steps across the parallel bars. The staff below were trying to hurry me up, trying to distract me on purpose: 'Come on down, Devereux, you're too fucking slow, speed it up.'

I blanked them out and concentrated on the task at hand. I was nearly half way across now, clinging on to the bars with the in-step of my boots. As there was mud on the bars, it was frigging slippery. That voice sparked up again. 'Fucking move it, Devereux! We haven't got all day. Straighten your back.'

Fucking idiot, I thought. At the halfway stage were two scaffolding clamps bolted around each of the other bars. At this stage I stopped, stood up as straight as I dared and shouted out my army number at the top of my voice; this was part of the test. 'Good,' I heard the voice say. I lifted my boots over the clamps, managing to keep my balance and not looking down. I then double shuffled across to safety. The barracking voice screamed for the next recruit to go on.

The Platoon losses on the 'Trainazium' were two refusals, one ricked neck, a twisted knee and a mashed-up right hand: the recruit had not kept his fist clenched when punching out at the cargo-net leap when he jumped. Result: three fingers on his right hand now facing the wrong way, having been caught on the ropes.

The end of P Company culminated in a ten-mile speed march

24

in full kit and platoon weapons across Long Valley. This, if we were all honest with ourselves, was the hardest of the tests, coming after an already long, hard-fought week. Niggling injuries which we carried through the training were now fully blown emergency cases. Some blokes could hardly walk after the penultimate day and eight hours in the 'wanking chariot' was not going to solve their problems. My thoughts of that final march are very much blurred now – but I passed, and that was all that mattered.

Having completed P Company at the end of summer, our platoon was now the senior platoon within the Depot, as Platoon 448 was at Advanced Wales and 447 had just passed out and had been posted to their respective Battalions.

Then our Advanced Wales came (much more demanding than Basic Wales). It was now turning cold – October is always cold in the Brecon Beacons. More tabbing, more advance soldiering skills, more tactics; digging in, defence exercises, ambushes. All we had been taught in previous months was to be used on this exercise.

We had been 'dug in' in a defence position for three days on a feature aptly named Concrete Hill and settled down to a routine of stagging on.We lived, ate and slept in the trenches we had dug.

One night I was on a two-hour stag (guard duty) with the GPMG. There was three foot of snow all around us. About half way through I realised I had been thinking every second, What the fuck am I doing here? What is this frigging exercise all about? when I was almost lifted off the ground by slippery Corporal H. He was nicknamed 'slippery' because he was always sneaking up on us, trying to catch us out. He planted one right into my rib cage and shouted 'Wake up.'

'I'm not asleep. I'm fucking *not* asleep, Corporal.'

He grunted – I guess he didn't hear the 'fucking' and said, 'Just watch it, Devereux. You haven't passed yet.'

I thought, Shit, hasn't he got anything else better to do at two o'clock in the frigging morning? But it was an extremely valuable lesson. Sleeping on stag is a crime in any part of the army but even more so in the Paras. Worse than going downtown and killing someone in a fight: at least there's a bit of machismo attached to that, but sleeping on stag, well, you might as well cut your frigging head off.

Eventually, Advanced Wales was over. We arrived back in Aldershot to find who had passed and who had failed. By this stage we all knew who was going to be back squadded. Twenty-five of us were left.

Number One Parachute School at RAF Brize Norton in Oxfordshire was a holiday camp compared to the Parachute Regiment Depot. We were there for four weeks as winter set in to be taught how to static line parachute (as opposed to freefalling) from 800 feet or below. The course was to include two initial jumps from an old barrage balloon and six descents from a Hercules C130 transport aircraft. These eight jumps were deemed sufficient to gain us that most coveted of badges, the British Parachute Wings. The whole course could be covered in one week, given favourable weather. In fairness to the RAF, UK weather is generally unsuitable for static line parachuting during most of the year, and of course, the RAF have their rules. But training the army how to parachute was a little hold they had over us; that's how I saw it and they weren't going to give that up for anything.

PCAU (The Parachute Course Administration Unit), at the end of a runway, comprised about a dozen Nissen huts in a line, relics of the Second World War. Nearby were the newly built, brick single-room barracks for the junior ranks of the RAF, with central heating and carpets. By contrast, a Nissen hut is frigging cold. In December it was warmer outside than in, no matter how much hot air was pumped in.

A thought followed me through the course, and it was with me some years later when I returned to PCAU to train in HALO (High Altitude Low Opening parachuting) with the SAS: Here we were, the students under possibly the most mental pressure in the entire camp, yet our billets were the noisiest, coldest, oldest and furthest from amenities. We were up at five or six most mornings, even earlier if the Met Check the previous evening was favourable. If a jump was cancelled, then we would carry on rehearsing ground drills, equipment checks, attending safety lectures, doing physical training.

Still, the RAF ran the course very professionally and the PJIs (Parachute Jump Instructors) could not be faulted. Safety was

26

paramount to them and that was just as well given the feeling I had in my stomach when the first jump was imminent; I didn't give a shit how many times they checked me!

Our first jump was from the C130 (the barrage balloon was not available for some reason): clean fatigue and single sticks. That is to say, we were not carrying any excess baggage such as weapons, webbing or 80-pound bergens strapped to our legs – that came later. Single sticks meant that we were all to exit the aircraft from the same side door. As we approached the C130 to board, I caught wind of a smell – the smell of fear: a mixture of aircraft fuel, urine and sweat.

Inside, the C130 had been gutted. There are no toilets (except a fixed bucket thing, at the rear of the aircraft); no comfy recliners, just collapsible bench-type seating. The feeling of fear was intense; my chest was heaving. It was a special type of fear, an 'Oh well, fuck it' feeling. A callous throw-away remark concealing the most profound of human emotions. All of us had seats of sorts; but parachutes were very bulky so we were perched half-on and half-off them. The parachutes, PX MkIVs with a front mount reserve, were, as my PJI said, almost totally safe and of accidents involving them, 95 per cent were due to human error, not equipment malfunction. That is, the parachute is great but will only open/function if it has been packed correctly and if the parachutist is competent enough to fly and land it.

Some days before I had read a comment in *The Parachutist* magazine on the 'Incidents' page. (You do this when you're training to become a parachutist, you take in every bit of information you can and try to absorb it to instill confidence in yourself.) It said that on the unfortunate death of a parachutist, the coroner will always record cause of death as 'death by impact', and not, as one might think, cause of death 'Roman Candle' or cause of death 'Crashed through aircraft hangar roof'. (To 'Roman Candle' is to spiral down, normally to your death, with the parachute canopy only partially open and the rigging lines twisted.)

With a deafening roar, the Herc kicked into life. Inside was dark and it smelt like all of Ali Baba's 40 thieves had 'cut one' at the same time. After taxiing, there was another loud shudder and we started our takeoff. A couple of retaining straps wriggled themselves free from the roof of the fuselage and dropped on someone's head behind me. We were all wearing helmets with our names masking-taped on to the front so I expect he was all right; he probably didn't notice. Then a push from the guy behind me really pissed me off. Here we all were on our first parachute jump, trying not to think about anything but the task in hand, and this guy behind me was constantly fidgeting. I gave one sharp push with my parachute, just to let him know that he was fucking me off severely. I shouted, 'Stop fucking pushing, Shit-for-brains.' He didn't hear me because the noise in the C130 was deafening, but he got the message.

The loadie did hear me. His ears had been trained through years of living and flying in the back of C130s. He was straddling the seats, hopping up towards me, paying particular attention to where he put his feet, aware that all his passengers were feeling the same way: apprehensive. I guess he didn't want one of these young Paras to jump up at him and release five months of nervous tension with a swift right hook.

He bent over really close to the side of my face and, with his right hand, half held back his right-hand earpiece and said, 'What's the problem?'

'That twat behind me, he keeps pushing my parachute.'

'That's OK, he's just puked up and he's feeling a bit rough.'

I nodded. Fucking typical, I thought. Then I asked, 'Hey, loadie, can you check my parachute?' I thought the bumping had done something to it; maybe the pack had been cut open and was exposing the chute. Of course it was a ridiculous thought. Common sense only comes with experience, or as the PJIs' motto on their badge reads, 'Knowledge Dispels Fear'. Still, I was worried.

'Yeah, bend forward.'

A second later he gave it a hard slap on the back, which really pissed me off. 'Yeah, Devereux, it's still there.'

Funny cunt, I thought. His idea of a joke. He grinned; I frowned back. He turned and balanced his way back down to take his place on the ramp at the rear of the aircraft. The aircraft suddenly banked to port and dropped, as I thought, through hundreds of feet. But I could see the loadie enjoying his job. He was grinning, talking into his mouthpiece to the pilot, hands on hips as the aircraft banked violently. Alley bastard, I thought.

You could not hear anything above the roar of the engines. The only way to communicate was eye contact, and everyone's eyes showed fear, pure fear. We had eyes like shithouse rats as we soared above the Oxfordshire countryside.

An incredible surge of adrenalin shot through me as the doors were opened. My first jump. Noise intensified as a rush of cold icy air spewed towards me and filled the aircraft. It was winter. We were travelling at 120 knots per hour and the temperature was minus 30 plus. I was waiting to jump with bollocks the size of peanuts.

The next thing I noticed was how peaceful it was. I felt suddenly warm from the adrenalin rushing through me. It was quiet and I was floating in midair. I took a few seconds to regain my posture, then checked if the parachute had opened; it had. Then it happened so quick, I landed. Shit, I thought, that was so fucking quick. Unbelievable.

One of the PJIs from the DZ (Drop Zone) party came up to me. 'You all right?'

'I think so.'

'Nice one. Get this parachute sorted out and get yourself a brew over by the trucks.' He left to walk towards a parachutist still in the air. With his loud hailer raised to his mouth all I could hear him shout was 'Steer away. Steer away you clown.' In the distance I could hear that same PJI giving Barney a bollocking.

'Didn't you see him? Well, didn't you?' He pointed to an object still wrapped up in his canopy on the ground some ten feet away. 'Didn't you hear me saying, "Steer away, steer away," Barnes?'

'No,' said Barney. I shouted across to Barney. 'Hey.'

Barney turned and we both gave ourselves the thumbs up. I thought, I've done it, I've fucking actually done it!

My second jump came and went; I was oblivious of it – my training took over. But my third jump was painful. The winds were up and for some unknown reason I found myself in total twists, when the rigging lines get twisted up around one another. The drill to get out of this (a self-induced act caused by 'not forcefully attacking the slip stream of the aircraft when you make your exit') is to get your head back as far as you can and pull the two main risers apart and twist *out*, rather like untwisting a child's garden swing. Because I had exited the aircraft like a wet fart, I was twisted so much that I could not get my head back to see which way the twists were going. In turn, the canopy was partially deflated. Thoughts of pulling my reserve parachute did cross my mind. I could see that I was falling but, it seemed, not at any great speed. However, I had missed the DZ and was now being blown over towards a dual carriageway. I was turning slowly all the time, getting a panoramic view of the landscape. The road disappeared. Thank Christ for that, I thought. Thoughts of pulling my reserve were well misguided. You only pull your reserve if you experience 'a total' malfunction. The Para macho view held that if you landed with two canopies flying at once, then you must have flapped during a jump and from that day on you were to be known as Flapper. It was on a parallel with sleeping on stag. I wouldn't have wanted that.

I kept my cool as I came into land. I was moving sideways to my right. It felt quite fast. I stopped rotating seconds before I landed. Very well timed, I thought. The ground was looming up at me. It was quiet, very quiet, just the rushing of the wind and the gentle rustle of a partially deflated parachute. I had had no real experience of 'ground rush', up until now, that was. Ground rush happens, and so does shit.

Knees and feet tight together, knees and feet tight together. Get in a good tight position. I remembered my training. Fuck me, I thought, I'm coming for a sideways right landing. Shit! Into what? 'Think, Devereux, *think*,' I can remember saying to myself.

By now I was flapping big style. Seconds before impact. All the drills I was taught came to me instinctively. I guess that's why RAF teach this style; it works.

I hit the ground with so much force that I was dazed for a few seconds. I wanted to lie there and get my thoughts together, only the wind got up, and my parachute started to drag me across some pigpens and through all the shit.

There was something drastically wrong with the right hand side of my body; I couldn't move my right arm to grab the bottom riser of the chute to collapse it. I came to a halt at the side of one of the (luckily empty) pigpens. I released myself as much as I could from my harness, then tried to straighten up to sort myself out.

A search patrol from the DZ party arrived quickly. Everyone in my 'stick' had been blown off course by some freak gust of wind. If

I believed that, I would believe anything. More like pilot error or someone on the ground party had cocked up the release point, I thought.

The DZ party radioed through to a medic who showed up soon after. He could see that I was in pain. There was no way I could carry on jumping, so I was unceremoniously dumped outside the parachute hanger and advised to go to the Medical Centre after lunch at 14.00hrs and to make my own way back to PCAU admin hut, where the RSM was waiting to see me. I put my red beret on, straightened up, adjusted my parachute smock and walked as smartly as I could back to PCAU, trying not to show the RAF what pain I was really in. I could sense a few sniggers from some RAF lads seeing my swagger: 'Fucking Para bastard, look at him!'

As I drew level I turned and said, 'Good afternoon lads' in my best Rupert voice.

A chorus of replies came back. 'Afternoon sir', followed by a volley of salutes. Dumb cunts, I thought. I grinned all the way back to PCAU, then dumped my stuff and went to report to the RSM.

At the admin hut, nobody seemed to be around. My shoulder was now really screaming with pain and for some unknown reason I had not looked at it. I knocked on the RSM's door. 'Come in.' I tried to march in correctly but the pain was too much. I came to a halt right in front of the centre of the RSM's desk. Without even looking up he said, 'Name?' I replied. 'You're the wanker with the bruised shoulder. I've spoke to the medic and he says that you should be alright tomorrow. Now fuck off and get that basha of yours sorted. I'll be around to inspect it later on.'

As I was just about to leave he told me to report to the doctor at the Medical Centre at 14.00hrs, then report back to him.

From the doctor I learnt that I had snapped half an inch off my right clavicle. He immediately hospitalised me and that evening I went for an emergency operation under a general anaesthetic.

I spent Christmas Day 1978 in RAF Wroughton Hospital in Wiltshire. The RSM of PCAU visited me and apologised for his tone. I was surprised at his concern and rather flattered. It was another valuable lesson I learnt during my parachute training. Respect and pride. He didn't have to come and see me at all. After all, who was I? just another faceless crow without his wings up.

31

I was downgraded for two months, then returned to complete my parachute training and shortly after flew to Berlin. I was posted to Four Platoon, B Company, The Second Battalion the Parachute Regiment.

I only spent six weeks in Berlin before I was posted back to the UK for preparation for a two-year tour of Northern Ireland. I was not worried about leaving Berlin; it seemed drab and very grey. The 'Wall' was still standing, which gave the whole tour a sinister, Cold War feeling: armed American, French and British soldiers cutting around the place; military vehicles on every street corner.

I was stationed in the old German Paratrooper barracks, Brooke Barracks. A year earlier the parade ground around the barracks was being relaid when the workmen dug up tons of live ammunition, stick grenades and MP39s (a very accurate and reliable machine pistol named the 'Schmeisser' which had laid to rest many a British soldier during World War Two). A heavy guard was posted around the parade ground while this old war stock was lifted. There was a rumour flying around the Battalion that many of these MP39s had been nicked before the guard was in place and for the next year there were 'snap' searches of lockers and personal kit. But nothing was ever found.

Being posted to Berlin did give me a chance to renew old friends and meet up with Barney. One evening he took me downtown to show me the lights. If Berlin was grey during the day, by night it certainly wasn't. One thing I learnt about the Germans was that they did like their beer and food. They could eat and drink all night long. Before I had always assumed them to be quite a sober and calculating race.

Over the past few weeks I had had an introduction to the pubs and clubs where the paras socialised. Imaginable and unimaginable sexual opportunities were on offer. If there was any doubt about a young soldier's sexuality, Berlin was the place to sort that out. I already knew what I liked. I'm a tits and bum man, strictly heterosexual. Mind you, with a few beers inside them, the bright lights of a strange city and a sense of adventure, it's not hard to understand why a few of the blokes mistook what they thought to be a beautiful woman's advances as the genuine article, only to find out, after a heavy petting session that the night was turning into a nightmare as groping downstairs to check out the 'old furry triangle' met with 'a meat and two veg' dish. These clubs were duly noted and frequented by those who felt the need for something different!

But if I thought Berlin was the 'Grey City' divided into quarters of nationalities, I was soon to learn how grey life could actually be in the religiously divided city of Belfast.

CHAPTER TWO

Northern Ireland – Legitimate Target

ANDERSONSTOWN WAS not a nice place to be in the late 1970s. This part of Belfast was a thousand times worse than the Turkish sector of Berlin. Certain inhabitants of this shithole regarded you as a legitimate target. Our task was to patrol four-strong in two cut-down, half-ton Land Rovers to establish snap VCPs (Vehicle Check Points) and maintain a continuous presence on the ground. It was the first time that a Parachute Battalion had been in the area for years, and stories of Bloody Sunday and Operation Motorman were rife. Those old sweats who were there at the time unofficially briefed us new blokes on just how hard and dangerous the PIRA (Provisional Irish Republican Army) were, and just how awkward and cunning their followers could be.

We took over the old rundown police station from an infantry Battalion who had been on a six-month tour. They had lost two men through sniper fire, plus one dead and four injured when the PIRA detonated a bomb under a culvert when a mobile patrol drove over it. Because of these two incidents it was their CO's policy not to patrol their area after 21.00hrs and certainly not before breakfast the following morning. This, of course, allowed the PIRA the run of the area during the hours of darkness, during which time they could basically do what they liked, from moving weapons and bomb-making equipment around, to carrying out knee-cappings and generally beating up anyone who didn't toe the party line.

I listened intensely to the brief given to us by my patrol commander. Two earlier briefings given beforehand as we were getting our kit sorted out were conducted by the Int (Intelligence) officer – a crow with no practical patrol experience – who seemed to be reading from a Sandhurst brief written for a full attack on Belfast. Brummie P was a Lance Jack (Lance Corporal) with one tour under his belt, back in 1976 in West Belfast. I was glad to be in his patrol. He was a no-nonsense guy who 'didn't take no shit'. More importantly, he knew the score all too well. He had been shot at, bombed and bottled, all in the space of one hour, during a riot on his last tour: a good guy to be around when the shit hit the fan.

During the day Para mobile patrols sent out before us were tasked to gain local knowledge of the area and to report any sightings of 'players' or anything unusual. But nothing was reported, the area was quiet and no events had occurred. A few stones thrown, the usual verbal abuse, that was all.

It was dark by the time we got down to the loading bay. I had signed for one Land Rover and made sure that it was all fuelled up, ready to go. I was the driver in the first vehicle, with Brummie in the commander's seat. The other vehicle was to follow at a safe distance, not letting us out of its sight. This, my first-ever patrol in NI, was the first night patrol ordered for at least six months and, going by previous Int reports from other units, probably a lot longer than that. The four of us lined up, weapons pointing towards the sand bank which made up part of the loading bay.

'OK! Make ready. Check your safety catches. Let's not have any NDs on this tour, you twats,' Brummie grinned, aware that he was taking a bunch of crows out on their first patrol and not wanting any Negligent Discharge of Weapons.

We cocked our SLRs simultaneously and applied the safety catches. Brummie told me to get the wagon started. In the meantime he was doing one last check with the other blokes in the patrol.

'Right, while Devs is getting the wagon sorted, Taff?'

'Yeah.'

'You got the FRG and rounds?'

'No probs, it's here with me.' Taff had the Federal Riot Gun slung over his left shoulder, and the plastic bullets to go with it were in his chest bandolier.

'Mark, the medical pack?'

'Yep.'

'And Paul, you got the box of tricks and make sure it's turned on, will you?' The 'box of tricks' was a piece of kit designed to pick up radio signals put out by Radio Controlled Devices (RCDs) – bombs.

The Land Rover roared into life. Brummie got in beside me and Taff and Paul jumped on the back. The rear vehicle was already waiting to go, ticking over on the far side of the compound. Brummie told me to drive over to Johnno, who was the Second In Command (2IC) of the patrol and IC of the second wagon, to emphasise that he was to stay close. It was a particularly dark night and since we would be driving with no lights, he didn't want to lose visual contact.

The guard saw we were ready to go and opened one of the two huge steel doors just wide enough for us to clear. This was it, I thought, out into the murky depths of shitsville. The patrol was to be about two hours and as I drove around that first night I felt, yes here we were, the Paras back in Belfast, ready to kick shit out of anyone who stood in our way. It was misguided arrogance.

We had not been going for five minutes when a crowd of kids started to pelt us with stones. It was pitch-black driving around these housing estates – the street lighting had been knocked out for obvious tactical reasons by the PIRA. A few gunshots rang out in the vicinity which we reported back to HQ. We were told to continue with the patrol. Setting snap VCPs became the order of the night and because our Limit of Exploration (LOE) was relatively small, and as it had only one main road running through it, there was a limit to how many we could set up without creating a pattern. I remember stopping one guy four times that night; on the last occasion he wanted to know why the army had, after all this time, started to patrol at night and that stopping him four times was an infringement of his personal rights, constituting harassment by the British Army. Being a bit naïve and actually seeing his point of view, I was just about to regard his comments as well founded when Brummie came over and asked me the problem. I explained.

'Right!' he screamed. 'Out of the fucking car NOW! Hands on your head. Come on, come on, spread your legs,' he ordered.

The man did as he was told. I could feel the situation building up. This was the first time Brummie had intervened in the VPC operation, confining himself before to radio-through P-checks (verifying a person's identity) when we asked for them. He had, up until now, been happy to take a stand-off position to allow us to get on with the job to see how we fared. Now he was showing what made him a switched on soldier. He told me to turn the engine and turn the lights off, and asked the man his name. On P-checking his name I found out that he was well 'Traced' PIRA. Brummie told me to cover him whilst he searched the man. He placed his weapon down on the road and put his boot on top of it. Brummie conducted a body search, then whipped out a plastic-cuff from under his flak vest and secured the man's hands behind his back as he protested profusely. Brummie picked up his weapon and said, 'Right, now let's have a look in the boot.' He began to search the rest of the vehicle. When Brummie was happy that nothing illegal was being carried, he cut the man's hands free and told him to fuck off. As he started up his engine he made one last stupid threat: 'I'm gonna get youse you fucker, you see if I don't.'

'Is that right?' Brummie said, and with that, threw a quick punch through the opened car window which landed square on the man's nose, causing it to break and bleed. Brummie then grabbed him in a one-handed Vulcan death grip, squeezing his cheeks together and said, 'Now, tell your cunts not to fuck around with my blokes!'

Two hours went by a lot faster than I realised. Back in the compound after the official debrief, Brummie gave us one of his own. He told us: 'If you drop your guard out there just once, you're in the shit. You could let a weapon, bomb or whatever slip by you if you switch off even for one second. Just because some pretty girl smiles at you and puts you off concentrating, or some fucker tries it on by driving into VCPs deliberately, just to see how switched on we are. You put us all at risk, not only that patrol, but possibly the next patrol who has to come out after us.'

'But he did have a point, being stopped four times in less than an hour,' Taff said.

'Fuck me, do I have to spell it out to you? The PIRA had years to get their game plan sorted out and will try absolutely anything to get one over on us. Taking a Para out would be like winning the football pools to them. So when you are working with me in this area you treat everyone as "Traced," you got that?' Brummie went on: 'I don't want my balls blown off just because one of you twats decides to play Mr Diplomat. Start switching on, the lot of you.' He finished with 'not a bad effort' to everyone.

We had 90 minutes to get some scoff, clean weapons and check our kit before the next patrol.

It was one of my unofficial tasks as driver to keep a supply of small nuts and bolts in the front of the wagon; the smaller the better. They were to be fired by catapult at the dogs which the PIRA trained to roam around the estates to attack the security forces, and for the kids who thought throwing stones at us was great fun.

During the next month we all had a secondary weapon, the catapult. Some of the blokes had shit-hot ones. Neatly welded together and fully loaded, they could stop a charging German Shepherd at 30 feet. We had quite a high doggie count. The dogs kept coming, but the stone throwing stopped.

When we left Andersonstown, we left the Royal Electrical and Mechanical Engineers (REME) guy wondering where all his nuts and bolts had gone.

Two months into the tour, the Battalion's Tactical Area of Responsibility (TAOR) changed. We were ordered into the notorious area of South Armagh, nicknamed 'bandit country', operating out of three locations: Forkhill, Bessbrook Mill and the town of Newry. The two main operating bases were Forkhill, with one company and Newry, with half of one company. A Quick Reaction Force (QRF) element was located at Bessbrook Mill, the other half of a company. The remainder of the Battalion was stationed at Ballykinlar, a camp set right on the east coast of the province and the main Rest and Recuperation (R&R) location for the rest of the Battalion, which also acted as our permanent location for the two-year tour.

I settled into the company's monthly routine of operations – Forkhill, R&R at Ballykinlar, operations from Bessbrook and Newry. There was still a lot to learn and Brummie, with his dry, hard approach to life, was a good teacher. Early on in the tour, August 1979, I was part of the QRF working out of Bessbrook Mill. I had just popped into the Ops room to pick up a map of one of the border check points – for a route-clearance operation the following morning – when a bomb contact report came over the net. Initially, all of us in the Ops room thought it involved a Royal Marine detachment who were patrolling in Warrenpoint, and sent the initial report. Later, when we were sent as the QRF to the incident, we learnt the truth.

Two four tonners and a Land Rover from A Company, 2 Para, had left Ballykinlar camp that afternoon and were on route, with stores and equipment, to help back up the route clearance operation. As they approached the Warrenpoint-to-Newry dual carriageway, they passed a trailer-load of hay, parked off in a lay-by. The trailer was parked at a place called Narrow Water, the nearest point to the Republic of Ireland along that stretch. A 500lb radio-controlled bomb detonated, catching the rear four tonner, blasting it into a mangled mesh. Six blokes from A Company had been killed outright, and initial reports coming back thick and fast into the Ops room at Bessbrook said there were only two survivors.

I was told to get the wagon ready for a fast drive to the incident. Then the orders changed. We were to be choppered in; quicker and a lot safer. Two Wessex helicopters were standing by. Rumour was rife. We all had mates in A Company and speculated who had been killed and who were the survivors. I knew of at least six blokes from 449 Platoon that had been posted to A Company, including Barney and another good mate of mine. My mind was working overtime. I had only been in the province a couple of months so although I had seen a few things, nothing had prepared me for the next 24 hours. It was to be the rudest awakening to the consequences of terrorism.

The chopper blades were already turning when we made the short walk from the compound to the heli-pad, the only place where you had to leave the relative safety of the compound. It always struck me as strange and stupid to have the only means of transport to get you into 'bandit country' detached and in a seemingly insecure site. (Some years later when I was back at Bessbrook with the SAS, things had not changed.)

As always, the Wessex strained to gain height to clear the high wire fencing which was the heli-pad's only protection from a rocket attack. Though it might be only for a short take-off time, we were now at our most vulnerable. The chopper shuddered and whined as it rose. The loadie was hanging out of the only door, directing the pilot over the top of the last part of the fence, a two-foot stack of razor wire. When he was sure the wheels were clear he closed the door. We were expecting an overnight stay so we had our bergens (rucksacks) as well as the usual complement of weapons, ammunition and webbing.

It was impossible to talk over the noise of the chopper. We were flying low-level and the pilot's actions indicated he was taking this particular task very seriously. He was flying into a hot DZ and we all didn't fancy being shot out of the sky by a fluke Rocket Propelled Grenade (RPG) attack.

Back at the incident, two Land Rover patrols from the Machine Gun Platoon, on patrol around Newry at the time, had also been dispatched. My mate Gerry was in that patrol. I remember hearing him on the radio, back at the Ops room, his voice full of seriousness at the thought of being first to arrive at the site.

The chopper ride lasted about 15 minutes, and I had time to reflect on what we were approaching. This was my first major incident and it was hard to deal with knowing that I was going to be confronted with my first sight of death. It could have been any of the Security Forces lying there. It made it harder when they were blokes you knew. Good mates. Paratroopers.

I gripped my SLR with both hands and squeezed my knees together, gaining some comfort from the thought that I had the protection of 100 7.62mm rounds to fire, should the shit hit the fan. The M79 I slung over my back gave me added security as it cut into my old parachuting wound. I could see Brummie becoming more agitated in a conversation with the navigator. He eased himself back down and shouted into Taff's ear. The message was passed along with a look of disbelief. 'There's another bomb gone off in the same area. No word of any casualties. The pilot's going to land us as close as possible, without ripping the arse out of it, and once he dumps us off he's fucking off, back to bring in more backup.'

There seemed to be a tone of apprehension in his voice. The

message had been passed down three blokes before it got to me, and I was just thinking what to make of it all when suddenly the loadie made a move to the door. The chopper banked violently and shuddered. The loadie was quick to slide the door open. The noise increased and the effect of cold air from the outside somehow seemed to dispel the fear that we were landing on one hell of a hot DZ. I could see the ground below as the chopper began to descend. With a heavy jolt we hit terra firma. We scrambled out to form an all-round defence position whilst the loadie and the last man threw all the bergens and other pieces of kit out as quickly as possible. Then, within seconds, the Wessex disappeared. The other chopper landed some way off in a different field. This was for security reasons rather than convenience; if the PIRA staged another ambush, two choppers together were a greater target.

When the second bomb had gone off, a Wessex that had landed on the dual carriageway to recover wounded from the first explosion had taken some of the force of the blast, making the pilot of our Wessex think very hard about *our* safety. This bomb was thought to be twice the size of the first; a 1000-pounder.

I looked around to get my first real experience of a terrorist attack. The smell was incredible. The only way I could have explained it, would be a fresh morning after Bonfire Night, mixed with an acrid barbecue odour – charred human flesh. I could see Brummie talking to a member of the Machine Gun Platoon who had run up on to the field when he saw the chopper land. Brummie beckoned half of us to join him; the rest were to remain at their defensive position. Moving toward Brummie I could see red berets and a couple of policemen who, I reckoned, had been called out from Warrenpoint RUC station, running around crossing the road and shouting to one another. Then more confusion as two other choppers landed. Both sides of the dual carriageway had been sealed off by the RUC. The debris of mangled Land Rovers, four tonners and 18 soldiers covered the area for hundreds of metres. This scene of total carnage was never to leave me. It was probably the hardest introduction any of us could have had to the horrors of what had been, and quite obviously is still, happening in Northern Ireland. That was the only positive thing I could remember from what I learned that day, 27 August 1979.

41

Waiting for the rest of the Company to arrive, our immediate task was to secure the area on the far side of the dual carriageway and face outwards towards the Republic. Gerry, my mate in the Machine Guns, came running over to me to tell his account of the past two hours.

'We were out on a mobile.' He stopped to get his breath. He was still shaking. 'We were just outside Newry when we heard this fuck-off explosion. Jimmy sent the contact report at the same time as a Marine did. We drove like fucking nutters.'

'Did you have a clue what was happening?'

'Yeah. We reckoned the PIRA had detonated a fuck-off device but we didn't know jack-shit else. We put two and two together and raced out here towards Warrenpoint to see what was what. When we got here, I mean, shit, there was crap all over the place, just like now, but it was still burning and the blokes were all running around, trying to do a body count and patch up the two survivors.'

I asked if he knew any names. He said no, not yet. He only confirmed that it was a platoon from A Company. We were cut short when someone from his platoon called him. 'Gerry, get your arse over here. The boss wants to know about the shooting.'

'Shooting?' I said. 'You've been shooting as well?'

'Yeah, give us a couple minutes and I'll come back over. I reckon the fuckers are still over there somewhere, waiting to get us with a third bomb.' Gerry shot off over towards what was left of an old, stone-built gatehouse, the lodge of a country house, and left me with a feeling of, 'Fuck, this isn't over yet, by far.' The PIRA could have put bombs all over the place and it was possible they were just sitting back in the forest, 100 or so metres across the estuary that divided the North from the South. They could be watching every movement we made.

I quickly looked around to see what the rest of the blokes were up to. They were facing south, watching their arcs of fire. Trying to make myself as small a target as possible and get into cover from view as well as cover from fire, I reminded myself that I was wearing the biggest marker for any would-be sniper, a red beret. Better keep the head moving! I waited nervously for Gerry to come back with more news. The smell of cordite was still thick in the air. It was a hot summer's afternoon with little or no wind so the smell was going to be around for a while. I was breathing heavily, and tried to compose myself and make sense of what I was witnessing. I told myself that many soldiers had seen all this before, but as I lay there looking around at the dismembered bodies, limbs ripped off in a millisecond, guts ripped open by the massive amount of secondary fragmentation, I wondered, Has anybody in this country witnessed carnage on such a colossal scale? I doubted it very much then, and still do.

I tried to make out where the bits of debris immediately around me had come from. A piece of angled metal embedded into the dry stone wall that I was using as protection I recognised right away: part of an SLR. I pulled it free and stuffed it down the front of my flak jacket. Everywhere I looked I could make out bits of body: the remains of a torso high up in a tree to the right; forward of me, on the estuary's beach, intestines and what looked like half a head, the face side. The explosion had cut the head clean off at the neck and had somehow bisected it from top to bottom. I looked for the back half, but didn't find it. Then Gerry rushed over to me again. I asked what he'd just done.

'Oh, I fired off a few rounds. We were taking incoming when the second bomb went off, so a few of us let rip into the forest over there. I saw two blokes, and taking them to be the firing point, I slotted one and then took cover, but as I did, I must have knocked my sight out of zero. I tried to slot the other fucker but he disappeared back into the forest. The boss wanted to know how many rounds I let rip.'

I was looking out across the water but kept nodding, suggesting that I was taking it all in.

'Anyway, we managed to get the wounded into the Wessex which happened to be in the air at the time. He's flying them back to Bessbrook. He landed up there on the road, just past the gatehouse. Someone had established the CP at the gatehouse, and as we were all trying to help out, you know, secure the area, there was this horrendous explosion. It threw me over and stunned me for a couple seconds. The place was covered in shit and stone. The dust didn't settle for ages. You couldn't see fuck all. Shit was still falling for at least half an hour. Well, you can see it's still in the air now.' He was right – a cloud of dust and crap was still visible above us.

43

He went on. 'We had a Gazelle landing with the CO QOH' – referring to the Queen's Own Highlanders. He pointed half right to where we were lying. 'He was running down to meet the boss when it went up. It took out our Land Rovers which were parked down by the CP.'

'Fuck me Gerry! Who did you lose?'

'Well, we're not sure yet, but at least 15. And we haven't accounted for everybody yet.'

Later on during the afternoon, I was detailed, along with the rest of 4 Platoon, to 'area clean' the incident of human remains. I picked up a pair of boots with the feet still in them, socks pulled up. The blast had neatly cut the legs off at the top of the socks. There was no blood. I could not find the rest of the body. Just a pair of booted feet with about 14 inches of leg still in them. Other blokes were assigned to stand guard over the remains of our mates. The amount of their remains grew and grew as the evening wore on.

Soon I was to learn the full extent of our Battalion's loss. Sixteen Paras and the CO and his signaller of 1 Queens Own Highlanders. Six blokes that I had come through Depot at Aldershot with had been killed, including my good friend Barney. Another close mate from Depot was badly injured. He had 80 per cent burns and was not expected to live. Later, on my first R&R back to the UK, I went to visit him in the Queen Elizabeth Hospital in Woolwich and saw the extent of his injuries for the first time. He was trussed up on a spitlike contraption, just like a pig roast, being turned constantly, ever so slowly. He had been like this ever since he was flown there immediately after the bombing, six months before: hung up like a piece of meat. But it was vital to his survival. It was important that his skin tissue repair to prevent scarring. His face had not been burnt and when I saw him that day he was smiling. We had a good talk and it was he who brought up the subject of Barney. Apparently he and Barney were sitting at the back of the four tonner. They tossed up for who was to get to sit at the rear. This mate won, so Barney had to sit one in from the back. When the bomb went off, he and the other guy sitting back-to-back were the only two thrown out. Only he could know what was going on in his head; the mental pressure must have been overpowering. It was about a year before he could actually stand up on his feet. The

NORTHERN IRELAND

Above: Me taking cover during a patrol near Forkhill, 1980.

Left: Colleagues on a border patrol in 'Bandit Country' – South Armagh, near Crossmaglen.

Above: Border patrol disembarking from a Wessex helicopter and running for cover.

Right: The aftermath of the Warrenpoint explosion which killed so many British soldiers. This is the wreckage of a four-ton truck. The water behind it is the estuary marking the border with the South.

EAST FALKLAND

Above: Argy photograph of my OP's Howitzer fire landing on an enemy-held target.

Left: Me after the battle for Goose Green. On the left, a dead Argy.

Above: The harrowing
view I had from Fitzroy
of the *Sir Galahad*
burning after an Argy
air attack. 8 June 1982.

Below: I took this shot of a fellow Para when we were under fire during the battle for Goose Green.

Right: I got a mate to take this of me on the victorious march into ravaged Port Stanley after the Argy surrender. All that remained of the burnt wooden houses were their gaunt masonry chimneystacks.

Left: Here I'm ready for the offensive for Port Stanley. You can see why I thought the Falklands landscape was like the Brecon Beacons where I had trained – except for the startling lack of trees.

Left: It's all over for them: Argy prisoners of war under escort in Port Stanley.

Left: Spoils of war: a
bayonet I took from a
dead Argy after the
battle for Goose Green.

Above: It's all over for
us: a packed landing
craft approaching the
MV Norland to take the
Paras home to the UK.

Regiment looked after him very well during his convalescence, but returning back to normal duty was not to be for him. He left the Regiment he loved so dearly and returned to civvy life the best he could.

Warrenpoint was not the only incident to happen that day. On the morning of 27 August 1979, Lord Louis Mountbatten, the 79-year-old uncle of the Queen, was killed when the PIRA detonated a bomb on his boat whilst he was holidaying in the Republic.

After such an incident one would have thought that the Battalion's morale would be as low as could be. Not the case. The Battalion went on to conduct its business as usual, carrying out the domination of South Armagh to such an extent that the PIRA kept their heads down.

There had been talk of revenge by the blokes – going out at night and taking out known terrorists. It would have been quite simple to get the right man because we all had access to the Intelligence Cell and it would have been easy to get addresses, photos, a routine of their lifestyles and last known sightings. To my knowledge, no revenge killings were ever carried out by the blokes; but I'm sure many came close to it.

Life on the border in South Armagh was a game of cat and mouse. Forkhill was a village just 200 metres north of the border and just down the road from the infamous town of Crossmaglen. It could have been a picture postcard village to an outsider, with a little river running through it, two single lane, stone-built bridges, a pub, a post office, a school and a little hairdresser's shop.

'Such a cute little village this is,' said an American tourist I stopped one day at a VCP. 'Yeah, but don't go out at night, will you? You might get your frigging balls cut off by these bastards.'

The only feature out of place was the RUC and Army barracks. It dominated this little village, with 20-foot steel walls, and a wire mesh and corrugated roof. It had several large sangars (fortified look-out posts) strategically placed around its perimeter, manned 24 hours a day. One overlooked the rear bedroom window of a house on a nearby housing estate, where a woman would regularly give night shows to the lucky guy on duty. We had all sorts of magic viewing aids in the sangars and since the bedroom was only 20 metres away you could view everything in intimate detail. One of her party tricks was to pretend that she was screwing some guy and she pushed all manner of objects up her vagina. And she was pretty good at it.

The OC knew about this, and quite rightly let the show go on. It was good for morale. You could always tell when she was performing; more than one guy would make his way up the sangar's steel ladder. The OC finally put a stop to it all when, some weeks later, a flatbed lorry pulled up at the far end of the housing estate and let rip with half a dozen homemade mortars. Luckily nobody was killed but they blew shit out of the heli-pad and the shithouse. The lady was subsequently arrested and brought into the compound for questioning. We didn't see her again.

Our job was to patrol all the surrounding area. We were given a TAOR which stretched as far as Crossmaglen and, of course, we had a few miles of border to look after as well. We spent the days and nights setting up ambushes, VCPs, house raids and arrests of suspected terrorists. You name it, we did it – generally in the pissing rain. That's all it ever did in South Armagh. I never understood why the locals lived there.

You could go for days, sometimes weeks, without any incidents, making it a hell of a strain for the soldier to take his job seriously. However, the odd snipe from across the border or the sighting of a suspect Improvised Explosive Device (IED) was enough to make us all switch on again.

None of the Security Forces ever drove round Forkhill or the surrounding area. It was far too dangerous. The whole area was full of suspect culverts and booby traps designed to entice the army into a 'come on'. When we did travel around in vehicles, it was to clear road routes in support of the REs (Royal Engineers), the police and other agencies; then we used armoured personnel carriers called Saracens: large six-wheeled, armour-plated vehicles with a top speed of about 30 mph.

On one occasion I was out on a mobile just coming in to Newry from Bessbrook Mill. The only route into town was down the Monaghan Road, notorious for getting a good stoning from the locals, followed by the occasional burst from snipers who used the nearby housing estate as a sanctuary. We were four up in two half-ton, cut-down Land Rovers; no roofs or armour plating, just a riot shield for windscreen protection.

Checkers was driving the lead wagon and I the rear. As we approached the downward slope of Monaghan Road, which took us past 'sniper alley' and then into Newry, we saw quite a large crowd of kids gathering on the playing fields on the left hand side of the road some 50 metres away. Then they started showering us with rocks and stones, bits of wood and milk bottles filled with shit and piss. The brief was to drive straight through. Checkers put his foot down and I followed suit. He got by, but I had trouble controlling the Land Rover: 50 downhill was as much as the wagon wanted to do. I was also late in pulling up the riot shield. Brummie was screaming for me to get a move on whilst the guys in the back were doing their best to cover themselves from the barrage raining down. The windscreen shattered; I swerved to keep control of the wagon. Braking heavily I brought us to a halt, the curb and a lamppost being our saving grace. We debussed rapidly and took cover behind the wagon.

By this time Checkers had seen what had happened and came screaming back up the hill. Brummie sent a 'contact report' back to Newry as Checkers reached us and gave cover. There was no way the four of us could fit in the lead wagon: all eight had to sit it out and wait for the QRF. Apart from that, we couldn't leave the smashed wagon for the rioters; that would have been unPara-like, and I would have got a fearsome slagging from the rest of the platoon.

'. . . roger, about 150. The whole place has erupted. Send ETA, over,' Brummie screamed into the radio.

'November Two Charlie. With you figures five, over.'

'November Two Charlie. This is Mike One Alpha. Roger that. Be aware that the mob is now on the road and blocking your entry. We are located halfway up the hill opposite the school crossing, over.'

'Mike One Alpha, November Two Charlie. Stand by for your crowd to bomb burst. With you, figures two. Wait, out to you, Zero acknowledge, over.'

'Zero acknowledged, out.'

Zero was the Ops room back at Newry, where the duty signaller was logging the exact movements of all the call signs out on the ground and plotting the route of the QRF to target.

The tension was growing second by second. I felt my heart beating in quick time. I had heard of many stories in the past where the mob would just engulf a patrol which didn't respond by firing to protect themselves. Patrols had been ripped apart by these mobs, weapons and kit stolen, the bodies found later, throats cut. What had started out as a routine mobile patrol had turned into a fullscale riot and the 'full Monty' of the Security Forces were being mobilised. Choppers were flying above us and RUC wagons appeared and were racing across the playing fields on their way to cut off the rioters in a pincer movement with the QRF.

Brummie shouted orders to the others, then turned to me, grinning. 'Hey, Devs, we're gonna have to put you on a driving course, you wanker, what do you reckon?'

I couldn't tell if he was serious or just taking the piss. In two years, I could never get to grips with his accent. So I said nothing.

The shelling stopped and the riot was dissipated as the QRF appeared – just like the cavalry. I could see the RUC fighting with a couple of the ringleaders, trying to make arrests. Then the QRF – two cans (Saracens) and four Land Rovers – appeared. On seeing this the crowd fled as quickly as they had appeared. The boss man came over to see the damage. It was the first time in ten minutes we were able to stand up. A security cordon was put up around us.

Looking around, the boss made his mind up. 'Hey Brummie, get your patrol together, get in the cans and let's get the fuck out of here – NOW.' 'Leave the wagon, it's fucked. This smells like a "come on".'

We all piled into the two cans and screamed off to Newry. That's when I found out how unstable these vehicles really were. The RCT driver was good, but not that good. As we came hurtling down towards Merchant's Quay, the main drag through Newry, he went out of control, mounted the pavement and took out a parked Morris Marina, squashing it flat against a brick wall before stabilising. Brummie ripped into him big style back at the compound. It was then the unwritten law amongst us all that can drivers were not to go over 30 miles an hour, even though the clock went up to 80.

The riot was another move up the learning curve of being in Northern Ireland. I learned that I had to be more confident within

48

myself. I could now control my fears and anxieties. I was a better soldier for that riot, although I didn't do anything. All I did was to get under cover and watch. I was lucky, I thought. Blokes in the early 1970s did not have the chance I had. I had time to think and take in all that was happening around me: how Brummie reacted; how the other patrol adopted good fire positions when they came up to help. I took it all in.

The riot *was* a 'come on' set up by the local PIRA. Twelve shots were fired during that incident: seven at us by the damaged Land Rover, a couple at the RUC during their arrests, and the rest at the QRF. The can that I was picked up in had a 5.56mm Armalite strike, smack bang centre of the driver's glass viewing prism – a ten-by-four inch slit the driver used to look through. Normally it was held in the 'open' position, but that day the driver had accidentally snapped off one of the retaining brackets so it could not stay open. You can talk about Murphy's Law, but I reckoned we had had our fair share of luck as well. For example, Pete T, a full screw (a two-stripe Corporal) from another patrol, was carrying out a routine border search. He stopped the patrol to do a snap VCP, and as he turned around to flag the first car down, a sniper fired at him. The round went under his armpit just close enough to cut the side lacing on his flak vest. On the other hand, some six hours before, we had a night contact down at Hotel 21 Alpha. (All metal roads and tracks which cross the border are prefixed by the letter H – Hotel. The letter and number pinpoints the position of any particular crossing.) One of the patrol thought he saw two gunmen moving into a snipe position, so they went to ground and waited for the two armed men to walk into their snap ambush. They waited for about 20 minutes. They could hear movement some 30 feet to their front but could not see anything. Then all of a sudden a bright light shone towards them. With that, one of the patrol shouted the standard warning, something like, 'British Army, stand still or I'll shoot.' Then they all let rip with a barrage of 7.62.

In the morning the Search Team with dogs could only come up with two blood-trails leading off across the border; no bodies or weapons. Nothing was known of the two men until one day when I was out patrolling, doing the usual VCP and P checks, and saw a battered old Morris Minor chugging towards us from the border. I thought, This bloke's having a laugh. We can't let people drive around in a vehicle in that state. Not even in Northern Ireland, where it seemed that there was no real law for the motorist. I shouted to Taff to pull him over. As I motioned to the driver to unwind his window I saw a sight which made me burst out laughing. 'Hey,' I shouted to Brummie to come and have a look. There was this guy covered in bandages. His wife was in the front and there were four kids in the back. Real ratty looking creatures. I said to the driver, 'What the fuck happened to you, mate?'

'Me'es and a fellow were out after rabbits the other week down on the border when some of youse feckers riddled us.'

I burst out laughing again. He told me it wasn't funny. As he replied I ordered him out of the car: 'Boot and bonnet, get 'em open.'

'I can't, I can't move,' he pleaded.

His wife obliged. I asked how the hell he could drive. He said that all he could do was steer and use his right foot, the other one carrying, I guess, the damage of a couple of 7.62. His wife had to change gear, use the clutch and brake. Info from Zero: 'No Trace'; there was no point in chasing him up. We thought he had suffered enough damage. Anyway, he would probably sue the British Government for thousands and what was the point in adding harassment to the charge as well? It wasn't to be the last time I heard of an Irishman taking a few rounds and disappearing off into the night to live to fight another day.

The living accommodation in Forkhill was unbelievable. Twelve blokes shared four treble-bunk beds in one room barely big enough to take two. Space was always at a premium and we lived together like rats. Trying to keep the bashas clean was a constant battle because of blokes coming in and out twenty-four hours a day: backwards and forward to the cookhouse; in and out from patrolling. There were only three places to congregate: the bashas, the cookhouse or the small NAAFI shop. This shop sold everything we needed from toothpaste to local post cards to send home!

The cookhouse was the main gathering place, in constant use every hour of the day. Everything happened in here. Guys would come in and get their heads down, not bothering to go to their bunks. It doubled up as an unofficial Ops room, TV room and,

50

sometimes, a boxing ring. The usual head-to-head between a couple of blokes who had been getting on each other's nerves would be set off big style in the cookhouse, sometimes only because there was no more salt left in the cellar or a table was wonky. It was just the stress of living in such close quarters and, of course, the thought of getting your balls blown off out patrolling.

On one occasion half the camp came down with severe food poisoning. The doc spent two days tracing the source: somehow the bog brushes were ending up in the cookhouse washing area. Brushes used to scrape the shithouses were getting used on plates!

Getting sleep was the other problem: you couldn't. We were understrength and tasks assigned to us pushed our manning to capacity, so stress levels were always at breaking point. Constant patrolling, stagging on in the sangars, dixie duties, QRF: the list of jobs we were expected to do was endless. When we did get a two- or three-day stand down, we were, more often than not, called out in support of some bigger operation, such as an outer cordon task for a route clearance or a RUC multi-arrest operation. It seemed that the hierarchy were intent on scoring brownie points. This used to piss the blokes off big style and a year into the tour, most of us were beginning to question why we were there in the first place: 'Let the fuckers bomb themselves into oblivion. Who gives a shit?' The reality was that only a small minority caused all the hassle, but at that point we were beginning not to give a shit about anything.

For my part, it seemed that we were being used as pawns in some much larger, career/power struggle, for the senior officers and politicians alike, at the expense of the blokes on the ground. We were doing all the donkey work, the dangerous work. We were working at the business end of the operation – the end where the blokes got killed.

At times there seemed no end to the problems in Northern Ireland, especially when most of the population lived 300 years in the past. How can you deal with people who constantly referred to wrong-doings visited upon their ancestors all those years ago? This may seem a simplistic view of the differences between the Protestants and Catholics, but that was my view, and it hasn't changed. The daily bombings, killings, kneecappings by both sides kept

51

happening no matter how many patrols we carried out or how many arrests we made.

I welcomed the short time we got off when our tour finished. Four weeks of hot baths, being clean and having space. I used to spend a lot of time running along the beach at Dundrum Bay and on the walks up in the Mourne Mountains. It was a time to reflect about absolutely nothing, get pissed, go out to the safe Prod areas and get laid.

We used to have fearsome piss-ups in the block. As long as we kept ourselves to ourselves, the OC saw no problem with it. As bosses go, he was one of the best. He was from the school of Bloody Sunday. Being a Major, he was probably as much under stress as his blokes.

One day I was having a few beers with a mate, who was fit as fuck and a bit on the 'punchy' side, in a place on the camp called the Placky Pub, named because its inside was done out entirely in plastic to resemble an old English country pub. It was run by an old sweat who had been in the Paras for years and had obviously found his vocation in life as its manager. I don't mean that in a detrimental way; he was a great character. He treated us like younger brothers, always ready to chew the fat and always eager to tell us what it was like back in the early 1970s: 'Our weekly routine was a shooting every day, and we used to finish off the week with a good old riot. Not like the pissy little riots you boys get involved in now. I mean a few thousand Molotov-Cocktail-throwing fuckers.' A few of us used to put him straight. 'Yeah, you were only here for four months back then. That was as much as you guys could hack. We're here for 24, you old bastard.'

Then a bunch of guys from 3 UDR (Ulster Defence Regiment) walked in. It was obvious that they were on their training because they weren't wearing their NI boots and their Stable Belts were pulled up as high as they could go. They looked like typical craphats: sewn-in creases in their denims and their berets pulled over the backs of their heads like ocean-going tadpoles. The beer started to flow and the pub began to fill out. I am not sure what happened next but I think I said, 'Hey, look at those hats over there. That's why we're working our bollocks off over here – to look after them. They think they look real "alley".' A couple of them obviously heard me and made the biggest mistake they could make. They said something derogatory about Warrenpoint. If they had retorted on the lines of, 'the only two things to fall out of the sky are birdshit and Paras,' then I think things would have turned out differently. But they didn't, and a fight ensued. Outcome: six UDR men nil, two Paras 14 days loss of pay and a full weekend washing dixies.

The following weekend, my mate and I were ordered to report to the manager for the SNCOs' mess. They were having a bit of a barbecue and the CO and RSM were due to give some presentation to one of the sergeants, and as the weather was good, they decided to have it outdoors. We were taken around the kitchens and given our tasks. All we had to do was wash up all the plates, cutlery, pots and pans, but not touch the glassware. That was OK by us. So we set about it on the understanding that as soon as we had finished, the sooner we could fuck off. Things were going great. We had a good routine together. I washed, he put away, not even bothering to dry anything. While all this was going on, we had been swigging the odd glass of wine from trays waiting to be taken out to the bash. After a couple of these, having finished our duty, we went on a tour of the mess and eventually found ourselves upstairs on the roof.

I still do not know to this day why we both started ripping off the slates and tossing them into sky like frisbees, but we were well pissed. We could see the party below: everybody seemed to be having a good time and so were we. Then some sergeant spotted us and told us to get down. We told him to fuck off – if he wanted us down he could fucking well come up and get us. Then they called out the QRF guard (who incidentally were our mates) plus the Provost Sergeant and a couple of corporals.

By the time they arrived we had all the Battalion's SNCOs shouting up at us, giving their ten-penny worth. Only the CO and the RSM showed restraint, perhaps because they were so shocked to see two of their men dancing, shouting abuse and pissed out of their minds on top of the mess.

We were each bundled into a separate cell and left to sober up. I took umbrage about being locked up and eventually broke the door down and released my mate. Big Tommo, the duty Provost Corporal, saw what we had done and locked the outer door which led into the guard room and then outside, in effect foiling our escape. Soon

53

the pair of us were running around the prison screaming like banshees. The prison had six cells and a holding room of eight bunks for prisoners awaiting sentence. We were the only two Paras, so we left the rest of the prisoners in their cells. Then, not being able to escape, we both retired to our cells to sleep off the effects of a couple gallons of red and white wine.

At 05.00hrs we were both awake. We were told of our charges and told to get a wash and shave and to change into prison overalls. Signing for one highly chrome-finished Para helmet and one very large, heavy, highly polished brass WOMBAT shell, we were told to take them everywhere we went, including the toilet. We obeyed. We were read the riot act and were told of our rights – we had none. We were asked if we understood the charges and our rights. We both answered yes. Then, oddly, we were asked if we had any complaints or requests. No. We were then taken out and given one of the biggest beasting sessions I have ever had in my life: two hours on the assault course.

I was charged under Section 69 of the Army Act: 'Bringing the Army into disrepute.' The CO asked me if I would accept his charge (in the army you have the option of accepting the charge, without knowing what the punishment is to be, or refusing it and going for a Court-Martial and guaranteed trouble). We accepted the charge and were given 28 days each and, of course, loss of pay. It was the maximum the CO could have awarded us without referring us to a Court-Martial, and, eventually, Colchester (the Army nick). We weren't bad guys, and it was the first time I had been in trouble. The loss of an ID card and the recent Placky Pub fight was all I had against me. What's more, the CO thought I had potential. It came as a shock to me when he told me that if I had curtailed my aggression until the next morning, I would have seen that my Company Commander had put me down for promotion. I said nothing in reply or in my defence.

Twenty-eight days in the Para nick gave me time to reflect on what I wanted to do with the rest of my life. I had let myself down, acting like a complete arsehole. Had I shown to my mates that I couldn't hack it any more? I thought I had really let them down. In fact, they all thought it was great and showed a bit of character. I'm not sure my boss did. My charge sheet had started to grow! Jokingly they would take the piss out of me when they saw me tabbing around the lines, with a highly polished helmet on my head and carrying the WOMBAT shell over my shoulder.

I looked upon my extra 28 days in the Army as a fulltime physical training period and used every opportunity to get stronger, physically and mentally. I promised myself to phone mum and dad more regularly, send them a letter even. I had spent only two days out of the past 18 months at home, the first two days of my leave periods. I couldn't wait to get home, but as soon as I was there, I caught the first train back to Aldershot the next day. I spent most of my leave time there, hanging out with the 'Para groupies,' making out that I was an 'Aldershot orphan', screwing around, having a laugh and pretending I had no real place to go home to. Subconsciously, I thought that my mum and dad and brothers did not understand what I was about. How could they know what it is like over there? I had nothing in common with them any more! I felt dead guilty that I thought that way about my family. It was as if the 'Troubles' (a local term for the situation in NI) had taken over me. I had to address all these problems and put them right at the earliest possible opportunity.

To keep the Battalion half sane and in touch with reality whilst serving a two-year tour in NI, the powers that be tried to keep the Wednesday afternoon sports day free if operational tasks allowed. For the whole of the British Army a Wednesday meant you go out, do a bit of training, maybe a short run or some weights in the morning and don't come back in the afternoon – it was regarded as a free day off, mid-week. I was feeling pretty pissed off at the thought of not being able to represent the Battalion at rugby, because I was still in jail on that particular Wednesday.

Then, to my surprise, the call to play in the match came. I was in a great mood when Tommo double timed me over to the pitch. A quick pep talk by my OC (who was also the captain of the team), gave me added inspiration to do really well. As I got changed into the Battalion's strip on the side of the pitch, I saw there was a good turn out. I could see the CO and RSM having words and pointing in my direction, so I thought I had better not fuck up this time. Most of the Battalion spectators knew who I was, or indeed what I was – a

55

prisoner; but I could see a few strange looks from the opposition benches when they saw me arrive with a shiny helmet and a very shiny anti-tank shell. We won the match and after running through the opposition's tunnel, I was met by Tommo and his sidekick. I got changed back into the prison outfit and was marched over to the jail. No comment was passed. Two hours later Tommo came and told me I was to report to the Placky Pub. He didn't say why, but I thought, Great, a celebration orange juice with the team. Wrong. When I arrived there, most of the team had just left: I was to help clean up the bar. What a bummer, I thought. I saw the OC in the corner talking with his opposite number. As he left he came over to me and said, 'Well done, Devs, you played a blinder today. You can't have long to do?' Five days, I told him. 'See you back in the Company lines then.'

That was a shock, because the general rule of thumb is that when you come out of nick, you get posted back to a different company. It's like moving house when you don't want to.

'Yes sir, and thank you sir,' I replied, very relieved and very happy.

At the beginning of 1981, there was a rumour spreading around the Battalion that our tour was to be cut short by three months. This was a shot of excitement and blokes started jockeying for positions on the advance party back to Aldershot. All of us who had started the tour back in mid-1979 just wanted out. We were pig-sick of NI and when I found myself for the last time in bandit country, I began to count the hours to do as opposed to days. A worrying factor about being in the Armed Forces was that you tended to wish chunks of your life away, be it six months here or five weeks there. Comments like, 'I can't wait until this trip or tour ends,' were frequent.

When the rumour was confirmed I was down in Forkhill. I was feeling really happy that this was to be my final tour, as I walked into the briefing for an ambush of the now infamous Kilnasaggart Bridge – probably the most ambushed in the history of soldiering. The first railway bridge into the North on the Belfast to Dublin line, it was always a PIRA target. During our tour, it had been bombed half a dozen times. Nothing too big, just enough to put it out of action for two or three days; enough to piss people off at both ends of the track. The monetary cost to the North of repairing the bridge was minimal, but in terms of putting soldiers on the ground to protect the civvy engineers repairing it, it was astronomical. A small repair would tie up a couple of hundred soldiers, police, bomb search teams and helicopters, as the PIRA knew all too well. It would take the Security Forces away from patrolling tasks for a few days, giving the PIRA more scope to carry out another incident elsewhere, with less threat of being caught.

In the briefing the Int officer stated that intelligence had been received from a half-decent source that the PIRA were going to plant a bomb sometime over this weekend, possibly with three vehicles involved. The bomb was to be planted under the bridge and not on top as with previous attacks. It was to be an attack on the structure of the bridge itself.

After the hundreds of briefings we had been given over the past 18 months, none of the guys was particularly worried about taking notes or anything like that. We had done this a thousand times, never with any success. Most of the time the PIRA wouldn't appear, so we were cynics. We weren't stupid and were all a bit long in the tooth now to be fooled by the term 'half-decent source', meant to heighten our awareness and interest in the operation. But we all knew that if there was half a chance of the job coming off, we would certainly not be put on the ground. Definitely not in the killing or cut-off group of the ambush. That would be left to the SAS troop. The most we could expect to get was the outer cordon, facing outwards, in the pissing rain; a real bummer.

I was always suspicious of the Intelligence Services in Lisburn, convinced they would rather sacrifice a couple of soldiers on a job in order to confirm the reliability of their source. I was constantly on my guard about being set up. The other danger was, of course, that no soldiers had been on the ground for a week or so and that gave the PIRA opportunity to get in and plant an Improvised Explosive Device (IED) in or around a good blast point. We could all be walking into a bomb. Another problem was getting shot by your own blokes. This had happened just over a year earlier on New Year's Eve. A four-man ambush was put out, right on the border. It was a particularly dark, cold, blustery night. At five minutes past midnight two of the blokes let rip at two other armed figures wearing

57

balaclavas, who walked right in on top of them: a lieutenant and another soldier, both killed. They had apparently walked around to wish the other members of the ambush a Happy New Year – a tragic incident.

Our ambush was now 'set'. We were late getting into the position. The chopper had dropped us off at the right grid reference, but the going to target was horrendous. It was sleeting hard and there was more traffic than normal, so we had to get down everytime something approached. We could not risk getting caught in the beam of a passing vehicle for a second. As we were tabbing across country I was worried that because of our lateness, the PIRA might have reached the bridge just after last light, planted their device and fucked off without us realising it. So I suggested to Brummie carrying out a quick recce of the bridge area to see if we could find a device. He agreed. We didn't find one, so the chances were that they hadn't yet turned up, if they were going to turn up at all.

Brummie, very unconventionally, set the ambush up almost on top of the bridge. It was a good idea, helping us cope with the shitty weather. The night was pitch black, wind was blowing in the wrong direction for us to hear any movement, and it was still pissing down with sleet. We lay in a surprisingly dry drainage ditch 15 feet away from the bridge, settled down for a long night. We were to pull out from the target before first light and take refuge at the Lying Up Position (LUP), then move back into the ambush the following night. This was to be the routine for the weekend. We were to be extracted by helicopter in the early hours of Monday morning, should nothing happen.

The traffic passing under the bridge started to die down after midnight. Just after 01.00hrs a car passed under and stopped. We could not see what was happening as the ambush was set on the other side and we didn't have enough men to cover both angles of the bridge. I saw a man getting out of a light-coloured Datsun Cherry, then heard him piss against the arch of the bridge. The vehicle registration check came back negative. It was impossible to tell whether it was the PIRA doing a Close Target Recce (CTR) of the bridge or whether it was just an innocent passer-by who had stopped to relieve himself. The vehicle didn't dip or turn off its lights and made no suspicious movements as it came into our view, or as it drove off once he'd finished.

A little incident like that was enough to keep us on our guard. It also warmed me up considerably. The thought of something happening was just the job to squirt a bit of adrenalin around the body. At 03.15hrs the sleet was still coming down, and now the drainage ditch had half filled up. We were up to our knees in freezing cold, thick mud. It was impossible to make any sudden movements for fear of making loud farting noises, due to the suction of the mud against our Arctic gear. We just had to grin and bear it until the following night when, hopefully, Brummie would select a drier ambush position, if possible. Movement within the ambush had to be kept down to an absolute minimum. A move of the right arm just high enough to take the weight of the body off it was as much as you dared do. Every bodily function had to be curtailed. There was no talking. The only way of communicating was in a very quiet whisper. Since we were all lying next to each other, that was not a problem. Any noise or movement heard from outside our little group was heard by all, so there was not much to say. We were four heavily armed guys, lying in a piss-ridden ditch, freezing our bollocks off, waiting to kill someone.

At 03.33hrs a shadowy figure appeared on the road beneath the bridge, came through the arch, got down and stopped just forward of our position. It was lost against the background. A slight nudge from Brummie put me on guard. My heart began to race. I was thinking, What if it should all kick off? Had I cocked my weapon? Of course I had. What if lying in this ditch had made my weapon waterlogged and caused a stoppage when I began to fire it? Of course it wouldn't. Had we been compromised? Was the PIRA now surrounding us for capture? We didn't dare move. All our weapons were trained on this lonely figure at the spot where we had last seen it. Lying up at night in a constant state of alertness, your eyes can play tricks with you. I thought this had happened to me until I saw the figure get up and go back through the arch. Brummie whispered to me, 'Did you see that? Was the fucker armed?'

'I couldn't see. Probably doing a recce,' I whispered.

The PIRA would do something like this just to draw out an army patrol from their ambush. It was a dodgy game to play but they would use some dumb fucker, probably a new recruit, so if the army did open fire it would be on an unarmed, non-traced civvy. If he or she was killed it was a useful piece of propaganda for the PIRA; if they were wounded, it would be a nice little claim against the Army, probably into tens of thousands of pounds. The PIRA would obviously take their commission from that as well. We knew all this and lying in wait for the next move was a great feeling. Whatever that figure might or might not have been, we had not been compromised, because ten minutes later we heard what was one or possibly two cars roll down the road, lights and engines switched off, just the other side of the bridge. A squeaky brake pad pierced the night, then we heard voices. The squeaking had prompted them to drop their guard; they appeared to be a bit pissed. We saw nothing for about a minute, then all of a sudden two armed men appeared under the bridge.

It's going down, the fucking bomb is being planted. Come on Brummie, you're the patrol commander. Challenge them. We can slot these two fuckers easy, I thought.

'HALT, HANDS UP, STAND STILL. I'M READY TO FIRE, YOU CUNTS.' Brummie had hardly got to 'Halt' when both men let rip in our direction. Screams and gun fire. I fired off a couple of double taps. Two tracers were my first rounds. I saw them hit and ricochet off the side of the bridge. The others were firing in its direction. The two gunmen disappeared under the arch and a vehicle started up. Brummie and I quickly leapt up from the ditch and ran across the other side of the road under cover from the other two in our patrol. In doing so, we had to run directly across the front of the arch. We were being shot at and I could see the muzzle flashes of weapons being fired through it. Amazingly, none of us had been shot. Brummie was screaming at Taff to stay put and put up a flare to light the other side of the arch.

Brummie got onto Zero. 'Zero, Brave Two Charlie. CONTACT. CONTACT. Wait out.' His voice harsh and to the point. We were both breathing heavy. I was gasping for air. I felt my whole body tingle with the surge of fear. My heart was pumping, my eyes straining to see through the darkness. The vehicle strained to get going, they were trying to make their getaway. It was too late to put an M79 round down through the arch. Everything was happening in a split second. I put more rounds down. A flare whooshed up in the night, lighting up the other side of the bridge without throwing too much light in our direction, but we were too late. One vehicle screamed off in the direction it came from. Then it went very quiet. I shouted to make sure everyone was alright. No one had been hit. Taff and Paul had stayed in the ditch, as briefed, while Brummie and I had made our way out. There was the smell of spent small arms; that fireworks odour again. We lay still for about five minutes, none of us moving an inch. We had no idea how many PIRA were about: they might all have fucked off; they might have been waiting for us in an ambush their side of the bridge. There was only a slight chance of this, but since there were but four of us, it would have been very stupid to venture into the tunnel to check out the other side of the bridge. Of course, the terrorists might already have planted the bomb and just come out to 'turn it on'. If so, we were better off crawling back into our ditch to await the inevitable hoards of bomb disposal and search teams, RUC and forensics. Our job was done and we were to be pulled out ASAP once all of us had been debriefed. A fuller debrief was to take place back at Forkhill. Two unexpected things happened that night. One, I had a full blown gun battle with the PIRA and two, I had compulsory 24-hour stand down. We were, as David Bowie once sang, 'heroes just for one day'.

The outcome of that contact, one of the last the Battalion had during the tour was: one AK47 machine gun with three magazines, two taped together for easy changing, one of them empty; one sawn-off shotgun, both barrels fired only once; four balaclavas; a home-made ammunition carrier waistcoat; three radios; and a half-eaten cheese sandwich. And once again, two separate blood trails, one leading over across the border, one leading out from an old, shot-up, yellow Datsun Cherry. No confirmed dead.

I left NI in March 1981. I was glad to leave, I had had a gut-full of pissing in the wind. The senseless patrolling, the inane operational tasks assigned to us, the 'need-to-know-basis' attitude from above, made me feel I was just there as a pawn in a power struggle waged by the hierarchy. The British Government could have resolved this problem years ago. They still can! It would mean a hard-line approach for a few months, but it could be done.

If one was to look at the problem from a different view, then you might come up with a reasoned answer as to why we have been playing across the water for so long. That is, every country has to have Armed Forces. They have to be paid; that comes out of the taxpayer's pocket. So why not have this Armed Force stationed in the same country, fighting a real war? That, of course, is a small part of it.

The spinoffs from this are considerable. Terrorism is the most common form of conflict being waged around the globe at any given time. The Brits are probably the most advanced force in the world to tackle this form of warfare; having fought it in their own country for the past 25 years or so, they are at a huge advantage. We can, and do, constantly develop skills to combat terrorists, new pieces of equipment, too. We are a world leader in developing ways to treat gunshot wounds, burns and traumatic amputations. These are all part of the offshoot of terrorism. Also bear in mind, prior to NI we had been involved in Malaya and Aden, all places requiring Counter Terrorist Operations.

One day I had a talk with an old boy from the village of Ballykinlar. I asked him what it was like before the 'Troubles'. He said that only one house in the village had a TV and that jobs were scarce. Ten years on, every household had a colour TV. There were plenty of jobs around. That made me think: had the 'Troubles' brought prosperity to NI in a roundabout sort of way?

I remember also, as I travelled around Belfast, especially on my trips to Aldergrove Airport, noticing that most of the cars in the airport car park were new. Potential new business from outside, or just internal prosperity? Certainly there was no shortage of contracts for builders in NI, with all the bombs going off. Once again, this is a simplistic view of a very difficult problem. Certainly people from both factions, Protestants and Catholics alike, have experienced generations of violence and I do not want to undermine the fact that they have endured a living nightmare. But it makes me wonder just exactly what the Government and PIRA were, or are, still up to!

Roll of Honour

Officers and men of 2 Para, killed in action in Northern Ireland on the 1979–1981 tour:

Major P. Fursman

Lieutenant S. Bates

Warrant Officer W. Beard

Sergeant B. Brown

Sergeant I. Rogers

Corporal L. Jones

Corporal N. J. Andrews

Corporal J. C. Giles

Lance Corporal C. E. Ireland

Lance Corporal D. F. Blair

Private T. Vance

Private R. N. England

Private P. S. Grundy

Private G. Hardy

Private J. A. Jones

Private R. D. V. Jones

Private G. I. Barnes

Private R. Dunn

Private A. G. Wood

Private M. Woods

Lieutenant Colonel D. Blair and Lance Corporal V. Macleod, 1 Queens Own Highlanders were also killed at Warrenpoint.

CHAPTER THREE

Sweat and Endurance

THE PATHFINDER PLATOON is a small select force within a Parachute Battalion: an élite within an élite. Its main role is to jump in ahead of the Battalion to select, lay and secure a suitable DZ for the rest of the Battalion. They would then go into their other rôle as a covert force, establishing Ops and reporting back to Battalion HQ. In effect, they are the eyes and ears of the Battalion and the Brigade.

2 Para had not had a Pathfinder Platoon (I will call it a platoon, although it was officially called C (Bruneval) Company – after the famous Bruneval raid in World War Two. It was only platoon strength) since the Government had disbanded 16 Para Brigade, so it was good news when I found out that they were reforming it. I was bored with routine Army life in Aldershot. Sometimes I wished I was back in NI. I needed a new challenge.

There had been only two guys in the Battalion from the original Pathfinders but they had now moved on. However, they were posted in to oversee the first selection and training course, and to pass on skills and experience.

Joining a platoon like this would be a downwards career move. I would lose all seniority of rank within the Battalion and, of course, the ability to get rank for at least two years. However, since I was still a 'tom' (a private) it didn't really matter. I was chosen for the four-week selection course along with 16 others. It was a great time; the platoon knitted together almost instantly.

We worked in four-man patrols and reported directly back to the Colonel – at that time Colonel H. Jones. It was his idea to reform this platoon, it was his 'baby'. We sharpened up our personal weapon and patrol skills, spending a lot of time in the field practising all types of tactics and unorthodox ways of operating in an enemy environment. In charge was Captain Stern. Definitely not from the officer mould, he fought for the Company on every level, and this being a newly formed platoon, he had a fight on his hands. Every company had their unit pride and thought that theirs was the best, so when faced with a new force, internal rivalry began. A lot of inter-Company slagging started, through ignorance more than anything, but that went when they saw that we could perform around the 'lines' and, more importantly, in the field.

We used to train every day: a ten-miler in the morning, a run in the afternoon was our fitness programme. We became the platoon to beat. Nobody could touch us for fitness, weapon handling, tactics. (We weren't too hot on drill or parades, though.) Captain Stern took the time out to learn from the blokes. He won our respect within a very short time and made the Platoon what it became. He regularly came downtown with us: a very rare officer. I was enjoying this period immensely. We were left alone by the rest of the Battalion and answered only to the CO. We *lived* for the Platoon. It was extraordinary to be part of this totally professional force.

Although achieving rank had never been uppermost in my mind before, it was now that I appreciated that in order to get anywhere in the Army you have to get on the ladder and start plotting your career. You have to take on responsibility sometime, otherwise you fester and just fade away. So with my new frame of mind at the back end of 1981, I applied for the January 1982 SAS selection. This went down like a death at a birthday party with Captain Stern. 'We've just formed the Platoon. Now you want to fuck off and join a bunch of "hats".' He was joking, and understood that I now had some kind of ambition. But I don't think he would have been too pleased if he had known that within 18 months, eight more of the original Pathfinder Platoon would follow me and pass SAS selection, and many more would do so in years to come.

That number of men accepted into the SAS from one Platoon within one Battalion was unprecedented: a whole Regiment could not expect such a number. It showed the Army just exactly what the Pathfinder Platoon, 2 Para was all about. The CO passed my application and the SAS accepted me for the January course: I would now be based in Hereford, not Aldershot.

The Brecon Beacons, December 1981: the first time that heavy snow had fallen on the town of Brecon in 14 years. The long-range weather forecast predicted things would get worse. Just my luck. As I was later to find out, on every course, be it winter or summer, the weather always throws up an extreme that has not happened before: the hottest summer on record, the foggiest January since King Offa built his dyke, the worst deluge since the great downpour of 1763. In South Wales you can experience all seasons, sometimes in one hour.

My transport for the duration was a Cortina Estate, bought off my brother. Money was always tight, and the sort of price I could afford did not leave me much of a choice: I was desperate for a decent vehicle, and at least I knew the history of this one. The last thing I wanted was to get halfway down the M4 only for the bastard to blow up.

My personal training pre-course schedule was hit and miss. I knew where the Beacons were, having been up and down Pen y Fan mountain, the highest in South Wales, with the Paras, but that was about it. As regards the other training routes, I was completely in the dark. My idea was to spend at least ten days training on the mountains with Ben, an old friend who had returned from the summer course because he failed to make the timings in selection week. That gave me cause for concern, because Ben was a lot fitter than me. My plan of attack was that Ben and I would tab around the hills to get my map-reading and fitness up to scratch. We met each other in the prearranged RV, a pub in Brecon, and confirmed our programme. Our first port of call was Pen y Fan; viewed from hundreds of feet above its summit, Pen y Fan would look like an elongated oval, almost slug-shaped, with the Storey Arms mountain rescue centre at the west end – the slug's head – and the Roman

Road end (named after an ancient route in the vicinity) at the east. We would start from the Storey Arms end, go over the top, down the Roman Road and back over again. A slow tab with a hot scoff at the top, stopping to take notice of the surrounding peaks. This would be a good day's training.

Snow was inescapable on the Welsh hills at this time of year. The following morning we arrived at the Storey Arms Mountain Rescue Post. The weather was looking good, a sharp frost and a clear sky, a nice crisp morning. The short-term Met check predicted snow later, but that didn't worry us; we would be off the mountain before it came. If not, we both had the right gear to deal with a night out in the 'cuds'.

Snow came earlier than forecast, so by the time we got down to where the vehicle was parked the wind had blown up a three-foot snow drift around it, by which time snow was dropping faster than a whore's knickers at party time. There was no way we could get back to the town so we decided to make a night of it and we tabbed to a phone box to 'report in' to the guard at Derring Lines, the nearest army camp, in Brecon itself. I gave our grid reference and added, 'Don't lay the table for us tonight.'

That was the extent of my training programme. The snow had screwed up my walking parts of the course. I felt pissed off and at a disadvantage, as I would have no knowledge of the marches to come. I had to settle for a map study of the routes but there's only so many contour lines you can look at before you go boss-eyed. I returned to Aldershot knowing that my prearranged training programme was to consist of tabs up and down hills I had tabbed in Depot. What a lovely thought!

I had a mega Christmas. A friend of mine who had passed the winter course had said: 'Don't let the course get in the way of having a good Christmas. You aren't going to increase your chances of passing by abstaining for a couple more weeks. Have a good time!' So I did.

I reported at Bradbury Lines at Hereford, as it was known then (now renamed to honour Sir David Stirling, founder of the SAS), on the second Sunday of January 1982. Once through the strongest security precautions of the MOD guard (Who was I? What unit? Then he gave me a vehicle pass, told me to display it in the vehicle at all times and put it away out of sight when leaving the camp.), I parked and remembered my friend Ben's words: 'You've gotta play the grey man up there. Don't get noticed by the Directing Staff [DS] for at least three weeks!' The rest of the day was spent filling out forms, drawing kit from the stores, including a 24-hour ration pack to be carried at all times in the mountains.

Over the years the Beacons have claimed many lives, civilian as well as Army, mostly those who were poorly equipped to deal with the notoriously rapid changes in climatic conditions. The previous winter course lost someone, found dead sitting against a rock with his bergen still on, stiff as a board. Rumour had it that the search party used him as a sledge to get down the mountain. Everything we signed for had a purpose and we were to carry all this in our bergens, plus whatever we had brought from our own units. This made up the considerable weight we were expected to carry throughout the course.

I found my bed space, dropped all my kit and went out to get the rest from the car. There were eight beds to a room. Had I got something vastly wrong? Did I not know about essential extra kit? There were blokes with all sorts of magical bits and pieces: special compasses that lit up in the dark; masses of go-faster pills; one even had a bag of his specially made-up Alpine breakfast. My room filled up; more blokes with all the extras I lacked.

These items were not on my instruction sheet: 'Things to bring with you'. There were four Paras in my room, which made me feel a bit better. They were all corporals and above, but the one that I knew quite well from my Battalion was Basha. He was a no-nonsense man, well respected in the Anti-Tank Platoon and the rest of 2 Para and expected to do well. I, on the other hand, was an unknown quantity. As the course went on, Basha was to be a source of inspiration to us all. I chewed the fat for a time with the blokes in my room when Basha said,

'OK fuck it, who's coming to check out the local boozer?' It was a command decision; off we went. There was a pub just around the corner from the camp, so we had a couple of pints and a bag of chips each, then went back to spend our first night with the SAS.

The following morning didn't come too soon; I didn't have a particularly good sleep. I tossed and turned nervously between bouts of heavy snoring from Basha. We were up at 05.00hrs, scoffed by 05.30hrs and out on parade by 06.00hrs, dressed in light order with boots, to run the BFT (the Army's Basic Fitness Test, a one-and-a-half-mile run) in 11 minutes. There were just under 200 of us. Basha reckoned that four blokes didn't even get out of bed that morning. Standing amongst some of the Army's fittest men (or so I thought) I wondered how many would be left at the end of the course. Many waiting for the off were wearing their unit's tracksuit tops, displaying their badges of merit. There were blokes with gold judo crested badges, blokes with Army football tops, some with the all-singing, all-dancing, fittest-dick-in-the-Army badges; everything to show how good they were at sport but nothing to show how good they were at their primary role in the Army – being a soldier. Fucking 'grey men,' I thought sarcastically.

We all heard the DS say, 'This morning you're all going to do the BFT, if you want to, that is. If you don't, don't.'

Someone decided that the occasion was all too much for him. I saw him standing to one side as the DS shouted the off. I completed the run within the time. No big deal, after all it was just the basic Army fitness test.

The rest of the week I saw myself moving from a run session to gym work-outs, to classrooms for basic map-reading and a few medical lectures on how to look after yourself in the mountains. To any infantryman this was pretty basic. It gave me more mental energy to focus on the ever-demanding runs that were getting longer. The circuit training in the gym seemed to go on and on. I could not remember a beasting session in the Paras like I was getting here. In between gym sessions, we would shuffle to and from more lectures.

I was pretty sure that this week was designed to thin out all those who had no intention of passing selection, but only wanted to tell their mates that they were, or had been, in the SAS.

This first week was to ensure that when we started on the mountains, we had all been taught the basics of surviving them. Blokes who had come from Corp units were probably under the most pressure because, to some extent, this was all new to them, tabbing around and map-reading, but for me, the first week sped by. I felt pretty confident but kept myself to myself, only talking to other

Paras. Nobody really knew anyone and I guess we were all apprehensive of each other, not trying to give away too much of what we knew to any outsider, in case they used it against us.

One morning we all paraded outside the Training Wing Office with our bergens, belt kit and a havabag (packed lunch), boarded the trucks and headed out of Hereford. From day one we had been split into four groups; now the course was down by 30 students. This day's training was to be split between a run and an orienteering exercise. The latter caused me no problems; about half a dozen checkpoints to find. The run was something else. It was over eight miles, it was hilly and wet, and since I had used up a lot of energy on the morning's orienteering, I thought, Fuck! How am I going to keep this bastard pace up? This was the real start of selection, I thought. Things had been ticking along too nicely!

In the Paras I was never really a runner, more of a plodder. I preferred a short run, say five or six miles, then a session in the gym. Luckily for me the first part was downhill for about a mile, on a slippery old logging track; blokes were falling all over the place, some careering into the pine trees. I began to pace myself, thinking that if we were running downhill, at some stage, we must go up. I reckoned I was about in the middle and tried not to let anyone pass. We ran on the flat for some time, then up we went. I overtook a couple. All I had to do was just hang in there with the main group.

After about 30 minutes I was dying. My body was covered in sweat, I was gasping for air all the time and my chest heaved as we approached the top of the long hill. I could see the trucks parked in the car park. We had obviously done one long loop of the forestry block. My head picked up ready to show the DS willing as I came into the car park. Then I saw what I thought to be my main group, just disappearing back into the forest. My worst fear was right; we were still going! 'Come on, come on, catch 'em up,' a DS was saying. 'Down the hill and back up again, that's all.'

Some 30 minutes later I found out that the car park had been only the halfway stage. Fortunately I got my second breath and found myself running aggressively to reach the main bunch. Just before the last hill I caught them up, now reduced to about half a dozen plus the original lead DS. I don't know where I got my energy from, it was the hardest run of my life.

There was not a lot to do once the day's training was over, apart from going out for a few beers. The talk was always about how many got 'binned' and what was in store for the following day. Some stayed in all that week, packing and repacking their kit. I couldn't see the sense in that. You just built up nervous tension with no release for it. The best release was getting away from the place, having a few beers and a 'lech' at talent downtown.

The end of the first week was our real test – the infamous 'Fan Dance' march. I had been across Pen y Fan in the Pathfinders a year before but never over and back in the same day, and especially not as a race. It was a basic, no-nonsense tab with a bergen weighing 40lbs over a distance of 22 ks up, across and down the other side and back over the highest peak in South Wales. The course was split into two groups, one at either end of the mountain; the two groups were to meet somewhere in the middle, and there was no advantage to starting at any particular end. The Storey Arms end was an almost immediate step climb, the Torpanto end (the start of the Roman Road) a more leisurely-looking incline. These two start points became each group's halfway stage, so we covered the same ground. My group started at the leisurely end. The game plan was to stay with the DS and just hang in there. All he said was, 'Just stay up with me and you'll be alright.' Easier said than done, I thought.

We huddled around in small groups until we saw the DS walking towards the start line. I was nervous: what if I got injured? I had to concentrate on where I put my boots when we got to the stepped, rocky bits.

In the Paras we were used to this type of tab. Past blokes from the course had told me that all you have to do is keep up with the DS: 'Don't stick up on his shoulder or even try and outrun him. That will piss him off severely. He knows just exactly where he has to go and what time he has to complete the march in; you don't. I thought, I will be lucky to come in with him. In the distance, I could only see part of the Fan. Most of the top was covered in mist. It looked daunting, a friggin' long way off.

Suddenly the DS went off at a blistering pace, no ready, steady, go. Some blokes were caught napping; we were 40-odd metres ahead before they managed to get their bergens on. I tucked in behind the DS. Basha turned around to me and said jokingly, 'Aye, this is the life, Devs!' I didn't reply, deep in concentration.

It was raining when we started and as we approached the first steep climb it began to hail. Although I was wet through, I was warm and felt good. Tabbing uphill suited me. I just put my head down, adjusted the position of my bergen so I got it as far up onto my back as possible, stuck my arse in the air and dug in.

We were getting near the top now and started meeting the other group. Silently we fought to stay on our part of the single-lane track which led up to the peak; giving way meant that you either dropped down a couple of feet or climbed a couple. That sapped your strength and you would lose two or three metres, so giving way was not recommended.

As I got down to the Storey Arms end of the mountain, my knees continued giving me shit from the jarring fast descent. I gave my number to the DS at the turn-around point and wheeled round for the return journey. The climb was a series of ball breakers. As soon as you thought you had reached the top, another higher false horizon would appear.

By now we were spread out like a long curving snake and for the past hour I had been tabbing on my own. I reached the top for the second time and started my descent. It was snowing now and all I had to go on was the trail of footprints winding down the hillside. I stuffed a Mars bar into my mouth, but it was so frozen I couldn't bite through it, so I sucked. Chocolate, saliva and sweat were blown over my face by the fierce headwind. My eyes squinted through the snow as I focused on the treacherous terrain. The Mars bar broke some minutes later as I raced the final furlong. Every step sapped my strength and concentration. I was burbling the tune of 'Bat Out of Hell' by Meatloaf to match the constant rhythm of the bergen bouncing against my back. The snow, rain and hail didn't matter now – all that mattered was getting to the finish as fast as possible.

I put the 'Para Head' on and went for it, picking out people in front of me and chasing them. I passed a couple and eventually arrived back at where I started from. There was no finishing post banner, no hot cups of tea, but it was a personal achievement for me. I had passed the first tab. Others were not so lucky. Twenty jacked and six were injured, one being blown over the edge at a place locally known as Windy Gap. Apparently the wind got up under his bergen, picked him up like a squealing pig and dumped him halfway down the ravine.

By the end of the first week we had lost 61 through injury or VWs (Voluntary Withdrawal). When we got back to camp at Hereford we were two short in our room. That left five of us. All Paras. Two from 2 Para, one from 1 Para, one from 3 Para and John, who was Para Engineers – 9 Squadron.

We were given the following day off to sort our kit out and grant the walking wounded a respite. A few of us took the opportunity to check out Hereford, staying well clear of certain pubs that were out of bounds.

Over the next two weeks the pressure was on. We were on the wagons at 06.00hrs, then a two-hour drive from Hereford to the Welsh mountains. We were never told where we were going or what the day involved. All we knew was to check the notice board in our basha every evening to see what kit to bring the next day. We always took the bergen (weight 40lbs); the only other extra thing we had to carry was a drill SLR to add more weight, carried at the ready. None of this over-the-shoulder stuff you see in the movies, or tucked in down the side of your bergen.

I remembered a Rupert who had just passed me as I came up to a checkpoint. He was about six foot six, really skinny and gangly. He clipped the side of my bergen as he passed, a really arrogant twat, I thought. Two DS were standing alongside the Land Rover to check us in and out again. This sight had obviously given the Rupert a boost of energy. As I stood off, waiting for the Rupert to receive his new checkpoint, I realised he wasn't carrying his rifle. The DS casually turned around and grinned at his mate. I thought, have they seen the Rupert doesn't have his rifle? They let him get 50 metres out, then:

'Hey sir, where's your rifle?' They chuckled. No reply was necessary. I last saw the Rupert scurrying back the way he had just come. He had probably left it up against a rock as he was taking a bearing. Who knows? He was binned two days later. Another rifle incident: one guy, every time he got out of range of the DS, would stick his rifle down the side of his bergen, for ease of carrying. But one march, quite unexpectedly he met the CO and the Adjutant on top of one of the high spots, out for a day's stroll. That was the end of *him*.

When we boarded the trucks in Hereford, it was always dark and raining. Out would come the doss-bags and those of us who were switched on would get a couple of hours' gonk en route. It amazed me that some blokes would just sit on the wooden benches, feet up on their bergens, arms just tucked under their armpits, and that's where they would stay for the journey. It was biting cold in the back of the trucks. The wind would get sucked in through the canvas sides and blow about. There was no warm place unless you were in a doss-bag. These blokes were fucked even before they started. It wasn't that there wasn't enough room for them, because we all just lay on top of each other. They were just lazy. You could see that as the days went on, they would lose a bit more heart. It was a grinding-down process, all part of the course.

There was no bollocking if you weren't on parade at a certain time, it was all down to you, the individual. It was hard to get out of bed at five on a winter's morning, knowing that all you had to look forward to was the same as the day before and the day before that. Getting out of the warm doss-bag was also hard. That rush of cold air, thick with water, would attack all parts of your body as soon as you unzipped. What's more, jumping off the tailgate of the truck would jar your already bruised and cut feet. But once on the ground I couldn't wait to get my first grid reference and get going. It was always a struggle at first. It would take five minutes for a strange comforting pain to enter my body and make me switch on. I would remember all those stupid little sayings that we were constantly bombarded with when I was doing P Company: one liners like, 'All the way Airborne, Airborne, Airborne all the way,' or, 'No pain no gain.' I reckon John Lennon had it right when he said, 'Feel your own pain then you know that you're alive'!

When the wagon arrived at the drop-off location, my routine was to roll up my doss-bag, take off my warm gear and stuff it into the waterproof bin-liner in my bergen, then stick on a sweat top and Para smock, find a bit of shelter out of the wind and wait to be called by the DS. He would ask me our exact location and I would show him where we were on the map, using a blade of grass or a thin twig, and give him the grid reference. He would give me a reference for my first checkpoint and I would show him where that was. Next, taking a compass bearing, I would tab off as fast as I could, get to the checkpoint and go through exactly the same routine. Some of the checkpoints were placed at specific locations, for example, the corner of a coppice or a bend in the river. Sometimes all it would be was a DS inside a bivvi bag (a small type of low-slung tent), on a flat ridge, and if the mist was down and visibility was 10 feet or so (which it generally was) all you could do was stumble around and hope to find it. Wind was also a problem and most of the time you would find the DS location only because you heard his radio transmissions. I'd get to the bivvi bag on these isolated checkpoints, call out my number and the zip would come down just enough for an exchange of pleasantries. I'd smell the waft of rich hot coffee from inside the bag, then be off again.

On one of these particular checkpoints I saw a guy huddled by the DS who had had to come out of his lair. This student had decided that the SAS was not for him. He didn't want any part of anything else. The DS was not pleased. He had to radio through to the nearest checkpoint and get two blokes up to deal with the situation. As I approached, I could see the fallen victim. It was one of the 'badge brigades'. The DS was trying to tell him to make for the road-head checkpoint. He didn't have a serious medical condition such as hypothermia, he was just at the end of his tether. Not wanting to stay around any longer I got my next grid sorted and raced off. It gave me just the encouragement I needed. I had been wondering why we were not losing as many blokes as we had done in the first week, and why all the 'go faster merchants' were still around. This was the first of many of the 'too-busy-looking-good' types to jack in the next few days. I had a grin as wide as the Windy Gap that day.

Generally, the faster you were on a particular day's tab, the better your chances of getting on the first wagon back to camp in Hereford. If you were really fast, and a lot of people jacked that day, you wouldn't have to wait long before the truck was filled up, and off you went. The advantage of getting back first was you had first use of the baths, showers, hot water, and first position in the scoff queue. Basha and I would race to get off the tailgate first and grab one of the two baths available. I used to get into the bath with my kit on, dumping the bergen by its side. You couldn't chance dropping your gear in your room first in case someone else sneaked in the bath ahead of you. There we would all talk about the day's tab and give our opinions on how we thought we did, how many had jacked, how many were left. After we got our kit squared away and had scoff in the cookhouse, we would wait for the duty DS to come in the billets and give us the 'good news'. He would come in, room by room, and tell the occupants if they were on OCs or not. If you were to have an OCs interview, it meant one of two things. One, that you were to get a gypsy's warning and told to buck up, or worse, two, you were binned. After this ritual the rooms would be quiet for a time, and then someone would chirp up and say, 'I wonder who's going to get binned tomorrow?'

The thought of the course being whittled down day after day didn't bother me at all. As long as I wasn't one of them, I couldn't give a shit. I wanted to be part of this Regiment so badly that I was prepared to take anything they might throw at me. No way did I want to go back to the Paras as a failure. The Paras attitude to that was, 'Why did you want to go on selection in the first place? Aren't we good enough for you?' or, 'We will still be here when you get RTU'd.' Blokes I knew had been Returned to Unit from selection, for not making the timings, or they had returned with a serious injury. Some fat knacker would say, 'Yeah, I knew he would fail.' With hindsight I could not blame the Paras for that attitude. They had lost a lot of good soldiers to the SAS. They had a right to be a bit pissed off.

At the end of week two, we had 18 officers join us which boosted our numbers, and by the end of week three we were 65 in total. A one hell of a bastard day sorted a lot of blokes out in week two. It was a 22 kilometre march across Radnor Forest in South Wales and then a march of about 30–35 ks that same night. It crucified me, and if all the horror stories of falling into bogs and getting caught in the pine forests were true, it obviously had the desired effect. A lot of blokes jacked, two with fractured legs. Week three saw another ballbuster, this time across some of the shittiest snow-covered bogs I have ever known; an 18k tab followed by a 12k night march.

On some tabs the weather got particularly bad and we were often told to buddy up with two or more blokes, to cut down the risk of getting lost or to ensure that if someone took a bad fall, there would be others to deal with it. We never knew what the cut-off times were for any particular march but quite often (especially on the winter courses) the weather could change so drastically that it could put one or two hours onto a particular march; and of course, our overall timings would show that. The Training Wing took this into account, but they never told us. It was always worrying when you would come off the mountain after a really shitty day in the sleet and snow, and you could only gauge your times against the others waiting in the back of the truck.

Comparing times against the elements became common. But you were never ever sure if you had done well until that evening's DS visit.

After the first three weeks, I don't think that there was anything else a man could possibly do to prove himself worthy. But there was: Test Week. We were to start it the following Saturday. Week three finished on the Thursday. Given the Friday off, I drove back to Aldershot to chill out a little.

The five of us left in our room were getting on great. We all used to go off downtown at night, sink a few beers and end up in a club, getting back about midnight. We were burning huge amounts of energy on these marches and it was surprising to see just how much food a man can eat at one sitting. Blokes would come back from the hot-plates with the scoff literally piled up as high as possible, only to go back and have the same again.

Getting a good night's sleep ready for the next day's tab was usually impossible until after midnight. There was always some sort of drama if you stayed in the block, so it was best to be out during the evenings. We used to ask the other blokes if they fancied coming into town for a few pints but usually they would refuse, saying, 'I need a good night's sleep.' But when we returned well watered they would still be up, fucking around with their bergens or studying maps. I couldn't understand it. The walk to the town and back used to loosen me up a bit. I would fall asleep as soon as my head touched the pillow, get a good five hours sleep induced by some of Hereford's finest ales, wake up, have a good hearty breakfast and then get another two hours kip on the wagons. That was enough.

I had been pretty lucky with my body so far. Most of my aches and pains disappeared after several minutes tabbing. Others had more serious problems. Medical masking tape wrapped around the feet was the norm to prevent blisters and skin being worn away. Some used to put this tape straight over burst blisters; some had their whole feet covered in the stuff. I could only imagine taking that tape off, seeing two or three layers of skin come off. I only had a couple of bits of floppy skin around the Achilles' tendon, on both feet, which I had taped up. I could live with that. What concerned me more was the old parachute injury to my right shoulder. It was beginning to play up and three weeks of constantly humping around my bergen on my back had done it no good at all. The right shoulder strap dug into it as soon as I had it on my back and because of its heavy weight it was virtually impossible to displace this burden off the afflicted shoulder for more than a few seconds. Every minute or so I would make a grunting noise as I attempted to throw the bergen over to my left side to relieve the pain from the right. This upset my pace and sapped my strength. I eventually said, 'Fuck it' and tried to ignore the fact that part of my clavicle was being slowly worn away by my bergen strap.

Then the first day of Test Week was on us. Test Week is a series of marches similar to earlier ones but longer, with more weight, culminating in a tab of about 70 kilometres. We weren't allowed on roads or to follow defined tracks or tab with anyone, and we were still against the clock.

All Test Week routes had names: one was Sketch Map, a tab around an undisclosed part of the Brecon Beacons where you were given a map with only three or four features on it. No contours, no grids, key or scale. Just a spot height, a blue line (signifying a river) and a feature such as a reservoir and a north pointer drawn on a piece of cloth.

This was a special week; the one we had been waiting for. If we got through it, stage one of the whole course was complete. Tension in the basha was now beginning to heighten: more map studies, more checking of kit, more nervous energy used to gain the extra information which might make the day's tab a bit easier. But no amount of checking kit or studying maps was going to help you in

78

the mountains. We all knew the score. We had to get up in the mountains and carry on as before; the only difference was that the tabs would be longer. So our room continued the nightly routine of the past three weeks: get out, relax with a few pints, chat up the birds and grab a bag of chips on the way home. If you were lucky enough to bag off with a girl, then all the better.

Before the start of Test Week our Training Officer gave us some advice. One of the longest serving men in the Regiment, with a very dry articulate way of putting things, he started to refer to our extra curricular activities:

'You people need to get a grip, and there are some men in this room who are flying with the eagles; remember, you people, you have to soar with the butterflies as well.' I never really knew what he meant until one of the DS briefed us up. He said that the OC knew that a few of us were ripping the arse out of going downtown and coming in later than usual. People in the camp were beginning to talk and that was a bad thing. 'You've got this far, what's the point of wrecking your chances by fucking some old trout downtown when you can go around to the local, have a pie, a pint and a wank? Understand me?' The DS winked and left us. We got the message.

At the end of the fourth day Basha was in the bath, singing away, confident he had had a good day. He was there 30 minutes later when the duty DS came looking for him.

'Is Corporal Pope here?' he asked.

'No,' I said.

'Can you tell him he's on OCs at 17:00hrs?' he asked, and disappeared.

I looked around at the other blokes in the room. They looked shocked.

'Fuck, I thought Basha was doing alright,' Bob said.

'Yeah, but when I saw him up at the checkpoint by the 502 [a mountain spot height], he told me he thought he had lost a bit of time.'

The others decided I should tell him the good news. Then Basha came into the room, soaking wet. He dried himself by his bed space.

'Who's been binned?' he said, roaring with laughter and towelling his bollocks.

'Only you, Basha. The DS came in to see *you*.'

'Fuck off! It's a wind up.'

'No duff, Basha. You're on OCs at 17.00hrs. Sorry mate,' I said apologetically. Basha didn't seem too unhappy about being RTU'd, but I knew deep down he was cut up pretty bad. A first-class soldier, he would have done really well in the SAS. But unfortunately, the first part of this course was not about soldiering, it was about pure mental and physical fitness. There were many men like Basha who had high soldiering capabilities but who would not pass this stage, good men who, when RTU'd, often decided to leave the Army, not being able to 'soldier on' within a unit when they had failed SAS selection. It was a personal choice: just because you didn't pass selection didn't make you any less of a soldier. But perhaps they thought it did. Basha did not know it at the time, but he was destined for the biggest challenge of his life. It was just around the corner.

The day of Endurance was upon me. The previous day we hadn't got back until about six o'clock, totally knackered. My shoulder was giving me shit and I was taking as many painkillers as I dared. We had to be up at 03.30hrs the following morning so I decided to have an early night. With Basha not around to lift our spirits, our room soon settled down; the light was out by nine. Minutes later it was back on. Matt said, 'Oh fuck it! Who's coming for a pint? I can't sleep.' Twenty minutes later the whole room was in the local, supping Guinness. Next thing I knew, the alarm was ringing: 03.25 hrs! For some strange reason, I felt totally refreshed and ready to attack the mountain. The pints and a chat really had helped me to unwind. The Endurance tab was a real slog. Because of the really foul weather conditions the average time was 20 hours, a really fantastic achievement for all of us. Nobody failed. Out of 183 who had started four weeks before, we were now down to 33.

The next part of the course was Continuation Training, a four-week build-up period before we went into the jungle of Belize, Central America. During this phase we were taught to handle all the weapons the Regiment uses in different theatres of operation around the world, tactics, and basic living and surviving in the jungle. Beforehand we had to mug up on our own personal weapons and tactics. This was because we were a mixed bunch from all over the Army: Corp men, blokes from the Marines, and infantry. A

80

Corp man might not be too hot on his basic weapon handling or too familiar with the basic platoon weapons, compared to an infantry-man.

There was no let-up in the gym. We were still under the eye of the DS, and had months of training ahead. I still played the grey man, although a couple of guys thought that having passed the selection phase, they could drop their guard and try to chew the fat with their DS – always a wrong move. They were digging them-selves into a pit, but it took the pressure off the rest of us.

The SAS range days were very good, and very different from range days in the rest of the army. The British Army takes a very sanitised view of firing down ranges, 20 rounds at 100 metres, then moving back to 200, fire another 20 and so on, until the NAAFI wagon comes; this was exactly as we were taught in the training Depot – by the book and no deviation from that method accepted. At times it seemed a senseless waste of time and ammunition. It was a question of rules being rules: don't question a well proven method for fear of being called a gobshite. I kept thinking, all that time spent in NI; that's probably why the Battalion didn't get any confirmed kills.

I was taught to be more confident with weapons, and my weapon handling improved 100 per cent. We carried out live firing drills in two and four-man units patrolling special ranges cut out of woodland. Targets would pop up, left and right of the Range lanes, static or moving. They could be ten feet in front of us or maybe even 40. Spotting these further targets was difficult – generally you only saw it because it moved. We would fire two rounds then get down in cover. The DS would shout 'STOP' and 'Change'. Then someone else would go point (lead man). We would carry out these drills endlessly, but it was really good training; I learnt more in that month about weapon handling than I ever did in the Paras. I often won-dered why the rest of the Army didn't take a leaf out of the Regiment's book and use the same training methods.

We were also taught contact drills, which derived from experi-ence gained in past conflicts, mainly the Malayan campaigns of the 1950s. We worked as a four-man patrol carrying out live contact drills, and had to get to know each other really well. I had to be sure that the guys in the patrol were proficient and, more importantly, safe when carrying out these drills; and they had to feel the same about me. Furthermore, we were going to live on top of each other for a month in the jungle. Any personality problems had to be ironed out before we went, to stop them undermining our chances of passing.

I remember my DS saying to us: 'Three things that really grip my shit. One, the patrols you have been put in will be the patrol you will operate with when we go to the jungle. That's if you guys get that far. Any fucker who I hear calling a patrol a "brick," I will personally nobble. A brick is what you build a house with.

'Two, no fucker will do any ballooning* here. It's a fucking stupid concept thought up by some craphat in some fucking range hut.

'And thirdly, the fucking Northern Ireland carry.** I've seen some of you do this. Another wank idea courtesy of the school of Northern Ireland. You will keep the butt of your rifle in or under the shoulder at all times, depending if you are on patrol or moving non tac.'

We were frequently in the classroom for lectures and tests on the subjects we were to use in the jungle: medical techniques, signals and Morse code, jungle tactics, hygiene and safety. The list was endless. We even had a crash course in Malay language (even though we were going to Belize!) and were tested on it. The real intention was to test the student's academic ability. This dispelled the myth that all in the Regiment are just switched-on killers: they aren't. They are a bunch of highly intelligent switched-on killers.

I had never been a 'course man'. Sitting down in a lecture and taking notes was hard enough. Rereading what I had written and putting it into order was worse. In the evenings when others went downtown, I would be left in the basha with the day's notes spread

* A patrolling technique used in NI. Looking through the sights of your weapon, you slowly move the rifle around so as to draw a figure of eight with the barrel end. The point was to make you switched on to any possible sniper, but all it did was tell that sniper that you were focusing in one direction, cutting down your peripheral vision.
** A method of carrying your rifle over the top of your arm in a sort of cradle fashion, meant to look non-aggressive. Because you can only hold the rifle by hand-grip, a few soldiers have had their rifles pulled from them by unruly mobs.

over my bed and the floor, in some mad effort to teach myself. This must have paid off, because at the end of the month I was on the list to go to the jungle. It was a brilliant feeling of achievement. Two blokes had been binned so we were now down to 31. This seemed a strange number if we were to operate in four-man patrols. Perhaps one guy might get binned before we went. In fact, one patrol had to have five in it, but if only nine guys had passed this stage, nine guys would go to the jungle. The sole deciding factor was whether you were good enough.

Belize is a tiny Central American country facing the Caribbean Sea. The former colony of British Honduras, its entire population, around 200,000, is less than many British cities. Here, midway through the third week of jungle training, we had just completed a night camp attack exercise. We were then expected to 'bug out' with little or no kit, only our weapons, belt kit, radio and medical bag. We had to live the next 24 hours on 'hard routine,' using survival rations carried in our webbing: usually a few bits of whitebait, an Oxo cube, maybe a tin of luncheon meat and a pack of AB biscuits.

For our patrol the exercise went well, but as we were moving back into our main camp we had to cross a huge piece of dead fall, about 15 feet across and seven or so feet off the ground, over a dry riverbed. The tree was wet and slippery. Halfway across, I began to lose my footing, then I was flying through the air, downwards. I landed with an almighty crash at the bottom. I couldn't move. I was lodged in the dead branches of this tree, face downwards, my feet in the air. It took the DS and a couple of the blokes a few minutes to make their way down through the secondary vegetation.

In a lot of accidents in life, you instinctively know just before impact that it is going to hurt big style. I was right. I had severely smashed my old parachute wound again. No way could I carry on. I was casevac'd out of the jungle, made comfortable at the hospital in Airport Camp and awaited a flight out back to UK. I had to be Taken Off Strength (TOS'd) and RTU'd back to 2 Para and spent three weeks recovering in the Cambridge Hospital in Aldershot. I spent my time thinking about what had happened. I cursed my shoulder. I cursed the fact that I was totally immobilised. Most of all, I cursed the fact that I had failed the course. All I could think about was getting back on the summer selection. More positively, I kept remembering a scene from a John Wayne World War Two movie, where his character was also laid up in hospital. He was paralysed in the leg, and in order to get the use of it back, his doctor instructed him to try and move just one toe. Wayne kept saying to himself, 'I'm gonna move that toe!' and I found that somehow inspiring – his refusal to give up.

A couple of weeks later I was fit enough to go back to the Battalion, but not fit enough to carry on soldiering. I was downgraded, not allowed to do anything physical for at least two months. I only existed. I was posted back to the Pathfinders in Aldershot and took over the Bedding store for the Platoon. The guys took the piss out of me about a hundred times a day. But it was good-humoured banter; all the blokes knew, there but for the grace of God go I. There was one perk that came with my new-found vocation – my own room, be it filled with sheets, pillows and mattresses. I used to hold court in there with blokes. We would talk about the course and I would try and give them pointers for future reference. Sometimes I felt a bit like an animal on display, working in my little store, but really I was left to my own devices. Although I became the proverbial 'grey man,' only coming out of my store to go to the cookhouse, I used this time well. I revised subjects I found difficult, and mentally I started to get ready for the next course.

It was when I had my own basha I met Annie, a friend of a girl who was going out with a mate of mine. I bumped into her one night and it went from there. She lived some distance away so we only met up at weekends. On a Friday night I would smuggle her into my basha and spend the days in bed and the nights downtown. She was a good girl and sensible with it, not like a lot of women who were only interested in was seeing how many Paras they could lay.

84

CHAPTER FOUR

Beach Assault – The Falklands

Para this and Para that,
and Para go away.
Special rights for Paras
when the bullets want to play.

THE TOILET WALL, THE GLOBETROTTER CLUB, ALDERSHOT 1982

AT THE END of March 1982 I was almost totally fit again. I felt good and I was glad to be back as a fighting member of the Company which, by now, was up to almost full strength and had split to form a Patrol Platoon and a Recce Platoon. Both were still trained in identical roles, that of reconnaissance and pathfinders. Posted to Recce platoon, I had one aim: to pass the summer SAS selection. However, these thoughts were brought to an abrupt halt.

News reports about a possible invasion by Argentina of a small dependency of the United Kingdom, namely the Falkland Islands, were increasing, and on 2 April 1982 it happened. They attacked, occupied and captured the Royal Marine garrison on East Falkland. Thatcher's government was outraged. United Nations Security Council talks to get Argentina to withdraw had no effect. When

Argentina was ordered to do so, Argentina determined to stay put.

Most of the men and NCOs of 2 Para, particularly those of us in C Company, didn't give a shit about the talks our Government had with the UNSC, and Al Haig's negotiations with Argentina. All we wanted was to get going and catch up with our parent Battalion, 3 Para, who had set sail on the SS Canberra with 3 Commando Brigade from Southampton on 9 April. 3 Commando Brigade also included elements of 40, 42, and 45 Royal Marine Commandos.

As it seemed an armed response was getting more and more likely, I wondered how far 3 Para had sailed and what were the chances of getting a piece of the action. There was an unofficial feeling in the Battalion that we were going to set sail as part of 3 Commando Brigade.

At the time, 2 Para was part of the recently formed 5 Infantry Brigade, still very new as an Airborne force, but we wanted to be a part of a Brigade such as the famous 16 Para Brigade; to have our own distinct independence as an Airborne unit. We didn't want our past battle glories tarnished and forgotten by being some part of a much larger 'hat' organisation, which had no interest in the workings and mentality of the 'Maroon Machine'. Like every Regiment in the British Army, we had our glorious histories, our battle honours, but the Parachute Regiment was still very young, having only been formed in 1941. Since then we had proved a formidable force, kicking arse all over the world for a succession of British Governments. So how dare they disband the 16th Independent Parachute Brigade, amalgamate us into a mass unit and lessen our capabilities? All the blokes wanted total autonomy from the rest of the infantry Regiments. An arrogant and somewhat short-sighted view, but it was the view of most of us while we sat waiting with 5 Infantry Brigade in Bruneval Barracks, Aldershot, listening to news updates, and getting more anxious by the day as 3 Para sailed south.

Something was about to happen. For the past two weeks the Battalion lines were full of activity. We were training for the possible retaking of the Falklands, but nobody was certain it would really happen. We did a lot of live firing, brushed up on patrolling techniques and generally made ready all our platoon and personal

86

kit, just in case we were called upon. Boxes of stores, equipment and ammunition were arriving daily into the Battalion lines. Then it happened. We were to join up with 3 Commando Brigade as soon as possible. We felt elated that we were going to get a taste of real war and over the moon that we were going to be part of the Commando outfit rather than the 'hat' brigade we were so keen to get out of; at least the marines had a reputation of being switched on. It was the most we could have wished for. 2 and 3 Para would be fighting together, we thought. Our third Battalion 1 Para was not coming – that would have been too much to ask, all three Parachute Battalions going off to war together. Maybe the Government thought that three Battalions of paratroopers would be too much of a handful for the 'Head Sheds' of the Commando Brigade to handle.

We sailed from Portsmouth on 26 April on board a passenger and roll-on, roll-off cargo vessel, the 12,000 tons *MV Norland*, a P&O North Sea ferry. Three days before we were given two days leave. I took time out with my mum and dad. My dad was convinced that the situation would be resolved through diplomatic channels; 'Nobody, not even Thatcher, is stupid enough to risk a fullscale military invasion just to retake these islands. Think of the political implications – war with Argentina, for Christ's sake.' Mum was not so sure. I guess she did not want to think about it. Those two years in NI had conditioned my mother not even to think about what might lie around the corner. In some sense, she had cut herself off from what I actually did. Not in a bad way; she often asked me what I was doing and where I had been, but I was very guarded in my replies. She knew that and that's how we got along. It was her way of dealing with one of her sons being a 'black sheep'. Deep down, she was really proud of me; I knew this when I used to get introduced to her friends.

I had never really been on board a ship. A cross-Channel voyage to France was all I had experienced. The thought of being on board for six weeks (the estimated time to reach the Falklands) was going to be something else. We settled down to the ship's routine. I was to share a cabin with a guy called Colin, a couple of years older than me, who had only recently joined. He was from Cumbria and had the dry Northern sense of humour. As we sailed we became good mates. We had to be; with all our personal kit, bergens, webbing and stores, there was very little room to manoeuvre in the tiny cabin. Our bunk beds were the only private places; we agreed not to encroach on each other. Otherwise, we just piled our gear up and tried the best we could to get on with it.

Our days were dominated by the radio. The World Service was on constantly, and its bulletins, plus the internal daily briefings, kept us in touch with the situation we were sailing into. A daily fitness routine was worked out and since deck space was at a premium, companies were allocated strict timings around the ship. When not running, we would find suitable places to do sit ups, press ups and chin ups. Chin ups were easy; there were loads of pipes and railings. We improvised with everything. A bar with two ammo boxes on each end worked a treat as free weights, for example. It was not long before every Company in the Battalion had its own homemade multigym.

C Company was allocated at the lowest level in the ship, well below the waterline. Every time we had to venture out on to the decks or go to scoff in the galley, we faced hundreds of steps. The officers, of course, were right up at the top with sea views. We didn't mind – it was the way things were. What did piss us off was when we started to enter the war zone and were issued with submarine attack orders: 'What to do in the event of an attack'. Our orders? stay down below. This was totally crazy, and when it happened the first time, we just sat in our cabins, waiting, waiting, waiting. The strain was unbearable and when the 'all clear' was given, we decided that on the next sub warning we would all go above onto the decks – no way did we want to drown in our tiny cabins. On Naval vessels some guys have to stay below because they have jobs to do, maintaining the ship if it has been hit. But there seemed no real reason for us to suffer the indignity of waiting to get killed below the waterline when we could take our chances on deck. This argument was voiced to seniors, who took it on board. They had no option; we would have mutinied otherwise. Luckily, the last sub warning the ship got was when we were all standing to on deck, so a mutiny below the waterline was avoided.

Weapon training and live firing filled the rest of our days. We sent mail, we received mail. It was all very nice and sanitised. I received two letters from Annie, she said she was doing well and missed me. But as I sailed further south my memories of our good times faded. Whether I subconsciously put the good memories out of my mind when things got going, I don't know, but what I didn't do was reply to her last letter, and I couldn't explain that.

The Haig negotiations continued. Meanwhile the *Canberra* had reduced speed and was waiting for us to catch up. We were slow to meet up with the rest of the Brigade, so when we did so up at the Ascension Islands, in the middle of the Atlantic south of the Equator, we had very little time to practise the landing craft loading drills undertaken by every other member of the Brigade while waiting for us. Obviously, there were no problems with the Marines – this was their bread and butter. 3 Para had time to do more than a couple of rehearsals and spend some time on the beach at Ascension. We, on the other hand, had only enough time to practise one embarking and disembarking. There wasn't even time to assault the beach and touch terra firma.

From the Ascensions the seas and the weather were expected to change. It started to get colder. Gone were the calm seas. Gone was the sun. Gone was the thought that this was just a show of strength by the British Government. Gone was the subconscious feeling that it wasn't going to happen. The skies turned to grey, and with the rain came storms. Sixty-foot swirls pitched us about. Sitting in the Continental Lounge, I saw vast green carpets of sea rise far above the height of the portholes and darken the entire ship. Chairs and tables turned over. The whole vessel shook and juddered as the waves crashed down across its decks. I was amazed that it could take such a pounding.

That storm marked the end of our six-week voyage. 'This is really going to happen, isn't it?' Colin said to me one night, after the fullest briefing yet.

'Well, if we have to be down on the car deck to prime grenades in 20 minutes, I reckon that's a clear indication that the shit is about to hit the fan,' I replied. 'I can feel a dump coming on,' Colin muttered as he scurried off to the heads.

The plan was that 2 Para was to be the first on shore. The rest of the Brigade would follow as we pushed on to secure a base around and on Sussex Mountains, then waited until the rear echelons had established a secure beach-head. From that the Brigade could organise itself and start to bring the essential supplies ashore. The next thing would be to organise a plan and strike out towards the Argentine forces in the area and finally to the capital, Port Stanley, where the bulk of the Argentines were entrenched. C Company would be in the second Landing Craft Utility (LCU) of the first wave along with Colonel H. If it was an opposed landing, we were to fight through, secure a safe area and await reinforcements. If it was unopposed, our task was to push forward inland, securing the area as we went and wait for the bulk of the Battalion to get ashore, prior to going up to Sussex Mountains, establishing a series of OPs and reporting back to Battalion HQ any enemy movement we saw.

Standing in the Continental Lounge on the evening of 20 May, I found the atmosphere a little strained. Under the weight of our enormous bergens, we were lost in personal thoughts. All of us had been issued primed grenades; this was a first. Here we were, standing really close to one another, each carrying one HE and one White Phosphorus grenade, all thinking: I hope that fucker next to me has checked that his grenade is screwed up tight! It was not a particularly good time to start cracking jokes. I didn't know how to gauge how I was feeling. The best analogy was the feeling I got when I did my first low-level, full-equipment, night parachute descent. My feeling of anxiety increased as we made our way down on to the lower cargo deck to wait in line to board the LCU.

By now I could hear what I was to face for next few weeks: the naval bombardment was in full swing. I pitied anyone underneath it. The noise was quite reassuring and as I waited to time the swell against the rise and fall of the LCU I caught sight of the steady stream of tracer and gun shells up in the night sky.

'Now, GO!' LCU Marine Corporal said. My timing was just right to clear the ship but the LCU came up a lot quicker than I had anticipated and my right leg jolted as 300 pounds of body and bergen weight met a 100 ton floating steel platform. I was in one of the first patrols to go. Basha the patrol IC, Buster, the LMG gunner and Pops, the 2IC were already on the LCU. It was pretty black outside and I took a couple of minutes to get my night vision. My leg a bit sore, I made my way across the LCU to three dark shapes huddled up in the far corner by the ramp. We had all woken up to the fate which might be waiting for us the other side of that ramp.

The entire Task Force was blacked out. Only the glare of a red light could be seen. There was not much to see or do whilst we waited for the LCU to fill up; a long slow process. Once everyone was on board, we drifted off to a semi-safe position and waited for the rest of the crafts to load. This would take a couple of hours. We had no life jackets on; it would have been impossible with the kit we were carrying, and I could not help thinking that we were sitting ducks just outside San Carlos Water. The sky was surprisingly clear and we could have easily been picked out by the Argy Airforce. Talking was kept down to a minimum as we waited. We whispered most of the time, but it was difficult to hear much over the drone of diesel engines, popping away on tick-over. The sky was occasionally lit up by a barrage of gun fire from the ships. It all seemed surreal.

There was a lot of pushing and pulling of bergens and guys accidentally poking each other with rifles, rocket launchers and machine guns. The occasional 'Fuck off you twat'; a bit of laughter; silence. Suddenly an alarm bell accidentally rang out loudly from wheel house. Anybody on shore must have heard it. It put everybody on edge. We all wanted to get off this friggin landing craft and onto a landing site. As soon as the alarm sounded, Buster turned to Basha: 'What the fuck was *that*?'

'A fucking mine alert or something. Buster, how the fuck do I know?'

Basha's mention of mines had everyone on the go now; whispers about mines erupted everywhere. Seeing Buster was about to have a sense of humour failure, he said that it was a joke and he did not think there were any around here. But the thought of mines made everyone switch on big style.

We started to move. I felt the LCU buckle and arch as it headed off towards the beach. We were all alert now. I could not see over the side of the craft, it was too high. The ramp was even higher. The guns seemed to have stopped. Fear was mounting. Some started to whistle nervously, some prayed and, like me, some just stared straight ahead, waiting for the inevitable 'Stand by' when the ramp would be lowered. There seemed to be some confusion as to where to land. A furious battle of words came from the cox'n and Colonel H. Our craft was now in the lead as the others had either got stuck in the kelp beds which surrounded this part of the coastline or had got lost and were going to put down elsewhere. But whatever the problem was, it was not as great as the one that faced us now.

'Stand by,' the cox'n shouted from behind. The engines were put into reverse thrust. Diesel fumes blew over us. My heart began to race. I was sweating, my mind was racing. Basha nudged me. 'Alright, Devs?' I grinned back. I tapped Buster who in turn nudged Pops. We all turned and looked at each other. The strain on their faces was emphasised by their dilated pupils. We waited, hunched over like little old men but poised, ready to meet force with force. Now the engines put in one last roar as the bottom of the craft scraped and slid up on the sand bank. A sudden jolt, and 200 men stumbled forward onto one another. Sea water which had been leaking into the deck of the LCU now formed a small wave which ensured wet feet for those of us who had, so far, avoided the water. Now all of us on board had soaking wet boots to hit the beach with. The ramp fell away. I could see nothing. It was pitch black. The ramp had fallen into deep water. We had not beached far enough. We were still in three foot of water, and had to get off the LCU the best we could. After having been cramped up for three hours like sardines, to find we had to skirmish to the beach through the icy waters of the South Atlantic was too much for some guys. Men were swearing and calling out for each other. Trying to find patrols and get into secure defensive positions was the priority. No enemy fire as yet. We hadn't made contact with the Special Boat Squadron (SBS) shore party. Had they been compromised? Were there Argies waiting in ambush? All these thoughts were going through my head. We knew which bearing to go on, so to get away from the noise of the landing we got organised and set off in the direction of Sussex Mountains, our second objective.

Once we sorted ourselves out we forged ahead. The going was pretty good. The sky was still clear and it looked like we were in for a crisp morning. My feet were soaking and I was cursing the cox'n of the LCU for not getting closer to the beach. It was a right pisser because apart from meeting the enemy, the last thing any soldier wanted was wet feet, especially if, like us, we had a long tab in front of us.

As we made our way up the steady incline we met no enemy, so after a few hours of tactical patrolling, I could just make out the base of the mountains. The going was very difficult. Every minute we would stop, get down on one knee and listen for the enemy. There was quite a bit of noise from way down below where the landings were now in full swing, but as we trudged up towards the high ground the feeling of being out on a limb grew with every step. We did not know what lay ahead of us. SAS intelligence said that there had been no sightings of enemy patrols in the past few days, but according to them, the enemy had been patrolling the area up until 17 May, which was only four days ago. The thought of bumping into an Argy patrol, or even worse, walking into an ambush, was uppermost in my mind. It would not have taken more than half a dozen of them to ambush us, then to disappear into the mountains, following a preplanned route. This could cause all sorts of problems for us. Certainly the tab inland would have been halted until we could call up enough fire power. The stopping, getting down and listening was increasing as we approached the base of the mountain. We were each carrying twice the amount of ammunition and more. We had also been issued four days' rations. Our bergens and belt kit were weighing well over 100 pounds, which knocked shit out of our knees and backs. When we stopped, some of the blokes just couldn't get down. Their weight was just too much. Once down they would probably not have got up, and in their attempts would have made more noise anyway.

As the dark faded away we reached our preplanned Lying Up Position (LUP) and awaited orders. The idea was that we were to go straight into the OPs once the rest of the Battalion had got itself sorted out. I took this welcome rest to check my weapons and equipment and, for the first time since the landings, have a chat with the rest of the blokes. We were still very much full of anticipation. Here we were, 8,000 miles from UK, pitched against the elements and half the Argentine Armed Forces. It was a time to reflect, to put a bit of faith in the Brigadier and his sidekicks to start making key decisions on how to use us, the men on the ground, to kick some arse.

I looked up at the sky. It was dry and crystal clear, not a cloud in sight. The sun was coming up. The only bad thing about the morning was the bitter wind which blew in from all directions. It was so strong at times that you had to shout to be heard if it was blowing into your face. I looked down and saw the Battalion winding its way across the ground we had covered some hours earlier. I was glad that they were down there with all that ground to cover. It would be some time before they reached us and that would give me more time to rest.

We were quite high up, but we had only reached the base of Sussex Mountains. That surprised me – I thought we had covered a lot more ground than we had. Since the landings we had been tabbing due south with a touch east, and as I looked down on to San Carlos Water, I saw the ships in the Task Force, making out the *Norland* and two Royal Navy vessels. The point at which I thought we had landed was obscured by a spur which ran off the mountain from the left. It was great to see the Task Force and I was feeling pretty good. The order was given that we were to stay put and wait for the rest of the Battalion. This was my first real sight of the Falklands. It reminded me of the Brecon Beacons. The only thing missing were trees. There were none. The air felt fresh and clean. The rain was holding off, but there was a definite breeze blowing up which I felt sure would bring the rain. It was now 07.30hrs 22 May.

In our patrols, we broke off the main track and went for cover. Within our four-man patrol we had a two-man routine. In each pair, one stood guard, while the other cleaned his weapon. We would change over, then one of us would get a brew on for the rest. Basha as patrol commander was always listening out on the radio or briefly disappearing to speak with other patrol commanders. He would come back with useful gossip to cheer us up. He was good for morale.

The day had started out well. We had reached our position of relative safety, and the weather was still holding. I had a brew on and broke open a packet of AB biscuits, the first scoff I had had in ten hours, and I was ready for business. Then I sorted out my wet feet. I always carried a sock in each of my trouser pockets and a small bottle of talc. Quickly I untied one boot, dried off the foot, squeezed a bit of talc onto it, put on the dry sock, then the boot. Within a couple of minutes I had two very warm, very dry feet. I would wring out the wet socks and when it came time to change, the socks popped back into my pockets would be nice and dry again.

Although having wet feet did not bother me, there was something nice about having dry feet and a hot brew in my hand that day. This routine was a lesson I had learnt whilst on selection. I was not to know just how valuable that lesson was to be until after the campaign when I saw the statistics of men who had actually gone sick with Trench Foot. This practice was SOPs in C Company, and we lost no men through Trench Foot.

As the morning broke we got our first piece of action. The Argentine Airforce was out in strength, but our first air raid was all over in a second. Two French-made Super Etendard jets appeared out of nowhere, over the top of the mountain, hugging the ground so low I thought they would crash before they got to their targets. The noise was deafening, yet they flew too quick for us to react. I could make out the pilots, no problem. I watched the jets scream off down the re-entrant from where we had tabbed up during the early hours, then level out and start to attack the ships anchored in the bay below. I watched the strafe and strikes on the water caused by the small arms and tracer fire: an incredible sight; real war. None of us was under any illusions as to what was about to happen, yet our mood was one of excitement. It was obvious that we were in the direct line of the fighters' approach to take on the ships. We were, in effect, at the start of Bomb Alley. We did not have to wait too long for the next sortie. A single Mirage appeared at the crest of the mountain following the same flight path. I took aim and fired but only managed to get off two double taps before it was out of range. I sat back and felt the warmth of the rifle. I was ready for another attack, we all were. The smell of spent cartridges was once again in the air. We were all shouting and giving our own versions of what we did. I thought I had hit it and so did the rest of the Platoon. After that I felt quite honoured and proud. There was something almost erotic about shooting at a multi-million pound jet fighter with a couple of tenpence rounds.

During the day the air raids increased. The Argy pilots were going for it, being either brave or stupid. Time after time they would come and attack the ships in the bay. By mid-morning they had learnt that we were up on the mountains and were more cautious in their approach, sometimes letting off bursts from their cannons just to get our heads down. Excitement built up when a lone Etendard screamed down towards us, head on. I don't think he had been briefed that there was a battalion of Paras dug in on the side of the mountain, because if he had, he would not have been so cocky. As he flew our gauntlet we let rip, about 400 men with SLRs, LMGs and GPMGs firing thousands of rounds. He was hit! His aircraft banked violently and in doing so, sprayed us with fuel. I saw him disappear down to carry on with his attack, only to be confronted by another 1,500 Marines firing the same assortment of weapons. He didn't make it back home: one of 16 enemy aircraft shot down that day.

The air raids continued through the day. As the last of the Battalion tabbed in we were behind schedule; the air attack had obviously scattered the Battalion with each pass. I was now beginning to get cold. I had had enough rest, now I wanted to get going. We all did. Spending much longer on the exposed hillside might cause a few blokes to go down with hypothermia, something our Company could not afford. Our OP tasks were paramount in supplying intelligence back to Battalion HQ – only then could those there assess the safety of the Battalion's LUP. There was no other means of gaining an idea of what was happening on the other side of the mountain. All the Harriers from *HMS Hermes* and *HMS Invincible* were looking after the ships, the limited supply of helicopters was tied up ferrying vital supplies and men ashore, and the SAS and SBS were now out of the area, assigned to different operations. We had to move soon. Colonel H knew this all too well and it was shortly after 14.00hrs we got the order to deploy into our OPs.

At 14.30hrs Basha came back from the HQ brief. He told us that we were to be the most forward OP on the ground and that Josh Winters from Support Company was going to be attached to us for the duration of the task, which was approximately three to four days. Josh was to be the Forward Air Controller (FAC) and our call sign, Charlie One Alpha, would be the only call sign to have the 105mm Howitzers on call. His task, should it be required, was to call up and conduct Fire Missions of artillery down on a main Argy position, which was apparently some 17 ks to the south at a place called Camilla Creek House. Basha went through his briefing quickly as we made mental notes of the main points. Since we had the furthest to go, my thoughts were on how we would get up the mountain. I did not fancy tabbing all the way, it would take us hours, and besides we would need rope, looking at some of the crags that stuck out like razor-sharp teeth. We were all having a bit of a chunter about the tab up, when Josh told us he had heard that a Wessex would be inbound in about 15 minutes, bringing the CO back from an O Group (an orders group) at San Carlos; we might be able to bum a ride. That was a good idea; quickly we made our way down to where the CO's welcoming party had gathered.

As we waited for our taxi, I got the latest rumours on casualties and losses of the war so far. It wasn't good. The Argy Airforce had blitzed the navy. In the morning, *HMS Antelope* had been hit and was now sinking. Almost all of the ships at anchor in San Carlos Water had been hit and damaged, including the *Norland*. News was sparse, but the general feeling amongst us was one of frustration and disbelief. We had been told constantly by the higher echelons of the Navy and Airforce that the Argies were no match for Brits and that whatever they did, we would react and return twice as much devastation. This did not appear to be the case as I looked down towards the bay and saw ships burning away. It was a pathetic sight. What I could not understand was why we had so many vessels all laid up in the bay so close together, given that the air raids started early on in the day and were still continuing. I thought the ships should have disappeared for the day and come back in at night. They looked like sitting ducks, and as time went on they were exactly that. News was also coming in on the casualties. At the time I really did not want to fill my head with rumours, but as it was the topic of conversation around me I had no choice but to listen. It reminded me of being back at Warrenpoint, where we all talked about who had got hit and who was injured. The news was vague, but it was noted that the Navy had lost a few guys and the casualties were beginning to stack up. 2 Para had not yet lost anyone, but we had our injured: a couple shot and about 30 injured on the tab in. I thought, that amount of injuries you don't even get on a full Battalion exercise parachute drop. What the fuck is going on?

I turned my attention to Josh, hoping to draw some inspiration from him. An old sweat, he had been a member of the Pathfinders during the life of 16 Para Brigade. When there was no job for him, he was posted to Support Company where he became an expert in all the Battalion's heavy weapons. Part of his work was to cross-train with other units such as the Royal Artillery, so he was well conversant with the calling in of Arty fire missions. Josh knew the score. He was certainly glad to be back with his old Company, the eyes and ears of the main task force. Our patrol was the furthest forward. That was why we had Josh attached to us from the Support Company. He was the only soldier on Sussex Mountains with the authority to bring down Arty fire on the target of his choosing. He was the longrange sniper of the Battalion, which made Charlie One Alpha one fuck-off good fighting patrol.

Josh reckoned that the sooner we pushed on and got to meet the Argies man to man, the sooner we might be able to stir up a bit of 'Airborne Morale'. He was right. The entire Battalion had been on land for less than a day and had seen the Navy get a good kicking. It was up to us to show the rest of the task force what the 'Maroon Machine' could do.

'Inbound,' Buster shouted. He had spotted the Wessex coming in low level, hugging the ground so close I thought at one stage it wasn't going to make it. It landed with a thump. Basha ran over to the loadie, map and grid in hand. We all followed them. Basha was so quick up to the chopper that the CO had hardly any time to get out of the door. They met head on.

'Ah, Corporal Pope! What the fuck do you want?' the CO shouted sarcastically.

'Sir. Can I borrow your chopper for five minutes? We need to get up there.' Basha pointed to the summits of Sussex Mountains.

'I know where you've gotta go, Corporal Pope, I gave the orders.'

'We're running a bit late, sir!' Basha pleaded.

The rest of us were standing off to one side. I could see the hand movements of the two of them, and reckoned Basha's bullshit had won the day. He beckoned us to come forward. We had got our lift.

The chopper was still turning and I could see the pilot getting nervous about hanging around too long on the ground, knowing the constant threat of the Argy Airforce.

'Ten minutes, Corporal Pope, and I want it back here.'

'No problems. Ten minutes. We can cover enough ground in

that time, and thank you sir.'

The loadie was getting agitated as Basha turned around to show him where we wanted to be dropped off. The rest of us loaded up and waited for the off. The CO helped us on board and wished us good luck. I replied with the thumbs up; it was good of him to say that. He must have had a shitload on his plate, what with battling on both fronts, the Argies and the Navy. It was the last time I was to see him alive.

This incident sped by: in less than three minutes we were off. The warmth inside the chopper was inviting. Standing outside waiting to board, I had been chilled by the downdraft, so it was good to feel warm. The door was open and the loadie was constantly looking out and talking to the pilot on his headset. The aircraft was banking more violently. We seemed to be flying a lot faster and lower than normal. At one stage I thought that the pilot had lost control. Dipping and turning constantly, we were weaving our way through the small re-entrants as we climbed up the mountain. Every so often I would see a bit of sky as the chopper climbed to avoid snapping its blades off on the sides of the valley. Then we would dive and the aircraft would become dark as we weaved and scurried just metres off the ground.

I looked round to see the faces of the rest of the patrol. Buster and Pops had their eyes closed, Josh was exchanging sign language with Basha. Basha saw me looking across to him. He was wearing a headset as well and was in constant comms with the pilot and the loadie. All of a sudden an alarm klaxon sounded. It kicked life into all of us, including the loadie. I didn't have a clue what was going on. At the same time a red light appeared from somewhere. We landed with a thud and the next minute the loadie was throwing out all our equipment. Basha ripped the head phones off and jumped out. Instantly we all followed him. Within ten seconds of landing the Wessex shot off and disappeared just about 50 metres from us down a re-entrant, where we could hear it hovering. A second later, two Mirage fighters appeared from nowhere. They screamed over low, heading up the valley from the north, the direction of San Carlos Bay. They passed literally within feet of us, an amazing sight. The noise was deafening. The episode lasted three seconds at most. Then the air became still and quiet again.

'Jesus Christ! Where the fuck did they come from?' someone said. Basha had heard the pilot tell the loadie that he was going to do an emergency landing to get us out of the chopper, then go to ground, because there were two jet fighters flying up the valley with a possible missile lock on. That's exactly what he did. He dropped us out and tried to hide. It was a brave manoeuvre – the pilot only had seconds to make that judgement. He wanted us out of the aircraft just in case he got shot out of the sky, thereby avoiding the deaths of eight men as opposed to just his two aircrew and himself.

When everything had died down, the Wessex reared its nose from its hiding place, spotted where we had laid up, flew over us with the crew giving us the thumbs up, and headed back the way it came. I felt now the war had heightened my awareness. That incident was the first direct aggressive action directed at me and my mates. The two Mirages had flown up the valley to hunt me down. They had seen the Wessex and had come in for the kill. For me, the war had now turned personal.

CHAPTER FIVE

Significant Enemy

Somewhere forward on Sussex Mountains – East Falkland. 22 May 1982.

THE RANGE OF Sussex Mountains stretched for about 10 kilometres, running north-west to south-east. Some five kilometres to the north lay San Carlos and the beachhead. It was made up of sharp, craggy rock formations. There was no vegetation of any sort on the top. No trees, no bushes or grass, just thousands of football-sized boulders which fell away from the highest ridge like rivers flowing down its side. In between these boulder-falls, there were sharp uneven rock runs which made the going very hard. Losing a foothold or getting your boot trapped down behind one of these boulders meant certain severe damage to your ankles and legs, exaggerated by the fearsome loads on our backs.

To our front, towards the south some 16 kilometres, was Camilla Creek House, an old farmstead made up of the main house plus a couple of outbuildings. Intelligence said we would get our first real sight of the Argy ground troops there: numbers unknown but confirmed sightings of enemy movement. This was our OP target.

After the dramatics of the chopper flight, we made our way

wearily up the mountain side. We had been dropped almost within our prearranged grid, so we lost little time in moving forward. The weather was beginning to turn and the wind, which had not ceased throughout the day, gradually began to get stronger as we scaled to reach the summit, bringing with it rain, then sleet mixed with snow. When we reached a point near the top, I went with Basha to recce a LUP and an eventual OP site. I covered him as we cautiously made our way up. I was constantly aware that an Argy fighting patrol or OP might be established on top of the ridge, might have spotted us making our slow ascent, and now might be waiting to ambush us from above. This was a real possibility, and we had to be careful in our movements. We stopped every ten feet, trying to listen through the howling wind to catch any noise, such as a radio or voices, that would compromise a possible enemy position. After a careful sweep of the ridge, we saw no Argies; there were no traces that they had ever been here. In fact, there was no sign that *anything* had ever been here. It was virgin ground. We found an ideal position for the OP, with only one route in; and two good bug-out routes should we need them, well covered by the OP. It had shelter and a good view of the target. Also, because we were up over 800 feet above sea-level, radio comms were near perfect. We radioed in our rough location and settled down to the night routine. Because it was nearly dark we could not brew up or get a hot scoff on, so I had to make do with a cold tin of baconburgers and few gob-fulls of water. It was a sure bet that the temperature would drop well below minus 5, and as there had been no let-up in the wind it was decided to do stags of one hour each man, as opposed to the standard two-hour stags. This worked out OK and because of the extra man, Josh, we all got a good four hours gonk.

Suddenly I was aware that something kept hitting me on the face. I had been in my doss bag for what seemed only a couple of minutes. I was now conscious of the icy wind on my exposed cheeks. I opened my eyes. It had snowed lightly during the night and a thin crust of it covered my poncho. The weather attacked my eye sockets and as I drew my first waking breath, I tasted the mucus that had dribbled from my nose during the four-hour kip and solidified on my moustache. I cleared it with the back of my left hand and instinctively reached down to feel for my weapon with my right. It was there. A reassuringly warm feeling spread through my body.

The realisation that I was now coming round from a very heavy sleep dawned on me. The brain was in gear. I switched on, in tune with my immediate surroundings, instantly alert. My stomach cried out for food and water as the previous day's tab had dehydrated me considerably. Raising my eyes I saw Basha just about to toss another stone at me. The look on his face was concealed by the Airborne helmet which covered his head and the two days of growth and cam cream covering the rest of exposed skin. He was half standing, half crouching against a large jagged piece of rock which made up part of the OP cover.

He made a slow but deliberate movement with his left hand towards the stagging-on position. He then gave me the thumb sign and turned it downwards, indicating 'Enemy in front.' His right hand was gripping his weapon. Once he saw I had understood the message, he turned to face the threat. I stared at him briefly. He poked his tongue out rapidly for a few seconds, implying he was going to enjoy the next contact with the Argies. Basha had many idiosyncrasies, but this was his most perverse to date.

Slowly, I extracted my body from the doss bag, my weapon close to hand. Everything we did in the OP was done with the minimum of movement and noise. The Argies could have deployed fighting patrols out anywhere on the mountain. They could have had OPs out like ourselves, especially as they had been here for weeks; time enough to get themselves well entrenched. Other Int reps we had been given via HQ said that SAS and SBS patrols, who had been covertly sniffing around for a few weeks, had reported no sightings of any significant enemy ground movement in our present area. I thought East Falkland was a fucking big island and, anyway, none of us was about to take the chance that the Argentine Army were just going to sit back and let their Airforce destroy us unaided.

On more than one occasion since the landing I had wanted to question the term 'significant enemy' used in the frequent Int reps radio messages. It would have been helpful to know if these Int reps were being sent back to the main intelligence HQ for the whole of the brigade, or whether they were sent to local command within the Battalion. The difference was that a sighting of one or two Argies by an SAS patrol, whose direct line of reporting was back to an aircraft carrier, would of been of 'no significance' in general terms. However, to a four/five man OP, this was of the greatest significance. The passage of hard-gained intelligence from the Special Forces OPs on the ground to other friendly ground troops was of the utmost importance for those in the thick of it and, of course, those frontline officers who had to control the advancement of the war. Later, as the war progressed, many of us 'grunts' dismissed the quality of the intelligence as R&F (Read and Forget) and relied on our own ears and eyes. To us, it was the pushing of paper around by the hierarchy, in the comfort of their cabins, that was 'insignificant'. The tactics drummed into me since Depot Para now made sense. I was not even going to fart aloud, well, not enough to compromise our position for no good reason.

Basha hadn't moved. I saw Pops stirring in his doss bag, just at the bottom of my feet. I guessed Buster and Josh were up on stag, looking at what had caused Basha to get me up. I picked my SLR up, keeping my finger away from the trigger guard and checked that the safety catch was still on 'safe' – I might have accidentally moved the catch to 'on' in my sleep. I released the magazine to check the rounds and to see if the top round was on the right-hand side. It was. A quick check of the rest of the SLR to see if all was well, then I crawled out of my doss bag, crouched down as low as possible and moved towards Basha, who was only ten feet away and still staring ahead.

'What the fuck's up? I've only been asleep for ten minutes!' I said.

'Fuck off Devs, your four hours is up, mate, and anyway, didn't you hear that fucking Argy Chinook fly by? It came so close Buster reckoned he could have punched the pilot in his face. It made a real slow pass. Poor old Buster was taking a crap at the time. That's why Josh is up there with him. He couldn't move, he didn't dare.'

'Does he think they saw him?' I said.

'Fuck knows, we will probably find out if he comes back soon.'

My body was now being heated by the adrenalin flow brought on by the thought of taking out the Chinook. While talking to Basha I was physically checking that all my HE and WP grenades were safe

104

and that all the pouches on my webbing belt contained what they should contain and were all done up. My belt kit was all in order and I was hot to trot. I tightened up the quick release belt, readjusted the webbing straps and for no particular reason touched the flattened pins of both grenades. I took a cursory look over to check that my 66 and M79 were still lying under my basha. It was a routine all of us did as a matter of fact, constantly: in the field, on operations, or back in the barracks in Aldershot.

I went back across to my basha, took the poncho down, and packed it and the doss bag away in my bergen. Then I stashed it away out of sight behind a rock before moving forward to the OP to see what was happening. Buster and Josh acknowledged me. Josh moved back to the rear to allow me to have a look. He was pinching his nose with his fingers, making out that Buster was stinking. Buster turned around to see this.

'Fuck off back you hat bastard,' Buster grunted to Josh. Although Buster was a good enough soldier to pass the Pathfinders Selection, he rather lacked a sense of humour. Still, Buster was as solid as a rock when it came to doing his job and a good hand to have around if the shit hit the fan.

Josh grinned and chuckled to himself as he left to go back.

'What was all that about?' I said to Buster, looking at the Chinook milling around some couple of ks in front of me.

'I was having a dump when the chopper came up out of nowhere. I mean it just suddenly appeared.'

'Didn't you hear the fucker?'

'You mean, like you did when you were dossing.' I just smirked.

Buster went on: 'I was having this dump when next minute I was looking straight into this fucking Argy pilot's face. The only warning I got was when the wind started to gusting about a million knots. It's so windy up here, you know, I just carried on until my shit started to go airborne. Then I knew. The downdraft of the chopper threw shit and piss all over the place. I'm taking that fucker out with a 66 the next time he appears. I fucking mean it, Devs. Ever had your balls and arse exposed to a wind chill factor of minus 100?'

Both of us were looking at the chopper whilst Buster was talking. Since it was my stag, I told Buster to go back and clean himself up.

Josh was right; he stank. He went back to sort himself out. We only had a limited supply of water, for drinking use only, and there was no grass on the mountain. Everything we carried in to the OP had a purpose, and because of the amount of ammunition, radio equipment, spare batteries and food, there was no room for baby wipes!

The Chinook disappeared beyond the horizon. More than likely it had gone back to refuel, or been put on another tasking. Basha reported the incident back to our HQ and we waited for its return.

We didn't have anything so luxurious as secure-voice frequency-hopping radios. Although we could use voice for short intervals and in emergencies, every radio message we sent back or received had to be coded and then decoded for security reasons.

I lay back and settled into two hours of stagging on. Because of the daylight we reverted to a two-hour stag system. Basha came forward to brief me on what was going on with the rest of the war and to let me know that he had been told to pass any other sightings immediately back to HQ. Should the Chinook come back, we were to remain covert and not compromise our position or that of other friendly forces in the area by engaging it. He finished off by saying that he would bring a brew up for me soon and that the rest of the blokes were sorting out their gear for a possible move. Move where? I didn't yet know. I guess neither did the CO, but I knew one thing about the Colonel; it wouldn't be backwards, back to the beach head where we landed yesterday, as Rumour Control had it, where the overall Commander of the Brigade, a Marine, wanted to reorganise the marching order and put the Marines in front, ahead of the Paras. I smiled in the knowledge that it would take many more Marines to push us off this mountain than the Navy had.

The first full day in the OP went by without further intrusion from the Chinook. Throughout the day we could look back down at San Carlos Bay and watch the enemy aircraft attack the Task Force. It was like being on the set of an action-packed movie. It looked unreal, but it wasn't. Our own men were being killed and maimed with every air strike that flew in. Once again I questioned the commanders' reasoning. Why did they allow the ships to remain idle during the daylight hours? It was frustrating to watch; I felt helpless and detached from it all. All I wanted was pure revenge for the devastation that was being waged on our men below.

There was not much to do in the OP when not on stag. The routine was to strip clean and double check our weapons and kit, and try and keep out of the appalling weather to stay dry. Getting rest was another priority. The radio was on constantly, picking up sit-reps from the Battalion HQ as to how the war was panning out. We seemed to be losing. It was not a good feeling I had in my stomach as I got my head down after the first stag that night.

First light the next morning saw the return of the Chinook. It was hovering two ks away, just off to the right of the OP, moving slowly and keeping low. It was obviously looking for something. Then it turned and headed straight towards us. Basha was already on the radio reporting the sighting. Josh had 'stood to' the rest of us, and now we waited to see what it was going to do. Basha sent a message, and after the necessary preliminaries got to the gist of it: 'This is Charlie One Alpha, we have an enemy Chinook heading towards our position. It's flying low and obviously looking for something. Request to take it out. Over.' Its position was requested. Basha replied that it was 300 metres away: 'We can take it out no problems. Over.'

'Roger. From Sunray this location. Negative. Negative. Do not engage. Do not compromise your position. Read back. Over.'

Basha grudgingly repeated the order back to Zero, confirming the message not to shoot the chopper down. He put the headset down and reeled off a series of 'Fucks' under his breath. We all got the message. Basha and I watched the Chinook ascend right in front of us. Divvy was hiding behind a rock with a 66 extended, ready to fire it off should the Chinook start firing for whatever reason. As the chopper rose up to our level the noise from its engines became deafening and the downdraft whooshed through the wall of rocks which made up the OP. I could now spot the pilot quite clearly. The chopper was painted in a similar camouflage pattern to our own, but splattered with a yellow spot design. It had guns on it and as it turned right, I caught sight of a series of portholes down the side of the fuselage. It was so close that I could see right through these: there appeared to be no bodies moving around inside. The tailgate was closed. I thought that a bit strange, because if it was on the lookout for something, then usually the rear loadie would have the tailgate down to get a better view. Perhaps, because it was so cold up here, the pilot had decided against it.

All I could do was watch as it flew off and once again disappeared the way it came. The decision not to allow us to shoot it down was totally stupid, without logic. Every man and his dog knew we were there. It was obvious that any attacking force would dominate the high ground and would have forward OPs out. It was senseless waste of a great opportunity to take out an important aircraft which would be used against us in a ground battle. It dampened our morale.

During that afternoon a message came through that there was a sighting of the enemy in and around Camilla Creek House. We were too far from that target to see for sure but Josh called up a Fire Mission from the big guns, 105s. They had been brought ashore the day before and were now ready to engage possible targets. We spent the rest of the day spotting the fall of shot of the artillery rounds and after six Fire Missions, Josh reckoned we had 'neutralised' the target. We could just make out the smoke of the shells exploding on impact. The afternoon's activities heightened our spirits; we felt that we had achieved some kind of a body count. That evening, we sat around chatting about the forthcoming move off the mountain and a possible attack on the settlements of Darwin and Goose Green. We were also left deep in thought as we watched *HMS Antelope*, a Type 21 Frigate, explode and burn away all night. She had been hit earlier that day by a Skyhawk fighter/bomber dropping a 1000-pounder on her port quarter, but the bomb did not explode until the evening when it set her magazines off. I sat there watching her burn all through the night, occasionally exploding as the heat burned through and set off the rest of the ammunition. I had never seen a ship go up before; a sad sight. Once again, I felt totally helpless. What was happening to our Navy? What was going to happen to *us*?

By the time we got our orders to move off Sussex Mountains and advance to Camilla Creek House forward of the rest of the Battalion, worse news had been picked up on the radio. *HMS Coventry*, a Type 42 air-defence ship (similar to *HMS Sheffield* sunk some days before), and the *Atlantic Conveyor*, a container ship, had both been hit and sunk. The *Atlantic Conveyor* was carrying all the warm clothing stores, tentage and 13,000 tons of vital supplies. It was also carrying ten Wessex and four giant Chinook helicopters, of which only one was lucky enough to take off when the ship got hit. There seemed no end to the severe battering the Royal and Merchant Navy was getting. Just what the fuck was happening? The Task Force could not go on without the stores it required to do its job.

It was a hard tab down the mountain and across to Camilla Creek House that evening. Although I had been static for four days back in the OP, it didn't make it any easier. The rock runs seemed to be getting wider, and the weather so atrocious it cut through to every opening on my body. All through the night we tabbed. I felt slightly lucky, in that having recently completed SAS selection, I was pretty much used to this slog. Some of the men in the rest of the Battalion were not so well equipped. Unfortunately they did not make it and were left either to bring up the rear or to wait until first light and try and get a chopper to take them back to the field hospital at San Carlos Bay, where they could be treated, patched up and sent back up the line. A lot of men went down with chewed-up feet caused by their boots, or sprained ankles twisted on the rock runs. Up until this stage, very few injuries were caused by enemy action.

The Battalion slogged its way all through the night. In my patrol we were very low on food and fresh water, burning up calories to such an extent that Buster and Pops had ripped into their survival rations just before last light.

The morning of the 27th brought more news and gossip. It was the first time since leaving the *Norland* that we had a chance to meet up with the rest of the Battalion. Stories were swapped and rumours of the Royal Navy's battering were confirmed. It was not a time for jokes. There were real concerns for the blokes who had been on board the ships when they came under attack. We were sad that so many lives and ships had been lost at this stage, especially since none of us had actually seen the enemy close enough to deal with him the way we had been trained.

Under the constant threat of air raids we made the best of a bad situation. We were fortunate to get a re-sup of rations and water purification tablets. No ammunition re-sup was required, but we had a choice of a Mars bar or 20 cigarettes. The cigarettes would come in handy. I would light three or four up at once and hold them in cupped hands to keep warm; also I found the smell of the tobacco reassuring.

Josh returned to Support Company. His Arty fire was pretty good. The area around Camilla Creek House was pitted with large craters where the HE rounds had done their job. Strangely, though, the house had not been hit.

We lay up for most of the day trying to keep out of the wind and trying to get some sleep. I found a peat hole. It was wet, but deep enough to get the four of us in out of the wind, so it was home for the next 12 hours.

The ground all around us was flat, peaty and very soft. In the distance to the north, I could make out the peaks of Sussex Mountains. They seemed closer than I thought they would be. Despite a hard night's tab, we had gone only 16 ks.

Some five ks to the south-east the ground gradually rose up and down again to a place called Burntside House another small settlement of a house and outbuildings. Directly due south of that, nine ks away, lay a much larger settlement, Goose Green, with about 150 people, an airfield and a school house.

Our order to move came far too quickly for me. I was quite happy in the peat hole, keeping out of the way of the rest of the Battalion. Our task was to recce the start line for the Battalion's first attack against the Argies. Eight of us had been tasked to go forward to Burntside House, and find and secure a position, so that A Company could lead an attack on it. Other patrols from C Company had similar tasks with B and D Company. This was to be our first encounter with the enemy, or so we thought.

A quick set of orders was given. We were to move out after dark on a fixed compass bearing set in the direction of Burntside House, locate and secure a start line, and send back four men to escort A Company. The attack was set to go in before daylight the following morning. Once all the rifle companies had taken their objectives, we would be held in reserve and brought forward if the situation got out of hand.

The night of the 27th was cold, crisp and black. We set off in light order – our bergens containing our warm gear and doss bags were to be cached and brought forward at a later time. It was to be a three-hour tactical patrol. We were now entering the enemy's territory, and there was no more messing around, we made no noise. I was switched on as we patrolled through the night. The going was good for about an hour. We constantly stopped and got down on one knee to listen and observe the ground all around us. In past conflicts it was not uncommon for an enemy patrol accidentally to walk straight into a defensive position without the occupants knowing anything about it. I was very much aware of this, and kept ears and eyes well tuned in. At about the halfway stage we started to find fence-lines made up of barbed wire which were not shown on the maps we had. The barbed wire looked too old to mark off a possible Argy mine field. Perhaps they outlined the boundary of our target. We crossed a couple of small streams and hit a track, also not shown on the map. We had been going for two hours now. A double check of the compass; we were heading in the right direction. The thing about working in the cuds at night is that you have got to rely on your compass, even if your instincts tell you otherwise. It could be fatal to choose the latter. As we were double checking the map and compass, a light appeared in the distance. We lay in wait. It came closer, growing in size. Then we heard the noise of what sounded like a Land Rover. As it came closer still, the noise was evidently that of a tracked vehicle. We were some 20 metres off the side of the track, and there was no cover to hide in – the ground was totally flat. As we lay in all-round defence, in a circle facing outwards, my heart began to pound. I felt it thumping my smock. I was now not worried about the cold, that feeling had gone. My body was once again filled with adrenalin.

'What the fuck is it?' Buster whispered.

'I think it's a LVTP 7,' I replied. I thought to myself that the ground was too soft for these armoured personnel carriers to operate on. But the sound was most definitely coming from a tracked vehicle.

Basha whispered to get a 66 and the M79 ready. Metallic noises filtered into the night from those who had the 66s, though getting them off our backs was a bit of a problem. The clicking in place of the retaining clips as they were snapped open to the armed position happened within seconds. The LVTP 7 stopped. No way could our movements be heard over the noise of the vehicle. I thought, That's

111

why the tracks aren't on the map, they have only recently been made by the Argies. We lay there for 20 minutes. The single beam of the vehicle was turning like a searchlight, but we were just out of range. If it had come forward another ten metres, we would have been caught in full view. The noise of its engines gave one last roar as it turned and headed off towards the south-west. We lay silent for another ten minutes before moving off. It was a close shave. We had been given no intelligence of sightings of LVTP 7s. It was a bizarre encounter, and we had been very lucky not to have been spotted.

Fortunately we reached the target without further incident. It lay some 100 metres to our front, and there appeared to be no movement coming from it. Maybe the Argies had all got their heads down or maybe they were, like us, playing the game for real. The last part of the tab was tricky. A series of small streams on our bearing made the going wet and slippery. It would be harder still when the 80 or so men of A Company came through. As planned, a patrol went back to Camilla Creek House and led A Company in. For us who were left to watch the target, it was a long four hours of lying down and not moving. One of the ships offshore, *HMS Arrow*, started to let rip with its one 4.5 inch gun. As we waited in the darkness the shells roared in to soften up the target. We were so close that sometimes they would fall short and shake the ground all around us, but on the whole the ship's fire was very accurate. Every so often the sky would be lit up with a mixture of HE and illuminating Starburst shells. My immediate thoughts were, I'm gonna get wasted by my own side! The firing would stop, then start again elsewhere in the distance. Then, without warning, it would shower down and around us again. It was terrifying. I just made myself as small a target as possible and waited until it was all over.

HMS Arrow stopped firing and it went very quiet. A Company had eventually got its men into position and formed up on the start line. The attack opened up with GPMGs, 66s, 84s and 2 inch mortars for illumination. There was nothing for us to do but lie guarded and watch the fireworks below. This was a live Company attack, the first the Parachute Regiment had done for many a year. The ear-shattering noise of 84s being fired and the screams of the men shouting out fire control orders as they assaulted down the hill into Burntside House were truly dramatic. It was an amazing success. The enemy had been taken out, and the rest had fled. In the distance I could hear other attacks going in. Our job was finished for the time being. We sat back and waited for further orders.

As dawn came I could see the devastation that we had rained down on the enemy positions. It wasn't quite light when we moved off down to where the Battalion was reorganising itself. Men were screaming an array of orders. Medics and support personnel were running around through the half-light trying to offer aid to those who had been injured, Paras and Argies alike. The air was thick with smoke from the fires caused by the anti-tank rounds hitting their targets and catching fire. The smell of spent ammunition and HE grenades wafted all around. As we approached along the track and into the madding crowd, I could see the bodies of the dead lying where they had fallen. Some were our own men. It started to drizzle. As we walked, I felt that we would not have to wait too long for this mopping-up to finish and for the day to begin with a big bang.

Firefights were still raging off in the distance and as the daylight became clearer I could see what looked like a scene from the Second World War: men with bloodied bandaged heads; prisoners being ferried away under armed guard; helicopters buzzing around look-ing for safe places to land and pick up the injured; supplies being dropped off; stacks of 81mm mortar rounds being ferried in on the under-slung cargo nets of larger helicopters. It looked like total chaos, but through all the mess there was a system at work.

The first phase of the battle was over, and as daylight came the momentum which we had gained at first light began to slow. The battles had been fought out in open ground and now all of us could see that we were targets for the Argentine Mortar Fire Controllers (MFCs) and snipers who had command of the high ground due south of us. We made a steady advance south towards them. They lay between us and Goose Green, our next main objective.

It was about 10.00hrs and we had tabbed only about two ks when all hell broke out. We were being mortared! There was nowhere to hide, so we had to get down the best we could and wait for the barrage to stop. Mortars were landing all around. Most of them exploded about two feet down into the peat, which was good news for us, because it deadened their impact. A few rounds fell that did not explode. Duds. There seemed to be no command and control. The boss man did not really have any idea as to what to do. He seemed to be just as frozen as us. Sods of earth and sizzling secondary fragmentation was being kicked up all over the place. We had to make a move. I screamed across to Jim, who was from another patrol and was the only one I could see, that I was going to make a dash for it, forward into some dead ground which lay about 80 metres in front, where the most forward patrol had taken refuge. It was a long sprint but it was the only option we had short of going back the way we came. I tried to let Basha know my intentions, but because in the confusion I hadn't a clue where anybody was, I screamed back across to Jim to let him know I was going to go for it any second. It took some time to build up the nerve to expose myself and make the dash, but staying where I was meant almost certain death. I got up and started to sprint. I then heard Jim, who was with another bloke who had split from his patrol, scream, 'DEVS, WATCH OUT, WATCH OUT.'

I halted, just as you would react to an order on the parade square. I do not know why I did it, I just did: for a second I stood there. He had seen a mortar round explode just in front of me and his warning was to stop me moving forward, just for an instant. As I froze, a piece of shrapnel the size of a packet of cigarettes came whistling towards me. It seemed to be flying through the air in slow motion, and missed my right femur by inches, embedding itself into the peat just behind me. If it had hit me, it would have been curtains.

It took ten minutes to reorganise ourselves in the bottom of the dead ground. The entire area was void of trees, rocky crags or anything which might have afforded cover; there was only the dead ground in the folds of the rolling terrain. All of us had been split from our patrols. I found Basha and Pops, but Buster was still pinned down with the rest of the Company, out in the open. There was a lot of confusion. Men had split up from their patrols and were yelling the names of mates. I did not know if some of the blokes were screaming in pain because they were hit, or just out of total confusion.

However hard you train for the real situation, you cannot train with real live bullets being shot at you. Some men react very strangely when real pieces of lead are coming their way: they just

114

stay put and don't move, they freeze. This breaks the Company's momentum, thus losing the speed and aggression which is vital to winning a firefight in any battle. This was partly the problem here on the exposed ridge.

We were safe for the time being because we were out of sight of the snipers and MFCs. It gave us time to stuff food in our mouths and take a swig of water. I was thinking that the morning had really started off with a bang. I looked at my watch; 08.30hrs. I had been on the go for eleven hours. We waited for the rest of the Company to catch up. Ten minutes turned into an hour. I heard news that A Company had moved another 2 ks to the south and were coming under intense fire from the ridge line at a place called Darwin, some 1 k south of our position and 3 ks directly north of Goose Green. It was vital that we had control of it before we assaulted Goose Green. We were waiting for elements of A Company to fight their way out of a situation they had got themselves into. I could hear the battle raging. It seemed to be coming from just around the next hill to my front. The amount of small arms fire I heard was incredible: both sides in the battle were giving it shit.

Buster arrived carrying his LMG, cursing everyone for leaving him stranded. Basha told him to shut the fuck up, take the gun, find a good position down the gully and face out over the bay. I was told to go with him. We did not know how long we were going to be in the gully. There was rumour that we were to go in and support A Company, should they need it. But the CO, who was on his way up to see what the hold-up was, came on the net and told us to stay put. We just did not know what was happening.

Buster picked a good position for the gun, and he and I laid up and watched our arcs down the gully and out over the sea. The gully was about ten metres high and 50 across. We had sentries out higher up it, should any stray Argies walk in on us, and our main arcs of fire were basically straight down it. Ten minutes had gone by when Buster suddenly made one quick movement with his left leg to get my attention.

'Fuck, Devs, did you see that?'

'No. What?'

'I'm not sure if they were penguins or not, I just caught their movement out of the corner of my eyes, but three of 'em have just gone behind that big boulder on the beach.'

'Jesus Christ, Buster, that's less than 200 metres away!'

Buster had no time to reply. The Argies came out from behind the rock, and as they did, I squeezed off several double taps. Buster opened up with the LMG. It happened so fast. Two disappeared back behind the rock and I claimed the one which now lay on the beach.

It was quite a sanitised firefight. No rounds came back at us; we were too quick. It was all over in a matter of seconds, then we covered the area for some time. Basha came over and wanted to know what the hell was going on, who were we shooting at. The boss man screamed over to us to stop firing. This was *not* an order I agreed with. We weren't allowed to go forward and check the body and do a follow-up. We just had to sit there and wait for further orders to move. My little shooting incident was soon to be forgotten as the A Company firefight was coming to an end. The noise of the small arms was also dying down and it wasn't long before firing ceased totally. The boss man was on the radio trying to confirm a previous message when the news came in that our CO had been killed up on the battlefield at Darwin Ridge. The radio messages were being passed around the blokes and everyone was nodding as though they understood. Not only had the Battalion lost the CO, but two more officers and a few blokes as well. We all started to speculate who had been hit. The loss of the CO had no real impact on myself or the blokes around me in C Company. It was nothing personal, it was a case of, 'Well, that's a real bastard and let's get on with the job.' The CO never really knew me or the rest of us lower ranks; it would be stupid to pretend he did. He never knew me as Devs and I certainly never heard him being referred to as H.

The death of the CO and his fellow officers did affect the boss pretty bad. When we got the order to advance towards A Company's location, I could see the boss physically upset as we tabbed off. I felt that there has to be some holding back of the emotions until a more suitable time.

When we arrived up at Darwin Ridge, we saw what was left of the battlefield. A Company had really kicked some shit; dead Argies all over, some still in their trenches, some lying where they had been

116

slotted outside their cover. The prisoners and the injured lay in little clusters all over the place, moaning, crying, shitting. Just doing, I guess, what a defeated Army that had just been shot to fuck would do. Some of the prisoners were being held on the ground and were being shouted at by the blokes. I saw one Argy shouting in Spanish, looking like he was having an argument with one of ours. I thought, Why doesn't he keep his big fat gob shut? I would in his position. It was strange to see prisoner and captor arguing just after a battle. A butt stroke into the Argy's stomach settled the argument. He doubled over in pain as two other prisoners were ordered to grab him and take him down to where the rest of the prisoners were lying up. I passed medics attending to the injured. The stench of battle mixed with the smoke from the gorse bushes that had been set on fire by grenades and rocket launchers. A thick cloud of greyish smoke hovered over the battlefield. This time there was not a lot of shouting; it seemed quite peaceful. There was a slight drizzle, which seemed to temper A Company's mood.

Walking further through the battle area I learnt that two of my mates had been killed and one injured during the action. Steve Prior, Chuck Hardman and Grabber G had been shot up pretty bad and had been casevac'd back. I felt stunned by the deaths of Stevie and Chuck, having worked closely with them across the water. Two very professional, switched-on soldiers, they died the only way they could, leading from the front.

The casualty figures for A Company's efforts were: six dead, 12 wounded. The Argies weren't so lucky: 20 dead and 76 taken prisoner, of which 39 had been wounded. Add on the skirmishes that B and D Company had been having during the day, and it looked like the tide was beginning to turn in our favour.

Because we had lost the CO, Major Chris Keeble, 2IC of the Battalion, took command. Some decisions were made and we were ordered to lie up on the reverse slope of the hill which led down into Goose Green – in effect, the same slope which A Company had so gallantly captured. Looking south over the ridge line and down into Goose Green I saw the ground run slowly away to the estuary which lay in front of the settlement. To my left was the sea, to my right just open ground. Everywhere looked devoid of cover. I could just make out a series of trenches about halfway between us and Goose Green.

I couldn't see if they were manned or not, but within the settlement itself I could see many Argies getting ready for us.

We had now been on the go for more than 14 hours, with limited water and food. I just had my survival rations and a couple of packs of issue Garibaldi biscuits stuffed down my smock. It was apparent in my patrol that the new CO had to make a decision very soon on what plan he was going to put into action. It would have been very easy for him to stop the advance and to sit back and wait for heavy fire support, but that might not be available for some hours. The logistics and support problem was obviously hampered by the loss of the choppers on the *Atlantic Conveyor*: heli-support was very limited. He could have turned away from Goose Green, headed east towards Port Stanley and follow to where the rest of the Brigade was heading. Or he could keep the momentum of the battle going and attack Goose Green head on. In a lot of decision-making cases, plan A turns into plan B, and plan B turns into plan C. Not in this case. There was only ever one option available to the CO: quite simply, C Company had to carry out a frontal assault on Goose Green. To the right of Goose Green lay the airfield; D Company would assault that, then B Company would go wide right and then sweep left and attack Goose Green from behind. The plan, simple and uncomplicated, did not require a full set of Sandhurst-style orders or a nice scale model of the ground and settlement for familiarisation. All it required was guts: guts on the part of the newly promoted CO to make such a command decision, and guts on behalf of the men who had to carry those orders out. By now, all of us were fired up to go and kick the shit out of the Argies.

It was late morning when we lined up in our four-man patrols. My patrol in front, then two behind us, then three behind them, and so on. The HQ element was located in the last line of patrols. Here the OC would be able to direct the assault by calling up the lead patrols on VHF radios and so control the progress of the attack. This was SOPs for the British Army, and today was no different.

C Company's strength was less than 50 men as we lined up at the startline of Goose Green. I was point man, the lead man of the attack. Basha, Pops and Buster with the LMG were slightly back and to the left and right of me. Basha had told me to take point. I was not particularly pleased about it, but someone had to be that man, and today it was my turn. On the other hand, there was my misplaced bravado about being point man. A Paratrooper's dream, one might call it. Plain fucking stupidity, I'd call it now. Had I known that this battle was later to be put in the same class as Arnhem or indeed the Normandy Landings, then a quick twist of the ankle might have been the order of the day.

The startline was just below the ridge line and out of sight of the enemy. We were all ready, some of us kneeling and some just lying on the ground deep in thought. I went through my usual routine of checking my equipment, took one last cursory look at the rounds in my magazine, and waited.

'Right Devs, let's move,' Basha said, very soberly. I got up and walked to the top of the ridge before I was halted again. The rear patrols were not quite ready. This waiting was beginning to get to me. I had this real judder of a feeling in my stomach and my guts were giving me shit. I was nervous and all I wanted to do was to get moving. I was feeling cold as well. I looked left, right and behind me. I thought, Here we all are, 50 men, good and true, lined up in a battle formation looking like something out of the Battle of Waterloo. Isn't there an easier way to fight a war?

This is not a criticism of the orders or the battle plan of the day since it was the only way to attack Goose Green. There was no air cover or Harrier deployment to loosen up the target; there were no Artillery 105 Howitzers on call; there were no magical high-tech weapons that we could fire off from a safe distance to, as the Americans say, neutralise the target, allowing us to then nonchalantly walk the distance into Goose Green with bin liners and pick up the pieces. All there was was us, a shit load of 7.62 bullets and our Slurs.

SAS intelligence said that there were minimal Argies at Goose Green: 400 or so support aircrew for the Pucaras and a platoon of soldiers for local protection. This turned out to be slightly on the short side. There were in fact 1,500 well dug-in combat troops with fat bellies filled with hot scoff, ready to do business with Oerlikon 20mm and 35mm anti-aircraft guns, multi-barrel rocket launchers and Pucara turboprop fighter aircraft.

I turned to Basha about three paces behind me and grinned nervously. I made a gesture that I was going to crawl forward to the top of the ridge and have a look. I was aware that I might be a target for some forward Argy trench position, so I was very cautious when I broke the skyline with my helmet. I took a brief look. I could see the enemy about 800 metres away so they could probably see me. Then, somewhere from the rear, the command was screamed out: 'Prepare to move!' An order that gives even the hardest Paratrooper the shits. Then the same voice, another order. 'MOVE.'

Although I was out of small arms range, I still shuffled back a couple of metres on my belly. I moved left, then stood up and ran towards the enemy, zigzagging as I went forward for a few metres, then breaking into a faster-than-normal patrolling pace.

This movement of getting up and advancing was called breaking cover, a basic technique used by the infantry. It allows the advancing soldier some sort of advantage against the enemy. The idea is that if the enemy had seen you go to ground, he would train his weapon on the point where he saw you go down, so, if you stuck your head up to see what was going on for whatever reason, in theory he would take your head off. Moving this way makes it harder for the enemy to catch you in his sights. It's a physically demanding manoeuvre which saps the energy from combat troops, but it's imperative to adhere to the principle of breaking cover for your own safety and well being. It's part of the basic soldiering skills drummed into every Paratrooper from day one.

I checked around me briefly to see if the others were with me. Who knows, some sad bastard might have set me up and let me advance to Goose Green on my own. But everyone was with me. Pops, the 2IC of the patrol, was talking to me and to other members of the Company. As I listened I was studying every conceivable fold in the ground for cover, just in case the Argies opened up.

I could see the Argies 700 metres or so in front, standing around looking back at us. Maybe they didn't have radio communications with their forward troops and thought that we were friendly forces coming down for a chat and a scoff. It was fucking strange! Surely this wasn't how it was supposed to be. Soldiers fire even if not in range, to expel fear and anxiety. It gets you worked up, aggressive, in the mood. However, *we* were disciplined; we were to conserve rounds, we were not to fire until we had been fired on. We were sitting fucking ducks.

An order rang out from behind me – *well* behind me: 'Hold your fire. Again. Hold your fire.'

I thought, It's OK for you, twat, *you're* not up in front. Wanker. I turned to look at Pops. His face was grey, drained; wordlessly he shook his head in disbelief. We were as one: Let's just fucking run into the dead ground 300 metres ahead.

Five hundred metres from target. This was getting frigging stupid. I thought what looked like a small bunker had come into view directly in front of me. My eyes trained on its entrance. I didn't want to be here. The wind began to gust. Then Basha whispered, 'Watch it, Devs, watch that fucking bunker.'

Hidden in one of the many folds in the ground, it was a command bunker of sorts. I could just make out the small bent-whip antenna sticking out of the top. As I approached, enemy trenches came into view. Tactically well-sited, they appeared to be unmanned, but were the enemy waiting to spring out in a well-rehearsed ambush? This was 'Serious City'.

My breathing was getting rapid, I was feeling every step I took, conscious of everything around me. I had never been so much alive. I felt confident: the safety catch had been off my SLR since we started the advance. No sign of movement from the trench, now 20 metres ahead. I went to ground without any warning, everyone behind did the same. I got the feeling that the Rupert way back was thinking, Why the fuck has he stopped the advance?

Nobody said anything, not even Basha. I guess everyone was pleased for the break in proceedings. I eased a 'warm persons' (white phosphorous grenade) from my webbing. Basha instinctively knew what I was about to do. 'Don't fire until you are fired on' went right out the window. Fuck that for a game of soldiers! This was my decision. I flicked the safety catch on the SLR to on, easing myself forward on my belly. The pin was already out of the grenade. The bunker looked flimsy and I didn't want to use an HE (High Explosive) grenade as that would totally blow the bunker out, throw secondary fragmentation my way, and fuck my day up.

I was within throwing distance. Still no movement from the bunker. A voice from the back screamed, 'What the fuck's the hold up?' He couldn't see what lay ahead – that was dead obvious.

Now I raised myself high enough to see the flap opening of the bunker and threw the WP, shouting 'Grenade' and thinking, Why can't that twat keep his big gob shut and let me get on with sorting out this fucking horrible predicament? The grenade exploded almost instantaneously, like two seconds, not the standard four seconds we were all used to. Was this a duff batch?

Instantly I was up, safety catch off, firing into the now collapsed bunker. I had been right; it was flimsily built. As it burned a scream rang out. Fuck me, I thought, there's someone in there. Through the smoke and fire, I could see two bodies inside, one totally fucked, burning and obviously a goner. The other was about to be fucked. I shot him in the guts. The look on his face was total shock as blood spurted up from him and covered my right leg.

Were they asleep? Didn't they see us? Why didn't they defend themselves? I thought. Fuck it, it's not for me to understand the personal behaviour of the enemy. Then I put two rounds in the other body for good measure. At the same time, all hell broke loose.

'INCOMING,' was screamed out all over the place. Obviously we had disturbed something more than 400 aircraft technicians. For some reason I leapt out of the relative safety of the bunker and sprinted forward. I could hear Basha shouting something, but I wasn't aware if it was directed at me, Pops or Buster. I just kept on running, trying to zigzag and not get caught in the sights of the Argy fire. I spotted a fold in the ground directly ahead of me and made for that. I was aware that there were two blokes close to me on my left: Buster and Dick. What was he doing up with Buster? I thought. He had started off with another patrol. But I put the thought out of my head, and ran like a man possessed. I couldn't return fire, I was too concerned with reaching that fold and getting into cover. I made it! I dropped down out of the field of fire then quickly spun around to see who was with me, at the same time taking in all my immediate surroundings. Heart pumping, I lay face down on the peaty ground, my helmet just supporting my head and keeping my face from touching the ground. I closed my eyes tightly, took a couple of deep breaths.

The noise of small arms fire had kept at a constant pitch and now the 20mm cannons started up. The stream of ball and tracer from both sides was unrelenting. I felt relatively safe for the time being, but knew the fold only offered me cover from view, not from fire, a problem that I would have to address very soon. But the thought of making another dash filled me with fear, and I lay there for a while, feeling very tired. It had been over three hours since I had first popped up over the ridge at Darwin and I must have been on the go for 18 hours. I wondered how much longer this battle could rage. Something had to give!

Tufts of earth were still coming up all around me. Every so often a little whizz would speed past me, hissing like a snake. Sometimes splintered rock or secondary fragmentation would pepper the ground around me.

Accurate mortar fire was now incoming and the small arms fire was getting closer. Fuck it, I thought. We can't all stay here waiting to get picked off. Someone has to make a decision – or am I just going to do it for them.

I lay there for – a minute? Half the platoon were still behind me, the other half lying about 350 metres back near Darwin Ridge. Lucky bastards! At least they weren't out in the open.

I looked for Basha and Pops but couldn't see them. I shouted for them, but in the noisy chaos heard no reply. All I saw was Dick with his tobacco pouch out, rolling up a cigarette. He saw me looking at him and shouted, 'Hey Devs, my rock's bigger than yours!'

He was right. I had taken cover behind a pebble compared to his.

'I'm coming over, fucking cover me,' I shouted.

'Cover you from what? I can't see fuck all.'

'Just frigging cover me, you arsehole. On three, got it?'

Dick was no more than 5 metres away. I prepared to move.

'One, two, *three*!'

I ran over and crashed on top of him, knocking the cigarette clean out of his mouth.

'You didn't cover me you bastard!'

'You're fucking joking. I can't see anything, can *you* see where the fire's coming from?'

'Fuck no,' I said.

Then Dick looked up at me in disbelief. 'You've been hit! What the fuck's on your right shoulder, Devs? It looks like someone's guts. Hey, fucking get off me, will you.'

123

I glanced at my shoulder. Had I been hit? I felt no pain and brushed off the guts, which must have come from one of the Argies in the bunker.

'You're a dirty bastard, Devs. Can't take you anywhere.'

'Fuck off, Dick. Hey, where's Buster? I thought I saw him with you.'

Buster was Dick's sidekick and drinking buddy. This, of course, was why I had seen Dick with Buster. He had obviously seen Buster and when the firing started, had made a sprint to get to his buddy.

'Just over there.' Dick pointed to another small fold to his left. I could just make out Buster's LMG sticking into the air.

'Hey, Buster, you alright?' Buster raised himself a little. He was lying on his back casually having a smoke. He put his thumb up.

'Where the fuck's Basha and Pops?' I shouted.

'They made a run for it over there when you let rip in the trench.' Buster pointed to a piece of dead ground some 20 metres to my left. 'The rest of 'em couldn't make it this far,' he added.

'Fucking brilliant, what the fuck do we do now?' I snorted.

The radios hadn't been working since we crossed the startline. We had been caught out in the open, and Argy mortars had homed in on our position, hitting us pretty good. It wouldn't be long before we would start taking casualties, if we hadn't done so already.

A round landed just down from where I had taken cover, spraying Dick and me with earth. The whistling noise was deafening. Some rounds did not explode, which told me that the Argies had not set the fuses properly; just as well.

It was impossible to get back to the main unit. I could see dead ground 100 metres in front of us, but there were still enemy trenches in front which looked ominous. The Company had been putting down suppressive fire all over the place, including on these trenches, but I couldn't see too much and really couldn't move for fear of being shot by the blokes behind me. Dick and I didn't know if the rest of the Company knew we were lying low ahead of them.

Again I shouted out to Basha and Pops. This time Basha replied and I looked back to where the voice came from. Basha's head briefly appeared from above the ground – just his helmet and his eyes. I pointed out my intentions but he waved back the wanker sign. He had just put a brew on with Pops and wasn't going to leave until it was drunk. I found Basha's humorous attitude welcome and strangely funny, given our predicament. Having a brew stop during a battle was not in the SOPs, but I supposed Basha's experience as a soldier told him that a nice cup of tea was now in order. That was typical Basha – always a brew in his hand.

Looking back, it was the only sensible thing to do, because we couldn't go anywhere for the time being. We were pinned down by a ton of Argy hardware. However, we were not surrounded: we had friendly troops to our rear. The enemy was in front, and the chances of the Argies attacking out of their relatively secure Goose Green settlement were about as slim as finding a pork chop at an Arab's birthday party.

'I'm fucking doing it,' I shouted to the brew stop, then turned to Dick:

'You ready?'

'Fuck aye, I'm not hanging around here any longer.'

We burst out from behind the rock together and ran like bastards down into dead ground ahead. Without being told, Buster followed. The mortars were still falling but we were out of their direct line of fire. Also, the small arms fire was now going way above our heads: another good thing.

Moments later all three of us moved forward to the top of the dip we had secured to see what was what. I told Dick to look to his right and ahead. I would keep an eye on the left and see what was coming from the rear. Buster, with the LMG, watched the front. We lay anticipating we would be joined by some blokes from one of the other patrols, if not the rest of the Company. Dick still had his unlit fag dangling out of his mouth. He must have picked it up after I'd knocked it out earlier. He said nothing, just winked and carried on watching his arcs of fire.

We waited for Basha and Pops to join us with their brew, but they didn't appear. Then the wind suddenly changed direction and whipped all around the fold we had made home for a while. The heat from my body was being sucked out by the wind and, conscious of the cold, I began to shake with the chill. A more intense noise filled the air, a sharp whistling noise. 'Mortars! Mortars!' someone yelled.

Instinctively we burst out of our position and ran forward as rounds landed close behind us. Unaware of where the other two were, I hit the deck immediately, and with my body hugging the ground, started to slither forward, not once raising my head even one centimetre for fear of attracting fire. I stopped and waited. I had gone as far as I dared! . . .*

---

*The story now continues with the events of the Preface.

PART TWO

CHAPTER SIX

Napalm and the Ridge of Death

'DEVS! *DEVS!*' DICK thrust something at me. 'Switch on!' Instantly I snapped out of my reverie. So that was my past, was it? Well, I had to deal with the present – here, now, East Falkland, 28 May 1982. Get through this – sort my life out later!

The brew tasted great. Dick served it up in his old one-pint American non-issue aluminium mug, with masking tape on the rim to stop you burning your lips when drinking. I slurped a couple of mouthfuls and offered it to Buster, still watching from the top part of the trench. I raised myself up and lay next to him. The picture was a lot clearer now. Some 200 metres directly in front of me was the schoolhouse, a wooden, two-storey building with a slate roof, and to the left of that I could plainly make out one of the 20mm gun positions. Its barrels were almost parallel with the ground, obviously trying to engage targets still coming down the forward slope. Immediately to the right and forward of the schoolhouse were a few tents and sheds, the biggest about 5 x 5 metres. Just a little off to their right was the airstrip, a Pucara fighter still on the runway. A single track ran from dead ground in front of me, across a little bridge that spanned the inlet from the sea to my left. It then ran straight up a steep hill and disappeared over the horizon into Goose

Green. Further away, behind the schoolhouse, were many more buildings. They were barely visible now, but I had seen them before, waiting on the ridge back at Darwin. On my right I thought I could just make out elements of D Company in the distance, but I could not be sure. Figures would only appear for seconds and then go to ground. Off to my immediate left and slightly back I could now clearly see some of my Company making a direct approach to have a go at the 20mm gun to the left of the schoolhouse. Buster and Dick couldn't make out the figures to our right, but we all agreed that to our left were a few of our guys who, like us, had reached this far down the forward slope.

The problem was, what to do now? Since the attack we had lost contact with the command and control element of the Company and been split from our patrols. Assaulting as a mass of bodies looked grim, because we had no real idea where everyone was. As far as I could make out the entire Company was split all over the ground behind me for a distance of 800 metres and we had no idea where B or D Companies were, only that they were somewhere to our right. It seemed very odd that despite all we had been taught as far as section, platoon or company attacks were concerned, we had never rehearsed the scenario we found ourselves in now. It was always the case that we arrived on the objective as a body of men, with the occasional man having to 'play dead', whom the DS had told to sit out a particular assault. I guess, because the British Army had not been in this situation for 20-odd years, most or all of the lessons learnt had not been passed on, or just forgotten. Despite all our training which was as realistic as could be in peace time, we had forgotten to learn the fundamentals: the cock-ups, the inability to plan for the unforeseen. In my opinion, our training was sanitised. I was lucky, having had the experience of being taught less conventional methods for operating on the ground and tactics when on SAS Selection. My weapon handling and my appreciation of possible unforeseen situations and how to deal with them, had greatly improved because of that. It looked very likely now that I was going to put them to the test.

Another quick Chinese Parliament with Dick and Buster – again, we were of the same opinion. The plan was simple: attack the schoolhouse and take out as many Argies as we could. All it required was a shit load of speed and aggression (the surprise element having been lost hours before). Very soon, when we were all ready, all three of us would get up out of the trench and make a mad screaming 200-metre dash down towards the bridge, cross it, then disappear into the dead ground and get our breath back. Dick and I would break open our 66s and Buster would make sure that he had enough magazines at the ready. We would then scurry up the track on our hands and knees to a point where we could safely off-load our ammunition into the schoolhouse. We reckoned it would take us about a minute to get across the bridge, a minute to sort ourselves out, a minute to crawl up the track and a minute to let rip. That was the plan. Short and sweet.

Buster was getting agitated about hanging about in the trench and he was swearing a lot. Dick and I joined in the chorus of obscenities, working ourselves up into a frenzy. Anyone hearing us would have thought we were mad. But screaming our heads off released the build-up of tension that we had all been carrying around. The thought of death did not enter our minds; dying was not on the agenda, at least for the next hour or so. Buster stopped; we stopped. Time to go. I tightened my webbing belt, pulled the helmet strap tight across my chin and grabbed my rifle.

'OK, NOW!' I yelled. We scrambled out and ran for all we were worth. Making it to the bridge was the only thing on my mind. Nothing else mattered. I didn't know if the Argies had the bridge rigged up with demolitions or not. It would have been the obvious thing to do but it didn't matter. Now we were charging down the slope. Both sides were exchanging a lot of small arms, but oblivious to it I ducked, dived and zigzagged further and further forward. As we neared the bridge I could make out a fence going up the right hand side of the track and beyond that the Pucara. Across the bridge and at the base of the dead ground beyond it was a small re-entrant containing boxes and boxes of ammunition and what looked like rockets, obviously for the Pucaras. At last I hit the bridge and ran across it. The track was now hard, it felt different to be running on something dry and flat. I made for its far side and dropped down to the left. Dick and Buster were right by me. Buster was struggling with his ankle which was giving him gyp but he said nothing. He also had the extra weight of the gun to carry as well, which didn't help.

We dusted ourselves off and in silence prepared the anti-tank rockets. I swigged from my canteen, aware that we were on our own. Unless they had seen us charge down, nobody on our side knew we were here. We didn't know it, but we were in a very vulnerable position. There seemed to be no Argies around, they must have all retreated into the schoolhouse and beyond. To my left, about 20 metres away, I could see threatening tents and sheds, in Argy hands. Still, we weren't going that way. We were ready. One last thing I had to do! I was wearing a gold signet ring with the Parachute Regiment insignia engraved on it, a gift made by my father. I said to Dick, 'If I cop it now, please make sure my mother gets this ring.' A slight grin appeared on Dick's face. Most of his cam cream had come off around his eyes, he looked like a photo negative of a giant panda. Dick acknowledged this request with an understanding nod.

We had to be totally switched on because we had now entered no man's land and could be targets for our own blokes. I was breathing fast. The run had worked my lungs to full capacity. I made a positive effort to control my gasps for air as I crawled up the track on my side, trying to keep the 66 and my weapon off the ground as much as possible, and looking left, right and straight ahead every second. The track was even, making the going easy. We stayed about five metres apart. This gave us a fighting chance, should we get spotted by the Argies, to return fire; being bunched up close made us an easier target. I was approaching the top of the track now and signalled Buster behind me to get ready; he passed it on to Dick. Two more metres and I would break the skyline and be in full view of those in the schoolhouse. To take out the schoolhouse, all three of us would have to expose ourselves to the open ground. It was pointless just one going up and letting rip, then another; we had to hit the target with maximum firepower, all at the same time. Without any prompting from any of us it was obvious that that was going to happen.

Within seconds we were out from the safety of the side of the track and in full view of the schoolhouse, no more than 80 metres away. Buster let rip almost immediately, emptying a full magazine, raking the windows and the front door. I fired off a few rounds first and got down, ready to fire the 66. Dick was firing away trying to cover me while I got my shot off. I had one chance: the 66 is a once-only fire weapon, light, small and relatively accurate. I was not aware of any incoming rounds, I was too busy concentrating on getting a stable fire position. With the launcher on my right shoulder, I tried to make out the sight pattern and remember what sight line to use. My mind blanked, a tremor of nervousness came over me. I was worried about being exposed. Then all of a sudden, I picked up the sight picture, aimed and fired. The rocket has a 15-metre back-blast, so you should always check no one is behind you. I forgot to, but it didn't matter; I knew Dick and Buster were to my left. The rocket whooshed off.

Meanwhile Buster was still putting massive amounts of fire power down. Windows smashed and doors and parts of the structure were being chewed up by 7.62mm. My rocket found the target. I had aimed too high; it hit the righthand side of the roof, halfway up. The roof exploded as the HE sent secondary fragmentation whizzing around inside and out of the schoolhouse. I had now picked my SLR up and was firing into the blazing building while Dick fired his and hit it almost square on. This caused it to burst into flames, big style. The Argies didn't know what had hit them. One or two made the wrong decision and came out of the front door. They were slotted instantly. Some might have slipped out of the back door around the other side and out of our view, but many were slotted by the rounds Buster was putting down and many more were obviously taken out by the two 66 rockets. Because of the sheer amount of rounds Buster had used, Dick and I had to re-sup him with extra LMG mags which we carried for the gun. I remember him screaming out for more magazines even as we made our retreat back down the track. He was covering us, still firing at a rapid rate. Dick and I dropped off two mags each, ran a little way back down the track and waited for Buster to finish. He was just at top of the track and only had to drop down less than a metre and he would be out of view. When he was ready, all three of us made a dash back down the track to the bridge. From start to finish, the firing took less than a minute. We had achieved what we set out to do: destroy the schoolhouse.

The battle was still in full swing, no let up. Men from D Company started to appear from across the airstrip on my right and moved down on to the track. I met up with ten men from C Company including Basha and the rest of Dick's patrol. We all lay huddled into the bank by the inlet, to the left of the bridge and below the schoolhouse. There were stories of all sorts of personal battles. A group of the lads had finally got up short of one of the 20mms and taken it out. Other members of Patrols had scooted around the seashore, behind the schoolhouse and caught some Argies trying to retreat. I had a quick chat with Raz, Mal and Sean, another group from Patrols. They told me that they had been pinned down for over two hours by this 20mm cannon and it wasn't until the gun switched its fire that they made a mad dash for it. Because the ground was quite steep where they were, when the cannon switched fire back on to them, it could not get its barrels low enough, so they let rip and took out the gunners: an outrageously brave thing to do. That was how the cannon pinning me down had been silenced.

The whole area was filling up with little groups of Paras that had somehow made it through the gauntlet of fire. Mortar rounds were now exploding all around the bridge. Some exploded in the inlet and sent up showers of water, others fell onto the hard track and didn't explode. The battle had reached stalemate. We could not penetrate further than the schoolhouse because the incoming was horrendously fierce and we lacked heavy weapon support. Our wounded were in and around the newly captured sheds by the bridge, but there wasn't a lot we could do for them. No way could choppers fly in and casevac them out. They would have been shot down as soon as they exposed themselves above the ridge at Darwin. So the wounded had to make do with what the patrol medics had on them. Dick was a key player in this, and because he was a patrol medic he opted to stay with the wounded for a bit whilst some of us skirted back up the track, across and through the sheds, trying to punch a way through the Argentine defensive position. Inventive but impossible.

As the day drew on, prisoners were taken, an added problem – nobody wanted to take responsibility for them, we were all too busy looking after ourselves. I only hoped that there weren't any brave bastards amongst them with a suicide mission, who might try to pick up a weapon and start shooting us in the back.

Buster, Dick and I had one last venture up the track to see what we could achieve. By now its bottom part was full of D Company who had taken the airfield and come across the wire fence to lie up in the dead ground. As I slithered up there, it was eerie because we knew that there were Argies all around. The assault by D Company had pushed those Argies who had not surrendered back across the airfield and up to the top of the track so they could make their escape. It was now, almost at the top, that I heard Spanish voices. I thought I was hearing things, but I wasn't – Dick heard them too. We went across to the righthand side over to the fence line. The voices were louder, and definitely Spanish! They seemed to be just the other side of the fence line, in an obvious trench system. We couldn't move to the fence without exposing ourselves to the fire coming from Goose Green, and because we were so far up the track, we could not risk going on and over the fence to take them out, as we had no idea how many there were. Deciding that discretion was the better part of valour, we returned back down the track. That incident later reminded me of a scene in the film *The Longest Day*, when the Americans had parachuted in and were in a forest at night, patrolling down a side of a metre-high dry stone wall. They were walking one way, a German patrol was walking the other, and they passed each other without even realising it.

As we got to the bottom of the track we saw the prisoners again. Most were lying down, comforting each other. A few were wounded and one looked in a real bad state, half his right leg had been blown off and its skin was just hanging down, as though someone had nicked the bone and left the skin. I felt no pity for any of them. It was survival and you had to look after yourself and your mates first. This was no time to think about showing compassion – as soon as you dropped your guard, you're fucked. Especially when we did not know who was winning the battle. Dick shouted at the three Argies who were not lying down and ordered them to do so. They did not appear to understand the universal sign of 'get down', so I grabbed one and shoved him to the ground. The other two, officers, started to object. I couldn't believe it. Here we were in the middle of a battle and the prisoners were not taking any notice of us. It was fucking crazy. Dick tried one last time. He went straight up to the two still standing when Buster, who was standing out from the prisoners covering us, shouted, 'Pucaras! Two of them coming straight for us.'

I ran out from the group of prisoners. The aircraft flew off out of range, but within a minute they were back, this time screaming in low from the sea and banking to their left, lining up for attack. We all fired like crazy. Buster stood up, firing his LMG just to my left. Everybody who saw the aircraft commenced firing too. Being so low, they were easy targets. Cannons blazing, they came in for the kill.

The shed where our wounded were was directly in their line of fire. The pilots must have seen the wounded there, but still seemed to make it their marker. The noise was deafening. As they came within 50 metres of us they dropped what seemed to be their fuel tanks. The canisters tumbled down to the ground and landed with a whoosh ten metres from Buster and me, round about where the prisoners were and just in front of the stockpile of ammunition.

'NAPALM, FUCKING NAPALM. THOSE CUNTS HAVE DROPPED NAPALM!' Buster shouted in rage. He was still standing and firing at the now fleeing Pucaras. As the napalm exploded the ground erupted into a massive ball of orange and yellow flame. It sucked in all the air around it for a split second as it breathed into life. I hit the deck, my face burning from the heat and the flames. The canisters had exploded so near me that all my facial hair had been singed and I had lost my moustache and sideburns. Luckily, their forward momentum as they hit the ground and exploded forced the blast away from us. It really was a close shave! This incident enraged all who witnessed it and blokes determined not to show any mercy to the enemy. For my part, at least, the gloves were now well and truly off. The use of napalm in war is outlawed by the terms of the Geneva Convention.

It was amazing that the napalm spread right up to the ammunition dump, but failed to ignite it. What it *did* do was to take out a couple of the prisoners, which shut the fuckers up for good, and when the Pucaras returned some five minutes later, they got a surprise as well.

After the first attack we all ran over to see if our wounded were alright. Dick did his best to try and reassure them and promised to stay with Jonesie, a good mate of ours who had taken a really bad wound to the stomach. Half his guts were protruding through a hole in his stomach, and he screamed like a stuck pig as Dick tried to comfort him. Most wounded had gunshot wounds and were all in obvious shock; some were dreaming in their own morphine-clouded world though others who looked to have head wounds were not allowed it. They had to suffer in their own silence.

The Pucaras returned for a second bite of the apple. This time we were ready. Down and out of the way in our little piece of dead ground, we hadn't a lot to do. Certainly we had no real targets left to fire at, so when the Pucaras returned, all weapons were fired in their direction. All of us who were around the area of the wounded bomb burst away. As we knew that the pilots would line up again on the shed, it was too risky to hang about there. It was nothing to do with deserting the wounded. They couldn't go anywhere, there was no place to hide them and it didn't make sense for all of us to hang about in a group just to appease our conscience. We adopted fire positions and gave the incoming aircraft hell. Dick, however, did decide to stay with Jonesie and the rest of the wounded. It was one of the bravest acts I was to witness.

The aircraft roared in. Not having to concentrate on dropping the napalm load, they could put all their efforts into aiming their cannons. The shed was hit and the ground all around us peppered with fire. We were all firing into the air with total disregard for our safety, about 100 men really letting rip. One of the Pucaras was hit. It twisted and turned and within two seconds the pilot ejected as his aircraft disappeared out of sight over the horizon. He slowly drifted down, getting blown towards us. There was still quite a bit of small arms being exchanged, so there was a possibility that he would take a round while he was descending. But he didn't. He drifted – and quite how it happened I don't know – and landed bang-smack in our position, not far from where, just ten minutes previously, he had dropped napalm.

It seemed like an act of God. We had in our possession the man who broke the Geneva Convention. He was paraded by his original captors and then told to get a grip of the rest of the prisoners and to look after his wounded. Once again, he was another cocky officer who had to be slapped around a bit to make him realise that he was in deep shit because he had dropped napalm, and that some of us didn't give a fuck if he was shot there and then, in front of the rest of the prisoners.

As dusk came, the firing was still raging. Most of us were really tired and hungry, and very low on ammunition. However, there were sufficient Argy rifles and bullets around should we run out of our own. I wondered how long this could go on, how long the men could stay awake. We had now been on the go for over 20 hours, and it wasn't over yet.

What we needed was a Harrier attack. So far, they had been so scarce throughout the war that many of us did not really think they existed. But they did, and late afternoon they came. Three flew in from the north-west and dropped their payload of 1000-pound bombs on Goose Green. The noise of the bombs exploding was heard all around the battlefield. I did not see them impact their targets, because they dropped on the far side of the settlement to the north. But it seemed that the whole of Goose Green had erupted, and then there was calm. A few stray rounds were zipping over the place, but now there was a complete change in the mood of the battle. The screams and groans of the wounded from both sides could be heard. The bombs had done the trick; they had virtually silenced the enemy's fire.

The battlefield took on an entirely new character. They knew where we were and we knew where they were; there was nothing any of us could do, so both sides decided to reorganise and resume business at first light. Because of the dark and the drop in gunfire we were able to stand up and walk about quite nonchalantly. Men were getting scoffs and brews on, little hexy stoves were lit up. Because we had fought so long and hard during the past 24 hours, we just did not care any more about maintaining a tactical role, whereby you were not allowed to smoke, get a brew on or use a torch. All that had gone out of the window. I guess most of us had just about had a gutful by that stage. If the Argies wanted to counter attack, we were ready; if they didn't, that was OK by us. Guys began to huddle around in small groups exchanging stories of the recent events.

There was one pressing problem; how to get the wounded back to the Regimental Aid Post (RAP). Jonesie was in a really bad way now. He had stopped screaming and was curled up on the ground waiting to die; nothing else mattered. Dick was doing his best for all the wounded, along with the other patrol medics, but there was only so much they could do, mainly comforting the dying as best they could. Someone had found an old wooden wheelbarrow and suggested we put Jonesie into it and wheel him 800 metres back to Darwin, where the RAP was. It was a good idea, so Jonesie and the walking wounded were escorted down the line by a few blokes. A couple of the Argy prisoners were also in a bad way, so they were organised for escort back as well. The Argy with one leg blown off, was, incredibly, still alive, and the downed Pucara pilot was ordered to carry him and make sure he arrived at the RAP alive. The pilot, an arrogant bastard, did not want to mix with non-officers but he was given a few slaps to make him come to his senses.

The battle scene was incredible: the wounded lying around in one place, the prisoners in another and all around, men dead, still in their firing positions. A picture I would never forget. To add to the atmosphere, the rain started to drizzle and when it mixed with the smoke from the burning schoolhouse and the smells of sweaty bodies and cordite, it made the air heavy. Then I started to notice how cold it was.

From a distance there was a sound of a chopper, a small Scout, buzzing around somewhere between us and the ridge at Darwin. It was obviously attempting to see if the Argies guns had gone to sleep or not. It came closer. A relative amount of suppressive fire was put down by the Argies. They had obviously heard it too and were firing at where they thought it was. The pilot was now pretty close to our position, but could not make us out. He had no lights on and we had no safe means of illuminating our position. He seemed to be taking his time. I guess he was worried and wasn't sure whether he might be landing on an Argy position. When he got close enough I pulled out my 110 instant camera which I had in the top pocket of my smock and fired off the flashlight a couple of times in his direction. He picked this up and came to land right by us. The chopper had a body pod on either side of its skids, so we quickly put Jonesie and another wounded in these and filled up the chopper with more wounded. Most of us were feeling pretty low at this stage. Seeing our wounded screaming and moaning around for hours, with not much chance of getting them to safety, had made us feel like shit. We had felt totally cut off, so when the chopper arrived to casevac our blokes out, our spirits were given a massive lift. It was time to thank whoever was watching over us during the battle, be it God or whoever. I was lucky, I was still alive. I still had all my bits and had come through relatively unscathed. As the chopper steadily rose into a sky filled with bullets, I said a little prayer for the pilot and those on board.

It was now early evening. There was nothing we could achieve by lying up all night where we were, and we got orders to march back up to Darwin for a re-sup of ammunition, food and water. Elements of D and B Company were left to guard the outer perimeter of the settlement. Some of us did not want to go back to Darwin, as we did not want to give up ground we had fought so hard for, but common sense told us there was no point in staying.

When we reached Darwin, we were safe, at least from any ground troops. The air threat was always going to be with us. We had no food left, and very little water, but we did have a stack of ammunition. When we refilled our magazines we got into our patrols and lay up in the gorse bushes covering the rear slope of the ridge. It was a bitterly cold night. Rain fell quite heavily, then wind and frost followed, but at least the gorse, still smouldering from the previous day's attack, gave off some heat. There we lay, huddled up, trying to keep warm. Every now and then a gust of wind would catch an ember and set alight another five or so square metres of gorse, then it would die down again. Sometimes I couldn't be bothered to move when it caught alight, I was too knackered. Only when it was really burning did I turn over or stamp on the offending bush. None of us could sleep but we didn't talk much. Most were too wrapped up in our own worlds, thinking about the coming morning's battle.

At around 10.00hrs the next morning the CO, Major Keeble, put his plan into action. He sent two of the Argy prisoners down to Goose Green, under a 'white flag' to give the Senior Commander of the settlement an ultimatum: Surrender or die! In the early afternoon they surrendered and we marched into Goose Green. It was very much an anticlimax because all of us had psyched ourselves up to do battle once again. Nevertheless, we accepted their surrender.

When I entered Goose Green in the afternoon I could not believe what I saw: hundreds and hundreds of Argies, all lined up and getting searched by our guys. All their weapons and equipment were being piled up in the middle of a field. The pile was huge, and

I couldn't understand why they had surrendered if they had so many men and so much hardware. They seemed to be coming out of everywhere, hands held high, heads hung low. This battle had cost 2 Para 15 dead and 30 wounded, not including those wounded who did not declare their wounds for fear of being hospitalised back at San Carlos. For the enemy it was a different story. Conservative estimates were 250 dead and over 1,300 captured, many wounded. We had captured a lot of spoils as well, including two Pucara aircraft, four 105mm pack Howitzers, six 20mm Oerlikons, six 120mm mortars, two 35mm AA guns and tons of ammunition and related stores.

We moved in and the Argies moved out.

An extract from a message sent to 2 Para on 30 May 1982 by the Chief of the General Staff, General Sir Edwin Bramall, GCB, OBE, MC (later to be Field-Marshal Sir Edwin Bramall, Chief of the Defence Staff):

For the Colonel of the Regiment and the Parachute Regiment from the General Staff. Greatly grieved the loss of Colonel Jones, his Adjutant and the other nine dead and 26 wounded* of the gallant 2nd Battalion: but wanted you to know how immensely highly I and my colleagues on the Army Board rate the performance of the Battalion against an enemy over double their number, determined to stand and fight. Not only was the task given the Battalion of vital and urgent importance to our country's interests and future at this time, but also in achieving all its objectives in a ten-hour battle after losing the CO and capturing over 1,200 prisoners, the Battalion has executed a feat of arms and gallantry probably unsurpassed in the glorious history of the British Army. It will certainly rate with the other great examples of courage by the Parachute Regiment such as the Normandy Landings and Arnhem.

*Later confirmed as 15 dead and 31 wounded.

We spent a couple of days resting up. Our patrol had been allocated the houses where the Pucara pilots had been living. As with every building in the settlement, the Argies had trashed them; the place looked like a pigsty. They had shat all over the place and they even booby-trapped a few areas, out of spite. But one of the booby traps had backfired on them. Because there were so many prisoners, we had to put them under guard in Goose Green's large sheep-shearing sheds. We had the job of guarding them. One day I had just changed over stag outside one of the sheds. The prisoners had complained that there was not enough room for them and asked if they could move a load of kit which was taking up room, but as they were shifting it, a booby trap went off and took out a few of them. I remember just walking away from it, not even bothering to go and help. Of course, the medics turned up to sort out the injured, but I just did not give a shit. As far as I was concerned, they could have all been blown up, because that meant I would not have had to waste my time looking after them. It was a cold feeling, but the war had made me that way.

The few days we had off went really quickly. Most of the time I spent wandering around the settlement looking for souvenirs and just chilling out before the day came when we were ordered to move out. The Brigade was tabbing towards Port Stanley and we had to go and catch up. For us, 2 Para, the war was not over. We were still required by the other ground forces to 'play'. The settlement of Fitzroy was our next stop, some 30 ks to our east, on the south coast of East Falkland, 50 ks south-west of Port Stanley. My patrol was tasked, along with eight others, to fly to the settlement, clear it of Argies and await the remainder of the Battalion. The short rest was over and I found myself packed in the back of the only Chinook that had managed to get off the *Atlantic Conveyor*. All it would take was one lone Mirage to see us, and that would have been the end of C Company! As I took one last look at Goose Green I was aware I was covered in the smell of Blue Stratos aftershave, the only thing left in the house that the Pucara pilots didn't smash. It's a smell which haunts me to this very day.

As the Chinook strained, juddered and bounced around under the enormous weight of its cargo, I wondered if we were not going 'a bridge too far'. We had no real Int about the settlement, so we had

141

to expect the worst – that the Argies were waiting for us or, at the very least, had left us with a welcoming present, such as half a dozen booby traps.

The flight was one hell of a risk. All through it I was waiting to die. I had this feeling that we were going to be blown out of the sky and that I would still be alive as I plummeted to the ground. I was so relieved when I heard the noise of the aircraft flare up as the pilot picked his landing point and started to drop. When we landed, I could not get off the Chinook fast enough. I made for a hedgerow and got into cover. We had landed in a field with a hedge on all sides which cut down our immediate view of the surrounding area. When the chopper took off, I was left with a real sense of isolation. If there were Argies about, we had to defend ourselves; it would be another hour or so before the Chinook would return. Out of nowhere an old man appeared. He had obviously seen the chopper land and had come over to investigate. He told us that there had been an Argy patrol around here but they had left some days ago and had headed off to Bluff Cove, about five ks north of us. He was really happy to see us and started to shake our hands. He then left and came back a short while later with some freshly baked bread – no butter but it tasted lovely all the same. The old man, in common with many Falkland Islanders, had remained in his own home while the Argentines occupied the area around. A quick recce of the local area confirmed that there were no longer any Argies about. That was good. We had taken Fitzroy without a single casualty.

Just like Goose Green, the settlement was mainly made up of sheep sheds and a few houses, plus a bridge which led over to an island that formed part of a natural harbour. The waters around Fitzroy were calm. They looked inviting but were icy cold. It was now 2 June.

Over the next few days we set up defensive positions all around the settlement. We dug trenches and 'stagged on' while we awaited further orders to join in the advance towards Port Stanley. This time gave most of us the rest we so badly needed. Although we had managed to get a hot bath or two and some sleep back at Goose Green, it was not the same as Fitzroy. For a start, we did not have the constant threat and worry of over 1,000 prisoners. It gave us time to get ourselves sorted out, as individuals and as a Battalion. If we weren't on stag we would be sleeping or getting our injuries dealt with. Myself and Stan, a friend from Patrols, went fishing in the harbour using a little ten-foot rowing boat we had commandeered for the duration of our stay. One of the locals had lent us his fishing gear, so we were well away. The only extra pieces of kit we took with us were our rifles and belt order, since air-raids were still very much part of our daily life. During the day we spent our time outside in the area of the trenches, and when night came, those of us who were not on stag retreated into the sheep sheds to get out of the wind and rain.

We were still getting daily sit-reps on the advance of the rest of the Brigade and realised that it would not be long before we would join in on the main assault on Port Stanley. Our victories at Darwin and Goose Green had lifted the spirits of the rest of the Task Force and had evened up the odds somewhat. The Navy were now doing a great job at taking out the Argentine Airforce. Visitors were flying in daily to meet with the senior officers within the Battalion. There seemed to be lots of handshakes and slaps on the back. The rest of us kept ourselves to ourselves. We weren't out of the fire yet! With the visitors came more stores and it was apparent that the Task Force had now established a firm beach head which allowed the continuing offloading of essential items for the big push towards and into Stanley. It was on one of these regular flights in that I met the new CO. He looked so clean and sterile, and so out of place. A lot of the guys thought it was a really bad move to demote our acting CO, Keeble, who on the face of it, did a brilliant job at taking over the command of the Battalion halfway through a major battle, and making the Argies surrender at the end of it all. The new CO was probably just as capable, but was it right, most of us wondered.

On 8 June, C Company had been allocated a live-firing after-noon up on the island overlooking the bay. We zeroed our own personal weapons and had a bit of fun firing all the captured small arms. It was a bright sunny day and we were just generally taking it easy. It could have been a day on the ranges back at Aldershot; the officer in charge even made us pick up our empty cases and load them into the back of a Snowcat. We had just fought a huge battle with massive amounts of ammunition and had not been told to go and pick up *those* empty cases, but here we were, on the same island, picking up brass!

After we had finished firing some of us sat overlooking the bay and took in the local view. Down in the bay at anchor were two LSLs (Landing Ship Logistic), the *Sir Tristram* and the *Sir Galahad*. We thought nothing of it. All we knew was that they contained more supplies for the main assault. As the last hessian sack full of empty cases was put in the back of the Snowcat, a comment was passed to the officer by a member of Recce, shaking his head in disbelief at the moronic order. 'This is fucking stupid, boss. Why the fuck are we picking up empty cases?'

Before the officer had a chance to reply four Argy Skyhawks flew in from the sea and up the inlet and started to attack the LSLs. It happened so fast that only a few of us managed to get rounds off. Within seconds they were gone, but they had hit both vessels and both were on fire. I saw the lifeboats being lowered and was shocked to see the amount of men trying to get into them. Some were jumping overboard to get away from the smoke and fire, others stayed on deck and took their chances on trying to get aboard a lifeboat. All the choppers were up and en route to the two burning ships.

Over two weeks before, I had seen *HMS Antelope* explode that night while I was on Sussex Mountains and had felt anger and sadness at that incident, but witnessing what I saw now was quite indescribable. One minute we were all having a bit of a laugh and firing off our spoils of war, and within seconds, two ships were blazing away with massive loss of life. It was totally mind-destroying.

Within minutes of the attack we had made our way down to assist the survivors and that's when the order came to 'offload the sacks of empty cases' and send the Snowcat down to help take the wounded back to the RAP. It was appalling to see all these soldiers who, a few minutes before, had been relaxing and probably watching a film in the ship's mess and were now totally fucked up. That incident left 38 Welsh Guards and 18 other soldiers and sailors dead, and many more wounded; a devastating reminder that we were still at war.

That evening the Skyhawks came back. We were all stood to in our trenches awaiting their arrival, and as they screamed down onto our position, we opened up. There was not much to see because it was a wet, pitch-black night, but we all had a go at shooting in their direction. I had my Walkman with me and it was playing 'Friends of Mr Cairo' by Vangelis. I had one of the ear pieces over my ear and was letting rip to the sounds. It was a good experience and reminded me of Vietnam news footage I had often seen years before. It helped get me through thinking about the tragic balls-up of why were so many men were left on board the ships, when they could have come ashore and into the relative safety of the settlement.

The days after the bombing of the LSLs became a lot more tactical. There was even a threat of a possible ground and air attack by the Argies, so this really put us on our guard. On 10 June we got orders to join up with the rest of the Task Force, now closing in on the mountain ranges just west of Port Stanley. We boarded Sea King helicopters and headed east for the cross-country ride to a LUP, from where we would have to tab the rest of the way. As yet, none of us had any idea what our target would be. All we knew was that we were heading east.

The next two days' tab across ground was hard going. Most of the Battalion had their bergens with them. We didn't, so were tabbing in light order, but the weight was made up with the extra ammunition we all decided to carry. I carried as much as I dared; no way was I going to be caught short again. I carried eight SLR magazines, a spare box of twenty rounds, a Colt 45 revolver with 9 rounds which I got off a dead Argy back at Goose Green, plus a box of 25 spare rounds for it, four grenades (two HE and two WP), one M79 and 12 rounds and a Schermuly parachute flare, plus spare magazines for our patrol LMG, three days' rations, and a poncho strapped to my back. The rest of the weight was made up of ancillaries such as a cleaning kit for my weapons and survival rations: a weight of 40 pounds plus. This, of course, was nowhere near the weight we had carried when we first went ashore, but it was still heavy.

The weather was foul. At night, because we had no doss bags or warm dry clothing, we tried to sleep in pairs, cuddled up together like newlyweds. But we couldn't sleep; it was far too cold. All I tried to do was not think about anything. Every ten minutes or so I had to turn over. When I tried sleeping on my side, it would go completely dead. I would then have to change sides, which meant that my partner had to do the same. I would have preferred to have lain up in some high ground and found some rocks to crawl into for the night, but this was not possible because our line of advance took us through vast open stretches of barren land, devoid of anything: trees, rocky crags or gorse, and that allowed the weather to eat into us.

When we left Fitzroy and landed at our position to start the long tab east, we were issued more rations, why I don't know – maybe someone had cocked up and we received some other company's quota. So we ripped open the one man rations and took what we fancied. Some blokes took the tinned fruit salad and pudding, although they were heavier than other, pre-dried, rations. They thought taste was more important than extra weight. I took a few packets of the Oatmeal blocks, packs of skimmed milk and all the boiled sweets that I could stuff in every pocket and spare space in my webbing. The rest we threw into one big heap for the sheep.

This was not good enough. We were told not to leave this mess around. We were in the middle of a war, but we had to carry *all* the unwanted rations – an incredible order! We had already filled our webbing up with as much as we dared, and now we had to carry an extra ten pounds of shit which was of absolutely no use to us. The blokes were livid. They wanted to kill the guy giving the order there and then. To leave his body in a peat bog would have been no problem. There might have been questions in the short term, but he would be forgotten until the war was over and then the loss would have been put down, like the fate of many Argies, as 'lost in battle'. At last light we chucked all the dead weight out, not even bothering to bury it, as we tabbed into the night. In any case we didn't see the guy who gave that order for the next few days.

On the second day of the march we were no wiser about our objective. Finally, we lay up just to the north of Mount Longdon at a place called Furze Bush Pass. All that day we had been bombarded with Argy artillery and buzzed by air attack. I could hear the battles of the big guns from both sides trying to bring rounds in on their targets. The war had now taken on a less isolated character for me. Ever since Goose Green, the rest of the Army had got their act together and there was a constant stream of choppers bringing in artillery guns, ammunition and all sorts of anti-aircraft systems such as Rapier (a ground-to-air missile system). I got the impression that our next battle would be with the full support of every 'arm' in the Task Force. It was comforting to know that.

Furze Bush Pass was about eight ks north west of Port Stanley. Two ks to the south was Mount Longdon, where the day before 3 Para had lost 22 men in a fierce battle for the mountain, which they won. Two ks south of Mount Longdon were the Scots Guards, waiting to attack Tumbledown Mountain. When the orders came, I was pleased that someone had actually made a decision and got us moving, even though it was to stage another attack. It seemed that our commanders in the HQ knew what was required but were always subject to the changing of orders by the Brigade. All this pissing around frustrated not only me but also the rest of the 'grunts' who had to go and do the dirty work. War is never easy and I did understand that the command and control of so many units was a very difficult and confusing business, but it still seemed a bit of a balls-up.

Wireless Ridge was to be our objective, three ks further east of Mount Longdon, the last feature before Port Stanley, which was a flat three ks east again. Parts of C Company task was to recce the start lines for A, B, and D Company to carry out the assault on the ridge. My patrol, along with the remainder from Recce, was tasked to mount an assault on a little pimple off to the east of the main ridge, once the main assault had gone in. This was going to be a full attack, with the artillery softening up the ridge before we went in under massive fire power support from the Blues and Royals' Scimitars with their 30mm automatic cannons and their Scorpions with 76mm guns, both equipped with the latest night-vision aids.

The attack started. Two batteries of 105s were firing a massive barrage onto the ridge and very accurate fire was being returned from the Argy big guns, their 155 Howitzers firing air burst shells all around. The noise was deafening. *HMS Ambuscade* was engaging targets with its 4.5-inch gun along with our own 81mm mortars. Our artillery stopped and the assault went in almost immediately. I was by one of the Scimitars which was firing hundreds of 30mm rounds. Tracer was being thrown up into the night sky, beads of 7.62mm tracer following it. Flares popped up all over the place and when the Scimitars and Scorpions switched their fire, the screams of men in battle could clearly be heard.

Within a few minutes of the main assault going in, we quickly skirted around all the firefights and dropped down into some dead ground out of view, then circled around behind, to arrive at the northern base of the pimple. I looked up to take my first sight of where, I thought, I might be killed. I could see it silhouetted against the night sky and the flare lights. It reminded me of an ancient burial mound, bleak and uninviting. If there were any Argies on top they could defend themselves very easily; all they needed were two machine guns and a box full of hand grenades. I sensed Basha close by. Pops and Buster moved to my left while Basha put himself between me and the rest of the patrols to my right. The flares being put up by the main assault were now dying down as we waited in silence, about two metres apart, to choose our moment to assault the pimple. Every so often a parachute flare would drift across in front of us. I tried not to look at it in case it blinded me for a few minutes and screwed up my night vision. The ground was soaking, pocked with deep holes filled with icy water, some covered in thick ice, and when you accidentally stepped into them, the cracking noise seemed to rise above that of the battle raging to our right.

Once again I found myself in the middle of the extended line we had formed at the base of the pimple: point man again! A stabbing movement towards the direction of the pimple from Basha told me that it was the time to get up and advance: no words were needed. I got up, took the safety catch off my weapon and advanced slowly. Eyes squinting through the dark, I concentrated hard, knowing that we might walk straight in on an ambush. I knew that the Argies might have put out trip flares so I had to think about that as well as checking the rising ground ahead. My sights were on the ridge as I tried to catch the enemy sky-lining. As soon as I started to advance I heard Spanish voices. The wind was blowing in our direction so they had come from the top, less than 30 metres away. I got down. Everyone followed suit. Basha had heard the voices as well. My heart sank. Were we walking into an ambush? What should we do: lie here and wait for the morning, go back and make up an excuse, or keep going until we come under fire?

There was only one way to go – up. I turned to look at Basha and

148

then around to see how close Buster and Pops were. They were right next to me. The rest of the patrols were still spread out along the pimple.

'Basha, did you hear that?' I whispered.

'Yeh. Those fuckers are waiting for us, I bet.'

'I'll just keep going, yeah, what do you think?'

'Fuck it, Devs, let's do it, just keep moving.'

Just before I got up the second time I reached for my bayonet and gently snapped it on the top of my rifle. Everyone else did likewise: 20 or so very faint, metallic clinks.

I got up and carried on. Slowly, slowly, we advanced up the hill. I could still hear Argy voices coming from the top. Every muscle in my body was tensed up and I was switched on to the fact that at any moment now a burst of gunfire could rain down from above. When we finally approached the very top, most of us were level with each other. I don't know why that happened, maybe I had slowed my pace down; perhaps some of the blokes just wanted to get to the top first. At the top, sleet and rain were being driven in gusts from every direction.

The top was flat, a mini plateau. It looked like the Argies had just bugged out. There was all their kit, still in the tents that they had been using. All they took were their weapons. A hasty enemy retreat meant that I had survived another phase of the war. We were mightily relieved that we had not come under fire, because looking back down the way we had come, it would have been the perfect turkey shoot for the Argies. Why the hell they didn't open up on us, I will never know. Buster cracked a joke about them getting cold feet, as he came out of one of the tents carrying one boot.

There was no need for us to hold the pimple so we advanced to a prearranged LUP and waited for the rest of the Battalion to win the firefight and secure the main part of Wireless Ridge. This took us about an hour of ducking and diving every time a 155 shell burst over our heads. We also had to stop dead in our tracks when a flare illuminated the sky around us. Eventually we made it to the LUP where we tried to find a bit of shelter out of the wind and sleet. We found a small mound east of Wireless Ridge, and until first light, huddled together the best we could. The 155s had now homed in on us so it was beginning to get really dangerous, and over the next

149

hour or so we were subjected to a fearsome barrage of shelling. The 155s were being fired from the middle of Port Stanley and could not be neutralised by our own guns for fear that they might drop short and take out the civilian population which had been housebound since the main assault began.

There was absolutely nothing we could do. Most of us got up and walked around in circles, just like prisoners do when allowed their daily exercise. We didn't care about the shelling any more, it was pointless taking cover all the time. If we were going to die tonight, then let it be through enemy fire and not through hypothermia. The hours passed by very slowly. The distinctive droning of an Argy C130 Hercules transport flying above us and into Port Stanley could be heard above the noise of battle.

Why were these cargo aircraft flying – hadn't the RAF taken these bastards out? Hadn't they bombed the runway with Vulcan bombers? They had made such a big song and dance about how they had bombed the runway into oblivion. What a bunch of wankers they were. It's a pity the Vulcan pilots weren't there with us; they could have heard the sounds of aircraft landing. It was another blow for our morale. I didn't know if the Argies were reinforcing the garrison or bugging out. More than likely they were bringing in reinforcements. That they were allowed to keep flying over Stanley pissed us off even more than the weather.

It was so cold we didn't even carry our rifles as we walked around in circles. At one stage a SAS patrol pitched up at the LUP. They had been organising diversionary raids across Port Stanley Bay, but some of them had got shot up and were now making their way back. Chatting to them livened up our morale as they told us how much damage we had inflicted on the Argy positions, and how many of them had run off the mountain and back into Port Stanley. It was then, as they were showing us their routes in and out, that they asked us how we had got to the LUP from the pimple without going across the minefield. We said that we had no idea that the route we had taken off the pimple was through a minefield; it certainly didn't show on our map. But for some reason it was clearly marked on theirs. Considering the continuous barrage of artillery and the fact that we had walked unscathed right through a minefield, we began to wonder if our time of death had been postponed

150

for the time being. It was a miracle that none of us had even been injured by the tons of shrapnel flying around.

Daylight on 14 June could not come too soon, and with it a feeling of warmth, yet I was frozen. My DPMs and boots were iced and it was so cold that even my body heat was not enough to thaw the ice. It was not until we started to move forward and inspect the night's damage that I felt some sort of feeling come back. My feet were the worst: although I had no problems walking, I hadn't felt them for more than seven hours. I began to wonder if I had frostbite, which was certainly possible. I had visions of taking my boots off to be faced with gangrenous feet, but tried to put the thought out of my mind as I concentrated on the push forward.

As the sun came up it was still very frosty but the wind had dropped; the makings of a nice day. News came through that the night assault had gone well and we were ordered to march to the forward point of Wireless Ridge. The scenes that confronted me there were of total, gob-smacking devastation. Wireless Ridge, just under two ks in length and at its highest point, no more than 30 metres wide, had been so blasted so much through the night by the artillery that there were bomb craters every 20 metres or so. The entire ridge was one mass of splintered rock. There were ten-metre slivers of rock, razor sharp, just sticking up in the air where a shell had exploded. The human remains strewn around made a sickening sight, even for those who, like myself, had witnessed the massacre at Warrenpoint. The ridge had an 'air' about it, as though something really bad had happened there. The way the men had been killed, it could have been by a monster. I had never witnessed the aftermath of a heavy artillery barrage before, so all I had to go on was my experience of what I had seen in NI, and of course, Darwin and Goose Green.

I was struck by the differences in how the dead had fallen. In Goose Green most of the dead had been shot; here almost all had been blown apart. Everywhere I walked were the remains of an Argy. Some were still in their fire positions, decapitated. Others had just been blown into hell, still others had their legs severed clean off from the pelvis. The look on one Argy's face said it all. This corpse's head lay propped up by his oppo's remains, right next to a bomb crater. Its eyes were wide open, its hands pointing up to the air as if

151

to say, 'Why me?' Its right hand was holding a small cross on a chain. I leant over and touched it; plastic. I folded it back in the hand. I stared at his face. Unexpectedly, the words of a Wilfred Owen poem, which had impressed me years before, came into my mind: 'Dulce et decorum est pro patria mori.' Then I made a vow never to call an artillery man a craphat again.

As the morning wore on, the Argy 155s were still dropping shells onto us, but not as intensely as during the night. They had obviously DF'd (Defensive Fire) the positions we were now commanding so it was quite easy just to fire at will. Every so often a shell would scream down on us and after a time we got used to its noise – you knew whether you had to get down or not. You could hear it whizz through the air and as it came closer it took on a higher pitched tone for a couple of seconds, during which you could determine how close it was going to land. It became a bit of a test of courage, guessing how close a shell was going to be before taking cover or not, like the 'I dare' game kids play on railway tracks when a train is coming. It was crazy, but then, we weren't exactly sane at the time.

We eventually left the 'Ridge of Death' and lay up on its reverse slope overlooking Port Stanley. I could see many Argies on the road into Port Stanley. None of us knew what they were going to do. Would they try to force a 'come on' and lead us into some massive ambush in the centre of Stanley? We thought about the battle into the capital. Some started talking about FIBUA (Fighting in Built Up Areas), others didn't even want to think about that option. A Gazelle chopper appeared just off to our right and hovered. I thought it might have been one of the Brigade 'head sheds' come to view the situation, but all that came off it was a bag pushed out by the loadie. He beckoned one of us to go over and retrieve it. No sooner had it appeared then it had gone, obviously not wanting to hang about and risk catching a piece of 155 shell.

The bag contained mail. A strange delivery, I thought. In all this madness, someone had dispatched a chopper to the front line for a mail drop. Not extra bullets or fresh rations like a nice juicy orange, just a bag of letters. It seemed to take the realism out of what we were doing. I actually received a letter. At first I didn't want to open it, be reminded of the nice friendly world outside these islands until my job was done. It was my way of dealing with the situation. Then I found myself a private space out of the wind between some rocks, and in the full view of 12,000 Argies, began to read the letter from my brother Mick, on holiday in Spain. But once I had read the first few lines, I quickly stuffed it into my pocket; I couldn't drop my emotional guard or let sentiment cloud my judgment. There would be better places to read it once things had died down.

The firing had almost stopped by now. A rumour spread around the ridge that the Argies wanted to talk about a ceasefire. Who had started it no one really knew, but it caused us all to cheer and come out of our hiding positions, though it was still not officially confirmed when we marched off Wireless Ridge in a race to be the first into Stanley. I took off my helmet and replaced it with my Red Beret which I had kept with me ever since the landings. A stream of Red Berets could be seen heading east.

As our patrol left the ridge we bumped into my old training OC from the Depot, Major Gullan. He recognised Basha, and jokingly shouted across, 'Hey, Corporal Pope, I *order* you to give me your red beret!'

'Fuck off sir! I'll die first.'

'OK, how much do you want for it?'

'What price glory! and by the way, aren't you in mixed dress, sir?' Basha replied.

The Major told us that the Battalion's losses during the night were three dead and 11 wounded, yet the Argies had lost over 100 dead, with 17 taken prisoner. Even though the cease-fire was still unofficial, the Argies had had enough, they were a beaten force. We left Major Gullan waiting for his HQ party to catch him up, still wearing the Royal Marine Green Beret but with a Parachute Regiment cap badge on it.

As we hit the road into Stanley I could see the remains of a retreating army. We approached a place called Moody Brook, the start of the metalled road we were all heading for. Half a dozen Argies were standing there, hands held high, stunned and pathetic. A feeling almost of pity now entered me, the first bit of 'negative emotion' I had allowed myself. The Argies had been beaten and we had won. I didn't feel *that* sorry for them, but on the other hand I did not hate or detest them, as I had done before the cease-fire. I guess

I was coming around to being human again.

The bodies of dead Argies littered the road to victory. We stopped at the war memorial just by Government House, the first troops into Port Stanley. I could see thousands of Argies hanging around further up the road towards the airport. At the time we were probably less than 200 strong, as the rest of the Battalion and the ground troops were still coming in from Moody Brook, and I had a strange feeling that this could well be a set-up. The Argies certainly outnumbered us by about 60 to one.

But as more of the Battalion and support elements marched into Stanley, I knew for sure that the fighting was over. We made our home in the garden and potting shed of the town's doctor, and set about scouring the local area for food and booty. For a time, a few of us commandeered an Argy jeep each, which we used to drive round in and pick up anything we thought might be of some use. One guy found a Huey helicopter and tried to get it going. All that could be seen was the blades turning and the chopper shuddering as the would-be pilot tried to get it into the air. On one occasion I was driving around with my 'Magpie' head on, looking for any bits of booty which might take my fancy, when I saw a bunch of longhaired men in dark blue mountain coats looking surprisingly fresh. I reckoned that they must be an SAS scrounging party, also looking for war trinkets. As I pulled up alongside them I recognised three of them: Paul, Ches and Knocker, from the SAS Selection course I had got casevac'd from in the jungle. I jokingly shouted, 'Hey, you fuckers, you've just missed a war!' They didn't respond to me at first; all of them turned to give me the 'ten-metre' stare.

'Shit! Is that you, Devs? I thought you were dead. Didn't think such an ugly bastard like you would survive the war,' Ches said.

It was like an old soldiers' reunion. We exchanged war stories. I found out that when they got badged they were immediately sent to B Squadron, involved with all sorts of weird plans to invade the mainland of Argentina. Then a change in the Squadron's MO meant they found themselves parachuting into the sea to be picked up by the Royal Navy a day before the cease-fire. They had indeed missed the war.

More ground troops poured into the capital. With 12,000 prisoners to be sorted out, we were put on guard duties watching sheds full of food and equipment. One of our tasks was to guard four 40-foot shipping containers of Argentine rations and equipment. We were not to let anyone near them. One day I was on stag with Buster, Basha, Brett and another guy when a helicopter landed nearby. That was no big deal; by now every man and his dog was flying in to take snaps of 'how they won the war', so when its crew came over to us to see what we were guarding, we had to tell them the score, that we'd had orders to let no one into the containers, that they should not even be in the area. As the party approached one of them broke away and came across to see us, wearing a flying suit and jacket. He piped up, 'Do you soldiers know who I am? Doesn't the Army salute Naval Officers anymore?'

Nobody replied. I asked him to leave the area, telling him they should not be here. The last thing we wanted was to get pushed around by some dick with the manners of an arsehole. We were still cam'd up and buzzing from the battle, on a 'high'. He wanted bits of Argy webbing, no big deal to us, and had he asked politely it would have been no problem; after all, we all won this war together. But he didn't ask nicely, and his last remark made even the rest of his party do a retreat: 'Let me tell you something. Over there is His Royal Highness Prince Andrew.'

'I don't give a *shit*,' said Brett. 'No one is to enter these containers.'

The officer saw Brett meant business and perceiving the state we were all in, did not want to push the point of who was boss. When they left, Basha had a word with Brett and told him to settle down a bit, not to get too excited. But Brett was adamant that while he was on duty, nobody was getting into the containers – I think the war had affected him a bit. But it was a really funny incident and it cheered us all up.

Something less amusing happened just outside the doc's house. We were just lazing around drinking tea and talking when a shot rang out from the garden. We all ran out with our rifles, thinking the prisoners had started a revolt or something when I saw two of our guys. One was standing over a body, obviously shot in the head but still alive. The doc was called. These two mates had been playing the 'quick draw' game with one another with two Argy 45 pistols. One of them was being James Arness, *alias* Matt Dillon from *Gunsmoke* when the other was accidentally shot in the face from ten feet. The round, the size of a Malteser but a bit longer, had hit 'the baddie' on the side of the nose, contoured underneath the skin around the outside of his face, and exited out of his neck. It was a million-to-one thing: normally the round would have gone right through and taken his head off. Amazingly, he survived.

We finally departed the Falklands on 25 June, leaving the mopping-up to fresh troops who were arriving daily. We sailed back to the Ascension Islands on the same vessel, the *MV Norland*. It seemed fitting that we should start the return part of our journey on her. She had taken her fair share of hits at anchor in San Carlos waters. When we got to the Ascensions three weeks later we boarded an RAF VC10 and headed off to RAF Brize Norton. I had requested that my parents should not meet me at the base, but to meet me back at Aldershot the day we landed. I was not really relishing a big homecoming and when we landed at Brize, I and a lot of the blokes kept out of the way of the limelight. For us there was no glory in what we had been through. All we had done was what was expected of us – our job.

When I met my parents outside the barracks in Aldershot, I thanked them for coming, told them I was alright and asked them to give me a couple of days just to get back in the swing of things. They were very understanding and within two hours they headed off home. I felt guilty that I could not give them my time, but I had to get my head together. I knew that I had a few mental problems to sort out and I still had the summer SAS selection on my mind!

It was during this period of self-exile I met Lynn. I was playing pool in the Queen Hotel with a few of the Aldershot 'diehards' when she walked in with a couple of friends. I spotted her as soon as she came through the door: small but very tidy. I felt attracted immediately, and made my way to where she was. It turned out that she was a 'pads brat'. Her father had just served 22 years in the REME and was now working in the Middle East. She had come to visit her sister for a couple of weeks. As I started to chat her up, it became clear that she knew the score all too well on Paratroopers, so I told her that I was not a Para but in the REME, an obvious wrong move – I knew frig all about them, and it became apparent as we chatted.

156

I could not have been anything else but a Para, standing there in my jeans and my 2 Para sweat top and desert boots. She told me that I had more moves than a Turkish belly dancer, but because of my 'neck' she agreed to go out on a date with me. I wasn't sure that I wanted anything more than a one-night stand, but on our first date I was hooked.

Roll of Honour

Officers and men of 2 Para, killed in action on the Falkland Islands:

Lieutenant-Colonel Herbert Jones, OBE
Captain C. Dent
Captain D.A. Wood
Lieutenant J.A. Barry
Colour Sergeant G.P.M. Findlay
Corporal D. Hardman
Corporal S.R. Prior
Corporal P.S. Sullivan
Lance-Corporal G.D. Bingley

Lance-Corporal A. Cork
Lance-Corporal N.R. Smith
Private S.J. Dixon
Private M.W. Fletcher
Private M.H. Holman-Smith
Private S. Illingsworth
Private T. Mechan
Private D.A. Parr
Private P. Slough

Attached arms
Lieutenant R.J. Numm, RM
Corporal D. Melia

Army Air Corps
Royal Engineers

CHAPTER SEVEN

SAS Interrogation

I ARRIVED BACK to the Battalion in late July 1982 after a four-week leave spent mostly at home with my parents. In some way I was trying to make up for the times I never came home, spending my leave in downtown Aldershot, raving it up. I didn't talk much about the war and I was not asked. It was good just to lie back every morning and take in the freedom of not having to make any decisions and knowing that I didn't have to be anywhere or with anyone. The silence was perfect.

I telephoned the SAS training wing in Hereford to find out if I was down on the next Selection. In the clerk's office was a large board with all the names and regiments supplying the intake of the next course, so at a glance he could find a particular name. A short pause; yes I was. I put the phone down and thought, Yes, *yes*!! The administration always seemed to work when under pressure. I had had a nagging thought that maybe, because of all the extra administration of the Falklands, my application might have been overlooked. I felt great.

Within a week of returning back to 2 Para I was off again. I missed all the celebrations, all the slaps on the back by every part of the media, all the free piss-ups and scoffs. I didn't really care about that, but I really missed not having the chance to sit down with a few of the blokes. But I didn't have much time if I was to get on the summer course. I left for Bradbury Lines with only one thought in mind – passing the SAS course.

The jungle phase had now changed from Belize to Brunei in South East Asia. In my patrol were Brian, a tough, sinewy-looking Marine; Taffy, an unknown from the Welsh Guards from the Guards Depot at Pirbright; and an officer, the boss of the patrol, called Blister, from some jock regiment. The boss and Brian seemed to be OK but I wasn't too sure about Taffy.

After a long flight to the other side of the globe (with a stop-off in Hong Kong) we arrived in the jungles of Brunei. We flew in part of the way by chopper and had to tab the rest. It took us four hours to walk into the base which the DS had cut out of the jungle, which was very wet and very humid. You could hardly see or feel the sun, although it was over 85 degrees, and we had to stop every 15 minutes to drink. We were not acclimatised and it would take at least a week to get used to the conditions we had to survive in for the next 30 days.

We eventually made it to the base where we were greeted by the Training Officer and the rest of the DS. Our first week was spent learning how to survive in this strange environment. We were shown how to put up pole beds, which we were to sleep on for the duration, and introduced to all manner of insects, animals and snakes. We were told what was edible and what was not, what could be used for survival. We had to be tactical, and that meant only ever whispering if we needed to communicate. We had to have our weapons and webbing with us at all times. We were playing it for real. Every morning, 45 minutes before first light, we had to stand to. That meant all of our patrol had to get up, in total silence, get out of our dry clothes and put on yesterday's cold, damp kit, then pack all the kit away and go to a predesignated guard point only a matter of two metres or so away, and stand guard, facing outwards, until daylight appeared.

We spent many days on ranges, live firing within our four-man patrols, under constant pressure and scrutiny from the DS. Every patrol had its own DS and you never really knew where he was. He would sit in the jungle well before first light and watch us standing to, seeing if we were doing it correctly or making a noise, observing whether there were any personality problems within the patrol, and whether a bloke was pulling his weight. All this was for a reason. On operations the Regiment has always worked in small numbers, well behind the enemy lines a lot of the time, so we had to be 100 per cent professional.

I actually liked living and working in the jungle, and our patrol was getting on really well. The boss was a good man, Brian was very professional and Taffy was trying his best. Things seemed to be going well. Nonetheless, it was exhausting, the heat and humidity at times unbearable. I couldn't stop sweating. When patrolling we had to keep off tracks, because of enemy ambushes or booby traps, so every time we had to be at a particular grid, we had to move through primary jungle. On one exercise it took us six hours to move less than 500 metres.

As the days passed we all changed. Living together in such a confined and harsh environment brings men to the point where they can't take it any more and in some cases, break down. The humidity, the constant noise of birds, animals and insects, the yearning to talk in a normal voice, the battle to keep fit and well watered were all constantly on our minds, plus the mental pressure of not knowing if you had done well that day or whether you had made a fuck up. You would wonder if you had failed the course; if so, what was the point of going on?

One day our patrol was told to report to Range Three at 14.00hrs. Range Three was the furthest range, at least 40 minutes away.

As we set off, it was pissing it down. The route was slippery and full of huge roots that came out of the mud every foot or so. I slipped every time I took a step. Foliage would come and whip me across my face every time Brian passed through a tree or bush. By the time we got to the range, the DS had been waiting for us for ages and was not too pleased that we were late, but he could see that we were knackered and told us to set down and get a brew on before he took us through the range. We were at least grateful for that. While Taffy prepared it the DS asked the boss where the ammunition was. The boss said we hadn't realised we needed it.

'Well, two of you fuck off back and get some. We can't start firing until you do.'

The thought of tabbing back up to the base camp and back again with a 30-pound box of ammunition was unbearable. But a quick Chinese Parliament saw me and Brian tabbing back. Both of us thought it a test to measure our reactions, and expected to be called back by the DS, but that didn't happen. Almost two hours later we returned and then went on to the live firing programme. By the time we started to head back it was pitch black. That journey back to our camp was probably as hard as the Endurance march we had done at the end of Test Week. Brian and I were completely exhausted, pushed to our very limits.

Days turned into weeks; the pace of the course increased. None of us had any idea of how well we were doing, as it was impossible to judge. We did not even know how well our mates were doing in the other patrols, even though we saw them every day. It was only at the end of the last week, when we 'broke camp' and carried out a squadron-size attack on a enemy camp that we managed to exchange our experiences with other members of the course. After the camp attack we were to be choppered out to a roadhead, picked up by trucks and taken back to where the rest of our kit was located, back at the army base. Even at this stage none of us knew who had passed or who had failed. We had to wait until we got back to Hereford to find out. Back there one Thursday morning we were all sat in the Lecture Room of Training Wing, desperate to know. We had got back from Brunei late the previous night, so the OC thought it best to tell us the next morning. None of us got much sleep.

The OC read out the list of failures, telling them to hand in their kit. The rest of us sat in a very happy silence. Out of the 28 that had made it to the jungle, only ten remained. My patrol had lost Taffy, but Brian, the boss and I had passed.

We were stood down for the next few days. Completely bollocked from the jungle, I had lost over a stone in weight. My body was in bits, I had insect bites and leech wounds all over me, my face looked drawn and I felt shattered. I intended to sleep the entire time. We were told to report for the start of the Combat Survival phase at 08.00hrs sharp the following Monday.

The Combat Survival Course, conducted in the vicinity of Hereford, is open to all branches of the Armed Forces, so the ten of us were fitted into a course of about 50 men, again split up into four-man groups. Over the next four weeks we were taught to live off the land, hunt and trap game, and build and live in our bashas, made from bits of wood and old sacking. The build-up phase was three weeks; the last week we went on the run in our four-man survival groups. This entailed surviving off the land for about five days, then we had to be captured and taken away for a 36-hour interrogation phase. When on the run we were to be chased by the 'hunter force', which happened to be 3 Para. If you were caught you were severely punished: put in a pen and left in the open for four or five hours in a stress position, come wind, rain or snow. Following release you carried on your mission until your eventual capture before the interrogation phase. Avoiding early capture conserved mental and physical strength, leaving you stronger when interrogated.

The Veterinary Corp instructed us on guard dogs. The dog handler would show us what his dog could do, then invite one of us to put on an arm guard, run off and let the dog give chase. When the instructor asked I was volunteered and could hardly back down as there were three Marines and two Para officers watching. In the true spirit of the Parachute Regiment, I left my beret on while I was helped into the arm protector. I was pissed off, especially since the dog handler thought it a great laugh to have a Para to humiliate. I asked him if it was true that 'the dog is only as good as its handler'. Yes, he said, so I replied that I had fuck all to worry about. He didn't find that funny at all and told me to treat this exercise for real, because the Alsatian was. With that one of the Marines threw me his commando knife and said 'If it's for real, you're within your rights to kill the dog.' Furious, the dog handler took it from me, told me to run off, and let the dog loose. I ran for about 20 metres before his 110-pound Alsatian came leaping up at me. Instead of going for my protected arm it ripped through my DPMs and bit me on the arse. To make matters worse, I could hear the handler encouraging his dog, so I was livid. I managed to turn around and face the class and present my covered arm to the animal, which it accepted. Its jaw locked over my arm; thankfully I felt no teeth. With the animal on my arm, I shouted to the class: 'Look, if I had a knife it would be dead by now,' and bashed the dog's nose with my clenched right fist. The force made the dog loosen its grip on my arm and sink its teeth into my right thigh. The joke was now over and I was deadly serious. I didn't dare move for fear that the dog would do more damage. I just screamed at the handler that if he did not call the dog off, I would rip its jaws open and do the same to him.

The result was that I had very nasty wounds in my leg and arse which had to be treated immediately. While I was in the ambulance the OC Training Wing, whom I'd previously met on Selection back in January, came around the back. He had seen the whole incident. I thought I'd fucked up in a big way, but all he said was, 'Young Devereux, I'm glad you enjoyed yourself out there, but if you *had* killed that dog, the Veterinary Corp would never come and teach us again.' It was always difficult to understand what he really meant, because of his very soft way of speaking. After that, I couldn't be the grey man anymore.

What worried me was that very soon I would be going 'on the run' and the wounds were going to take weeks to heal. My leg was stiff and I had trouble running. I started to think I was a lame animal and bound to get caught by the Hunter Force.

When the 'on the run' day came, we were stripped naked, had every orifice checked for goodies that could make our next five days bearable, and were given an old Army trench coat, a pair of boots, a small tobacco tin containing a couple of wire snares, a Durex for holding water and other bits of survival items, a rough sketch map (drawn on parachute silk) of the area we were to be deployed in, and a bin liner. We were then let loose and 'on the run'.

The weather was appalling; it didn't stop raining. The first night passed without incident but the second day our patrol was almost caught by some over-eager Paras. Somehow I escaped by whacking one of them across the legs with my makeshift walking stick. I didn't see any more of them until the final day when we were all due to be captured. Those of us who had not been captured had to make ourselves known to the Hunter Force. We had all split up for some reason, and I had teamed up with Archie, a Marine Captain who had also been on Selection. We got on well together and managed to get food and water organised for the duration so we were quite well stuffed when we entered the dark, cold rooms of the Interrogation Centre.

For the first few hours the interrogation was no problem because I was relatively fit and switched on. I was stripped, made to put on loose pyjamas, blindfolded and put into two stress positions: one standing up facing a wall with legs and arms wide apart; then, after 30 minutes, I was forced down into a squat position with my legs bent and arms forced behind my head. None of the captors said a word from start to finish. The only sound was loud 'white noise', like a radio not tuned in. The place was freezing cold, like a refrigerator.

As the hours wore on, I was led into a room where my blindfold was taken off. In front of me was my first interrogator, a big man with a beard in a white fisherman's jumper who looked nothing like a serviceman and who spoke in a Northern Irish accent. He looked like something from the PIRA photo checklist I used to carry with me when I was in NI. We had been taught not to say or sign anything in interrogation, apart from giving number, rank, name, and date of birth and responding 'I can't answer that question,' to anything else. My interrogator was sitting down, writing, and did not even look at me when he said, 'Everything OK? Have you been treated alright?'

'I can't answer that question.'

'Look, I don't want to know anything, just that are you OK?'

'I can't answer that question.'

'OK. If you're not going to tell me you're alright, just sign this chitty to say that you have received the pyjamas that you are wearing.' I didn't move. I was still standing to attention.

'I can't answer that question.'

The whole interrogation went on for about 30 minutes. When he said, 'Now look here, you cunt. I know you are Special Forces and I know that you are a Paratrooper, because your mate has been telling me. Go back and when I see you later you had better start talking,' I still said nothing. I had my blindfold put back on me and was led through corridors to the room with the white noise. This early in the exercise, I still knew that it was an exercise and was feeling pretty good. I was brought before the interrogators again about six hours later. At this stage I thought I had been in for about 12 hours or so. It was the same routine, but a different man, tall and skinny, who kept insulting me. He came right up to my ear and shouted a string of insults, from things about my unit to the one that my mother was a whore. I was now beginning to feel a bit fatigued

164

– having to stay in stress positions for hours on end was hurting my injury big style. Eventually he told my guards to take 'this piece of Para shit' away.

That last comment started to worry me. How did he know I was Para? I wasn't wearing a uniform when captured, certainly hadn't said anything. Then my mind started to do flick-flacks. I *really* wanted to know why he said I was Para, so much so that my mind was starting to go. (In fact, it was probably just a shrewd, educated guess on his part.) The white noise was still there, all the time, and the guards were watching every move I made. If I just dropped my arms down for a little bit they would be held up again immediately without anyone saying anything.

I was very relieved to be taken to an interrogator again. It was warm in those rooms, which gave me something to concentrate on. But I wasn't going to be interrogated. When my blindfold was taken off I was in a hospital, of sorts. A stern-looking nurse asked me if I had an injury and did I want the dressing changed. This threw me. I knew that my injury was bad because it had got infected when on the run, and it was now pussing up quite a bit. But still I replied, 'I can't answer that question.'

'Now, come, come, I am a nurse, I am here to help you. Now do you want me to change your dressing?'

I felt like saying, 'I'm sorry, I don't mean to be like this but I'm on this exercise ... ' – she was being so nice. But I resisted the thought and stuck to my routine: 'I can't answer that question.'

'This nurse is trying to help you, at the very least you can show a bit of courtesy and answer her,' a commanding male voice said from behind me. I did not turn around. I still stood to attention. In this type of interrogation, if you start off by stating your date of birth a certain way, then you must stick to saying it that way all the time. If you change at all, the interrogators know they have got you, and will work on you until you crack. The vital information we carry in our heads during a war situation is really only of value to the captor within 36 hours of capture. After that, the interrogators are not interested.

'I can't answer that question.'

'Well, what's your name then?'

'Private Devereux.'

'Is that with an e or an a?'

'I can't answer that question.'

The questioning went on. The interrogator never revealed himself. The nurse did eventually put a fresh dressing on my leg, then it was back to the white noise room. I had a couple more interrogators before I was led into a similar room for, I thought, my fifth interview.

This time there was a very attractive auburn-haired woman sitting at a table, quite provocatively dressed. She started talking to me, asking for my name, my rank and army number. The usual routine. What puzzled me was her American accent. It should not have really worried me but it did. She said, 'Do you find me attractive?'

'I can't answer that question.'

'No, really, I'm not joking, do you find me attractive?' She moved off the table and stood behind me, quietly talking into my ear.

'I can't answer that question.'

'Strip off, please.' Her tone was more sharp and abrupt.

I did not know what she really meant. I started to pull the pyjama top over my head. 'Come on, come on, I want to see how big you are.'

I stood there naked, looking straight ahead. I knew she was looking at me. She was trying to get me to say or do something. But I just stood there and took it.

'Well, you're not all that big at all, are you? In fact, you're the smallest I've ever seen! Do you know what I'm referring to, Private Devereux? I thought you Paratroopers were meant to be big boys!'

'I can't answer that question.' I had nothing else to say. I felt totally embarrassed. Having been freezing cold for the past six days, my dick had gone into hibernation. I didn't dare look down in case that provoked even more ridicule. Eventually she crossly shouted to a guard to remove me.

On another occasion I was led into a different room. It seemed a long time since my previous interrogation and I was really beginning to feel the pace. I heard the door close behind me and a voice told me to take off my blindfold. I was not sure if I should do that or not. It was the first time I had been asked to do it. So I said, 'I can't answer that question.'

'It's OC Training Wing. Peter, take off his blindfold.' I recognised the OC's voice, and when the blindfold was removed, I recognised his face. He was wearing a black arm band. With him was Peter, one of the DS.

'It's over now, Devereux, you can relax.'

'I can't answer that question,' I replied. I started to think. My mind was in a jumble from the white noise, but now I remembered the OC saying to us that when we saw him with a black arm band, it meant the end of the exercise.

'Take your time. Do you recognise me?'

'Yes.'

'How's that leg of yours?'

I had to think. Was I still in interrogation? I paused.

'It's OK sir, no problems.'

'Good. Let the doc take a look anyway. Well done.'

I was shown the way to the cookhouse and got a brew, my first hot drink for four days.

Two guys out of the ten left on the selection failed the interrogation: one was taken out by the men in white coats; and the other, sadly, got so far into the course only to get hospitalised during the 'on the run' week. But I had passed.

Getting 'badged' was an anti-climax. I was ordered to appear outside the Adjutant's office with Brian and Archie at 10.00hrs on a Tuesday two weeks after the interrogation. We were called in and, one at a time, went through the adjoining door to see the CO. When my time came, I marched in, came to a halt and saluted smartly. I received my new beige beret.

I was posted to 18 Troop (Mobility) D Squadron in December 1982, almost a year since I'd first set foot in Hereford. I had the rank of Trooper. Since being a private in the Parachute Regiment I hadn't moved very far up the rank ladder. I was 23.

CHAPTER EIGHT

White Water Disaster

D SQUADRON WERE on the Anti-Terrorist Team. This was lucky because I was looking forward to getting out of the 'green' kit and learning a different soldiering skill. As I walked to the Squadron office I could see a building with several garage doors. This must be the place, I thought. The doors were open, it was a hive of activity, blokes running all around the place. Weapons of all descriptions were out on pallets, and equipment I had never seen before was stacked up along the walls. A Range Rover was in every hangar doorway.

Normally, an SAS Squadron is made up of four Troops – Air, Boat, Mobility and Mountain – but when a squadron is 'on the team' two Troops become the Red Team (Air and Mountain) and the other two become the Blue Team (Boat and Mobility).

Having made myself known to the OC and the SSM, I was introduced to my troop officer, a Staff Sergeant, Eric. A tall, fair-haired man, he looked like an old campaigner. He told me to drop the rank and call him Eric.

'Call everyone around here by their first name except for the OC, you'd better call him boss.'

He told me to give him a hand to off-load some boxes from his wagon and come back first thing in the morning, when I would sign out all the 'black kit'.

A tour on the Anti-Terrorist Team was for six months. The team is split up into the Red and Blue teams. One team is on 30 minutes stand-by, the other is on three hours. Each is a mirror image of the other, with an assault group, a sniper group and a signal and medic back-up. During my years in the Regiment I spent two and a half tours 'on the team'. I started off as a sniper, that's when I first joined the squadron, then moved on to the assault group where I eventually became in charge of all aspects of Method of Entry (MOE) – a demolition skill, breaching entry points with explosives or non-explosives for the assault groups to gain access to buildings, aircraft, etc.

I settled down into squadron life. I was on a year's probation and in that time I had to get a troop skill in order to get my Special Forces pay, so I was put on a six-week signals course. I learnt all aspects of every radio the regiment used in operations, including Morse Code. On passing I became the patrol radio operator for about six months until another bloke was posted into the Troop from selection.

I liked D Squadron. All of the Squadron had been down in the Falklands, so I had something to relate to. My first Squadron operational trip was to Belize. I was looking forward to it because 2 Para had been posted over there for a six-month tour. Our task was to operate in the jungle along the border of Guatemala and gather intelligence of any enemy movements.

We operated as F Troop. There were only 12 of us, left very much to ourselves. We would disappear for a few weeks at a time, come back for a bit of R&R, then go off again.

Four of the blokes were from Boat Troop so whenever we could, I got cross-trained on their Boat skills. I was taught to dive and work with Geminis – small inflatable boats – and all manner of other boats. Three guys were from Air Troop, one the overall boss, Dan, a really nice man who didn't let anything or anyone get up his nose.

The first year flew by. I had done a stint 'on the team', two trips to Belize, a signals course and we were now going to Fiji with the entire Squadron for six weeks, another jungle operation. We landed in Fiji at Nandi Airport, and after getting all the stores and equipment loaded onto wagons, we got on two beaten-up old coaches and started the 80-mile journey eastwards to the capital, Suva, on the other side of the island. As soon as we had got five miles out of Nandi limits the road became a dirt track. It was mid-morning, the sun well up. About 20 miles out of Nandi a tropical rain-storm turned the track into mud, and the coaches had a terrible time trying to stay on them. Every so often, my coach would start to slide as we climbed or descended one of the many gorges we had to pass through. A few times we jumped out of the coach's windows just as it seemed about to slide into a ravine. It was a nightmare journey.

Within two days of arriving in Fiji we were in the jungle, setting up our base. The idea was that we carry out the training programme in full, work hard, cover everything we had to, spend time with the Royal Fiji Military Forces and maybe see a bit of the island and get some R&R. Some of the Fijians who had served in the Regiment and were finishing their time in the British Army had also come across with us and were going to show us the sights. That was the plan.

There was no let-up in the rain: day one, day two. I settled down to making my pole bed and living area as dry and comfortable as possible. Then we heard that the leftwing Fiji press had got wind of our arrival and made a big thing about it. Derogatory articles started to appear and our 'stand-in' OC deemed it best that we stay in the jungle for the duration to avoid adverse publicity. So, on the first day in the jungle we were told to pick up ten days' supply of one-man ration packs and, on the second, another 25. There was hardly enough room to put them all away. I had to make a cupboard out of wood for those I couldn't keep under my pole bed. We had fresh rations once a week: two oranges, an apple, two eggs, a couple of potatoes, an onion, two rashers of bacon and two sausages. For the rest of the time we survived as best we could on our dried rations.

Time passed very slowly. Rain had turned the camp into a quagmire. It was on a hill, so to get anywhere required the skills and dexterity of an acrobat. By the end of the fourth week we broke camp and started the final exercise. Throughout the Regiment, most Squadron trips, in whatever context, end with a 'final exer-cise'. We had to do a three-day tab in the mountainous jungle, stage a 'camp attack' on the Fijian enemy, exit down a river line to a road-

170

head by the lower reaches, then get back to civilisation.

Over the month, a number of us were casevac'd out for one reason or another: insect and snake bites, fever, sprained limbs, trench foot or groin pox, mainly caused by being constantly wet. It became evident early on that things were not going to happen according to plan. Firstly, our maps hardly showed any of the hundreds of pimples which covered the landscape, and secondly some of the jungle we had to go through was secondary (that is, jungle cut down then left to grow back – at double its original density) which made our patrol timings go to rat shit. Along with the rain, these factors started to turn the exercise into a genuine survival operation.

We had still not located the enemy position by the second day. Eventually we had to be told where it was; the enemy also had to make noise and light fires to assist us. We attacked at first light. They had located themselves up the steepest pimple they could find, impossible to assault in real life.

After a two-hour climb to get to the camp, it was all over in a few minutes. Then we turned our attention to getting out of the jungle. Fijian trackers led us to the river which we were to follow down to the roadhead, some 23 ks downstream. The problem was that since the exercise had been recced some weeks previously the river, the Wainavombo, had swollen to five times its usual size. We had to cross it because it did a dog-leg some ks downstream and it would take us at least three days to get out. The river did not look inviting. It was dangerous – the flow was a good metre per second at its worst with large pieces of dead fall running with it. A request to HQ for a heli extraction was denied, so we had to cross. Two Fijian trackers who knew the river volunteered to swim across – about 20 metres – with an extended loop line. To cheers they made it and we all used the loop line to get over, but on the crossing one Fijian came off the line and was swept downstream. I watched him drift. He seemed to be in control but once he drifted out of sight, I never saw him again. By now we all knew the score. This was survival at its most basic. Man against Nature.

The rest of us crossed in relative safety. Then I saw what lay ahead. Because the river had risen so high, we were forced to traverse along the side of a sheer cliff about ten metres above the water. We all had our full equipment with us, full bergens, webbing and weapons, so had to hang on for dear life. We played follow the leader, one man leading, the rest in a snake. The rain was still falling and the only thing in our favour was that we still had ten hours of daylight left. The traverse went on for about 30 minutes until the rock formation made it easier to walk along. We could not go up the cliff because of the dense jungle which covered the top of it, so we had to make do with keeping as close to contours of the Waina-vombo as possible. Within two hours of crossing the river we were on a small sandy beach having a brew, looking forward to a relatively easy tab back to the main base before tea-time. The Fijians had told us that it was all downhill as the river widened out and became easier. They started to cut lengths of bamboo to make rafts to float the next 20 ks, and as they were locals we thought they knew the score, so we followed suit. We sorted ourselves into patrols and started to cut bamboo to make our own rafts. Some blokes decided to try the SAS bergen raft – four bergens lashed together in a square with para cord and karabiners. (The waterproof bags inside each bergen are sealed to hold in a small amount of air. Each man holds onto a corner of the raft and floats with it, forming in effect a buoyancy aid.)

Once we had made them we launched them into the river. Our Fijian raft was four metres long and a metre and a half wide. We tied our bergens down, but kept our webbing on and of course held onto our weapons. Two guys, Fred and George, sat on the raft, with Vinnie at the rear and myself in front at opposite corners, in the water. We set sail, not really considering that we were still hundreds of feet above sea level. All we thought was that in two hours' time we would be floating down to the roadhead; all of us had forgotten one of the basic SAS rules: 'Never take the easy way out.'

The river was still flowing fast, but it had widened out so the flow looked OK. As we approached the first major bend, the water seemed to drop and rocks started to appear in mid-stream. The current started to get up and we began to increase our speed. White water started to appear, as the raft buckled under the flow. We were now in about six foot of water. I found myself trying to lift my body up out of the way of the rocks, but it was impossible, the current was too strong. The bamboo oars that the two blokes sitting on the raft

Above: Jungle training:
four-man river
crossing operation
in the tropics.

Above: In the jungle,
accommodation is basic –
you build a one-man,
A-frame tent like this out
of branches you cut
yourself.

Right: For desert operations in the Oman we were issued with shemaqs – the local headgear.

Above: The exhilaration of freefall parachuting – assuming the chute opens!

Right: On a mortar course in the Oman.

Left: Our Lying Up
Position in the
spectacular Oman
desert.

Right: Myself (left) and a colleague preparing Plastic Explosives for a jungle ambush.

Below: In the aircraft preparing for a High Altitude Low Opening jump from 25,000 feet – that's five miles up.

Right: Here I'm by the open tailgate of Chinook helicopter, about to jump.

Left: 'Go, Go, Go!' An RAF dispatcher gives the instruction for Static Line Jumping.

Right: This is training in the use of a non-explosive breaching entry device when assaulting a building.

Left: For SAS Method of Entry training we were let loose in an obsolete council tower block to do our worst. Here, we've just blown an internal wall with a Rosette charge.

Below: Helicopters are essential for most aspects of SAS operations. This is a jungle resupply – in combat, timings for these are crucial.

Above: Night patrols demand their own particular skills. We went to Jordan for this desert operation.

Above: A Chinook helicopter banking during an operation over the Jordanian desert.

Right: Security Advisor. I'm on the bridge of a supertanker needing protection from sudden assaults by gunboats – 'Boghammers' – in the Persian Gulf during the Iran/Iraq conflict, 1988.

had were no use. One snapped as it was held against a rock to stop us from smashing into it. By now we were in the middle of the river speeding through white water at a ferocious speed. It was hard enough just to stay with the raft. Downstream I could make out four or five guys who had come to rest on a small beach on the right bank, screaming at us and waving their arms furiously in an attempt to warn us of what lay ahead but there was nothing we could do. Another raft went by just a metre from us, the guys hanging on like grim death. Somehow we got drawn into its wake and followed them. We passed the guys on the beach as there was no way we could stop. They were the lucky ones. Another corner and the entire river was white water. To my right I caught sight of the four-man crew of another bergen raft. They had been caught in an eddy and were tucked in under a cliff, hanging on for dear life. They didn't say anything to us as we sailed past, they were too busy saving their own hides. Anyway, it was pretty obvious that we and the raft ahead were no-hopers.

Now we entered white water for real. My legs were knocked and bounced around as they hit the rocks. Then suddenly the raft in front hit a rock and flipped over, disappearing into the rapids with its crew. My raft managed to avoid *that* rock, but 30 metres on the right, in mid-stream, was a rock the size of two semis. We hit it smack bang in the middle. The raft buckled then cleanly snapped in half, throwing Fred and George into the water. I was on the front right of the raft and went under the water where the current kept me under. I was trapped against the rock by the fierce force, with the stricken raft stuck above me, and took a couple of seconds to come to my senses. I still had hold of my weapon, yet somehow I managed to grab the top of the raft and force my way up to the surface. My webbing was not helping – it had twisted around my body and was restricting my efforts to hold on to the little amount of air I had left. Disorientated as I was, as I broke the surface, I realised that I could not feel any broken bones, but blood was pissing out of a wound in my left hand where I had grabbed the splintered bamboo. My head had also taken a bash and I could sense blood was trickling there, too. I was facing upstream, the stricken raft at my right shoulder, being pressed against a rock with the flow. Calling out proved useless: my cries were drowned by the roar of the rapids. I had to manoeuvre myself across the face of the rock and somehow cling on to it as I went further into the river.

I had two options: one, stay there, await help and take a chance that another raft would not crash into me, or two, get back into the fast current and try and see what was on the other side of the rock. I had no idea where the other guys were but they certainly weren't near me. I took the second option. I clawed my way across the rock, cautiously, as the current was not making my escape any easier, when all of a sudden a piece of dead fall hit me square on the back so violently that I was dislodged from the rock like a wet rag. No sooner had it hit me than I was around the other side, hanging on for all I was worth. I heard Vinnie call out and I turned to look downstream. He was clinging on further down the rock. I could see he was in a bit of an eddy, his M16 on a ledge just above his head. Where he was the rock face looked quite climbable. He called to me: 'Devs. Let yourself go and as you come past I'll grab you. Hold out your weapon. I'll try and grab that.' It took some nerve because although Vinnie was as strong as an ox, I knew he was not the strongest of swimmers.

Without further prompting I let go and was swept off towards him. I tried to get some sort of balance but before I could correct myself, I was already parallel to Vinnie. After a quick struggle with my weapon I pushed it towards him; he grabbed it and pulled me in to the eddy. I was safe.

'Cheers Vinnie. I didn't fancy a solo trip through the rest of it.'

'No probs, mate. What happened to Fred and George?'

'I haven't got a clue. They weren't on the raft when I came up!' I said.

We scaled the rock. At the top it was relatively flat. We were some 15 feet above the flow and as safe as we could be for the time being, on our own private little island. I couldn't see much upstream. There were no more rafts coming down. Perhaps one of the guys I had seen on the small beach had gone back upstream along the cliff and warned the rest off. Downstream was like a scene from the film *The River Wild*: smashed rafts were trapped in between rocks. The guys were everywhere. Some had made it to the bank on the right, some had made it to another small beach on the left. I could see a radio out; obviously they were sending a major sit-rep back to HQ.

Vinnie and I were knackered but alive. We were concerned for Fred, George and the rest of the Squadron but couldn't do anything. Our only hope was that the radio was working and that a chopper would be on the way soon. From my survival rations I made us a brew and in between slurps I thanked Vinnie for saving my life, but he just told me to shut the fuck up and keep the brews coming.

It was two hours later that we heard the comforting sound of a Huey helicopter. The distinct sound of its rotor blades making a *whoop, whoop* noise was music to my ears. It was a civvy one and as it came into view above the canopy of the jungle we waved our arms. It spotted us and the pilot tried to negotiate down through the jungle. It took him several attempts, the rotors kept clipping back the vegetation. Now it was hovering directly above us and in the co-pilot's seat I could see Harry. He was acting as ops officer, and I could see his face, almost white with tension. The Huey turned backwards and forwards, trying to avoid contact with the jungle.

The pilot, unable to find a level place to put down, hovered to allow Vinnie to grab on to the skid and heave himself on board. I passed him our equipment then grabbed the skid and managed to pull myself into the chopper, grateful to see Harry.

As we flew low towards the roadhead, every now and then in between the gaps in the jungle I could make out groups of guys who had made it further downstream, in relatively calm waters out of immediate danger. I was just glad to be alive. The adrenalin was wearing off and I was starting to feel tired. Although it was very warm and humid outside, I was wet and cold, but took comfort from the warmth inside the chopper.

Those of us who were on the Wainavombo River now put it down to experience and have a laugh about it, but at the time it was 'serious city'. There was the story, for example, about a patrol getting swept under the water and sucked through a natural tunnel just big enough for a man.

George and Fred were picked up further downstream, slightly worse for wear. The furthest point downstream guys were found was ten ks, where they were found by locals, washed up on a beach.

How they got that far without getting their bodies smashed was a mystery. Sadly, two Fijian bodies were found a day later. One was the guy who initially swam across with the loop line, the other was from a bamboo raft which had met the same fate as mine.

As we arrived in dribs and drabs at our main base, many wondered why the Squadron hadn't been extracted once the dangerous condition of the Wainavombo became apparent.

Back at Hereford, I had a question for one of the old sweats.

'As you know, this was my first Squadron trip. It's been a bit dodgy, hasn't it?'

'Fuck off, young'un, that trip was a piece of piss.'

CHAPTER NINE

High Altitude Descent

WITHIN TWO WEEKS of returning to Hereford I was moved over to Air Troop. Air Troop trained in all aspects of infiltration into an operation by air, especially freefall parachuting by HALO (High Altitude, Low Opening) or by HAHO (High Altitude, High Opening). I had already been trained in static line parachuting but needed the freefall skill to be a complete member of the troop, so I was pleased to hear that the Squadron was to be deployed to the Oman with two RAF freefall instructors. They had been given special clearance to train me and five other guys in Accelerated Freefall.

Life was sweet and I was happy as a pig in shit. But Lynn wasn't. Since joining the SAS, my life had been like riding a nonstop rollercoaster and I had not had time to think about anyone but myself. Lynn, my family, the Falklands experience were things I had not made an effort to address and they needed to be. I used to talk with Lynn a lot on the telephone and when I had time off, I used to shoot off down the M4 to see her. The weekend before I was due to fly off to the Oman, Lynn came up to Hereford and there we talked about what we both wanted from this relationship. We agreed that when I was away, she would put her house up for rent and come up to Hereford and look for a flat to rent for both of us. We were going to give this relationship a go. I had committed myself and as I flew off to the Middle East, for the first time in my life I found myself thinking about Lynn and remembering how beautiful she looked when we said our goodbyes.

In the Oman for the next four weeks my home was to be a four-man tent in the middle of the desert. We were to train in desert warfare as a squadron from this tented camp, then split into troops and disperse for two weeks' troop training, finally meeting up to carry out a final exercise incorporating the techniques and skills we had been taught.

On the last week of training at the tented camp we had a small exercise playing the parts of a mortar team with live 81mm mortars. The team had the Command Post Operator (CPO), the Mortar Fire Controller (MFC) and then numbers one, two, and three on the mortar. The CPO is the boss, whose job is to run the mortar line. He notes the details of a target passed onto him from the MFC and orders the mortar crew to fire at it. He also gives them any MFC corrections. Once a target has been engaged and neutralised the mortar crews would automatically reset their tubes to the FPF (Final Protective Fire), a prerecorded target. The MFC's job is also to act as the mortar crew's eyes, directing rounds down onto the enemy and making any required adjustments to the fall of shot.

All went well until one of the final five missions of the day. The FPF was a large rock on its own in the bottom of the wadi (a dried-up riverbed) about 50 metres long and wide and 20 metres high. When we got to the top, the acting MFC, Graham, sent our new location to the CPO, and decided to bring rounds down on one of the pre-recorded targets. Graham called up the CPO and ordered a fire mission. Three mortar crews jumped into action – they were to fire three HE rounds each at the prerecorded target. Within 20 seconds of the fire mission being ordered there were nine rounds in the air at any one point, all due to land within five and 20 seconds of each other.

The first and second rounds were on target. Then I was aware of a distinctive whistling noise heading towards our position, a lot nearer than the last two rounds. The round started to fall off its trajectory, and the noise increased in pitch. We all thought, Oh fuck, it's a round that's dropping short of its target. I covered my head and ears and waited for impact. Luckily the rock had a natural furrow in it, about two feet deep and just wide enough for a man to lie in, side on. It ran the whole length of the rock, but was at its deepest on top. Graham screamed into the radio, 'CHECK FIRE, CHECK FIRE.'

A second before impact, the round whooshed past and exploded just off to my right. Fragments of rock shot up and covered us in debris. I stayed down. The radio crackled into life again. It was the CPO, his voice abrupt and precise, telling us two more rounds were in the air, ETA, two five seconds.

As I lay curled up, hands over my ears and my mouth open to reduce the over-pressure created by the explosion and prevent my eardrums bursting, I could hear the second round on its way. Then it was here. Another whooshing sound and then a deafening crump. It had landed off the rock and into the wadi bottom. Another five seconds. I heard the other round flying in. A whistle, then the whoosh, and then the ear-piercing explosion, closer than the first. The force of the explosion sent splinters of rock spinning all around. It had, for a split second, used up all the air around us. My ears popped and my brain seemed to rattle inside my head, but I knew instantly I was OK. I heard the rest of the guys sound off. As I rose out of the trench, that familiar smell of explosives was in the air. The two mortars that had landed on the rock had not penetrated it, but rather split it into slivers. It reminded me of a mini Wireless Ridge, where the occupants had not been so lucky. It was a miracle that none of us had been hit. We knocked the day's training on the head and spent the later part of the afternoon discussing what had gone so wrong.

At the end of the four weeks I moved off to the base of the Omani Parachuting School, to start the Accelerated Freefall Course, but it was apparent on the first lift up (first jump) that I could not clear my ears. I had blockage within my sinuses, which stopped me from jumping. That was me grounded, and after an inspection by the Regiment's doctor, arrangements were made for me to be flown back to UK ASAP to go under the knife and have my nostrils drilled. His parting words to me were, 'Have you been exposed to any loud bangs recently?'

'I've just come off the mortar course, if that's what you mean.'

'I wouldn't have thought the noise made by mortar rounds

179

being fired could cause the damage I'm looking at,' the doc said, strangely.

I said nothing and he left it at that, so I put the damage to my sinuses down to friendly fire.

Days later I was in the Queen Elizabeth Hospital in Woolwich, London. Luckily the operation was a success. When the surgeon was working on my nostrils, he had time to look in my mouth, and suggested that I get my wisdom teeth extracted as soon as possible, because they would cause trouble if I HALOd as they were. I took his advice and he phoned up my HQ and explained the circumstances. Since I had just gone under a general anaesthetic, I had to wait at least four weeks before they could operate again, but I was back fighting fit within six weeks and had two weeks to convalesce which I spent with Lynn. We had a lot to sort out and I was grateful for those several weeks off. It enabled me to sort out all my admin and settle any fears Lynn might have had with our relationship.

While I had been in the Oman she had rented out her house and found a small cottage, just out of town, for us to set up home in. It was for sale, not rent. The change from renting to buying was about commitment and the future for both of us. I didn't need to think about it too much. Lynn was a great girl and we had got on well in the past, so I couldn't envisage the future being any different. I bought the cottage at the beginning of 1984 whilst Lynn rented her house out, back in Aldershot.

Once again I found myself back up at PCAU, Brize Norton, in the same Nissen huts. Even those of us who were on the HALO course came under the control of the Paras. There were eight of us on the course, four of us badged, two attached and two from the Path-finders. One turned out to be Buster. I had not seen him since leaving the Battalion some 18 months before. I thought to myself, This is going to be one hell of a social course.

The aim of the six-week course was to teach each student the skills of HALO: two weeks at Brize and four weeks in Pau, the French Airborne base close to the border with Spain. The weather in the UK does not lend itself to parachuting, so we might spend two weeks not doing even one jump because of it. It was hoped, however, that we were to get in at least 40.

Our instructors were all from the RAF. They had progressed up from the 'mats' as a static line instructor via the Blue Falcons, the RAF Freefall Parachute Display Team. I knew quite a lot of them from when I was in the Pathfinders.

The first week it did not stop raining and it was not until the middle of the second that we had the chance of making our first jump. We all piled into a coach and were driven down to the DZ, Weston-on-the-Green, near Oxford. Because the cloud base was so low, jumping from a Herc would not be easy so the RAF had arranged for us to make our first jump from a Puma helicopter, as it could quickly take off when there was a hole in the clouds, and we could then be kicked out. We had it on call for the whole day so, at the very least, we might get two jumps in.

The Puma landed. Everyone was outside on the DZ waiting for the pilot's weather report. The skies didn't look too bad to me – a bit cloudy but relatively clear. All fitted up and checked, we waited nervously to board the Puma. Then there was a change of plan. Four instructors and 'Gungy' Gaz, a fellow member of my troop down at Weston on two weeks' leave looking for freebie jumps, were going to test the cloud level and if it was OK, jump. The minimum cloud base for us students was 7,000 feet. I would have preferred 10,000 plus, working on the principle that if anything went wrong it would give me more time to sort myself out.

The Puma took off with Gaz and the instructors. I relaxed as I watched it climb. At about 7,000 feet they jumped out. I watched nervously as the jumpers reached 3,500 feet and started to see their canopies deploy. One jumper had a bit of a sniveller with his Tactical Assault Parachute (TAP). All the time an instructor on the ground was giving us a running commentary on what was happening above.

'You see, he's got a bit of a sniveller. His canopy is taking a bit longer to deploy. He'll sort it out by grabbing the rigging lines.'

'He's fucking leaving it late!' someone perked up.

'Yeah, he's got a problem, he'll have to cut it away and pull his reserve,' the instructor said, nonchalantly.

Even my inexperienced eyes saw he had a big problem. The commentary continued. 'What he's gonna do now is cut it away, and pull his reserve.' The instructor's voice increased 20 decibels, and the uncertainty in his voice alarmed me. 'Oh no, oh fuck no! He's pulled his reserve, he's not going to make it.'

I had been looking up all the time. The jumper should have located the cut away hooks on either side of his harness up at the shoulders, released them, allowing the main canopy to eject, then pulled his reserve, leaving it to fly freely. Instead, without cutting away, he pulled his reserve and as the air caught it, it snivelled up and got tangled in his main parachute, causing both canopies to deploy only partially. I watched in amazement as the helpless jumper plummeted to earth. The horizon came up and the last I saw was him disappearing behind a hedge some 200 metres from the DZ. There was nothing any of us could do. Some of the guys took their parachutes off, sat on them and lit up cigarettes, the rest of us stood around in a stunned silence waiting to hear of the jumper's fate.

Gaz had seen what had happend and was the first on the scene. The guy had adopted a tight parachute position, knees and feet had been tight together. His knees had been driven up into his face and smashed both sides of his jaw. He was barely alive, and only because he had landed in a freshly ploughed field.

The DZ was closed until a Court of Enquiry could take place. The day's jump programme was also cancelled. We were glad. None of us fancied jumping after what we had just witnessed. They say that lightning doesn't strike twice, but there was no way I fancied putting it to the test.

We only got five jumps in before we went to Pau, so were ten jumps behind the course quota, and there we had to jump our arses off in order to get the jumps in. Our initial jumps were made on a parachute called the PB6. It was a front-mounted reserve 'rig' and had the flying qualities of a wet handkerchief, but it was safe. On my third jump in Pau with the PB6, I got into a bit of a spin. I jumped out at 12,000 feet, totally lost it on the exit and spent the next 9,000 feet spinning like a bastard. This caused me real problems when my 'rig' automatically deployed. I was still spinning and falling very fast as the instructor tried to come in and stop me. The canopy did open, but it was badly twisted, so much so that I couldn't check it to see if it was deployed or not. I picked a spot on the ground and tried to gauge my rate of descent. I could not make out if I was falling faster than normal because I was so high up. Within a couple of seconds I made my decision: go for my reserve. Fuck it, I thought, you only live once, and I ain't about to die just yet. There was no device to cut away my main chute on this rig, so I grabbed the underneath of my reserve with my left hand, held it firmly and, with the strength of ten men, ripped the reserve handle from its pocket with my right. The reserve flew almost immediately, which told me that my main was only partially deployed and that I needed the extra nylon (more canopy) above me. I then checked to see where I was drifting. I had no way of controlling where I wanted to go. I was prepared for a hard landing and the pain of a broken leg or two. My vision was very restricted because my head was still held firmly forward by the twisted rigging lines. I could see leafless trees, lots of them. The ground looked hard, uninviting and rocky. I tried to look to my left or right but I couldn't and though I heard my instructor shouting to me, I couldn't understand what he was saying. All I was doing was concentrating on my landing. I was close to the ground now. A tree appeared from below me; I tensed my body and tried to cover my face. A second later I went crashing through it and came to rest about ten metres up, embedded in branches. It was full of little spikes which had ripped into my jump suit, and I was impaled on these tiny thorns so I couldn't move. A quick mental check to see if I could feel any pain. There didn't appear to be any broken bones. I had survived. That was good enough for me.

I was brought to my senses by the instructor. He had landed right by me and had kept a eye on me from my exit. It took me about an hour to get myself free. In the meantime the instructor had sent back for a truck, so I could drop on top of it rather than climb down. I spent the night having thorns picked out of my body. (It would be months before they had all gone. Every so often I would feel a little prick somewhere on my body, only to discover that it was another one.) But the next day I was back jumping.

The course was now progressing well and within two weeks we got ready to do our first HALO (with oxygen) jump. To jump above 12,000 feet safely you need oxygen, because the air gets thinner and without oxygen you would most certainly experience hypoxia. This is a state where insufficient oxygen gets to the brain, giving you giddiness and memory loss, the last thing you want when you're just about to plummet to the ground at 120 miles per hour. The danger increases tenfold, the higher you go above 12,000 feet, and up at 28,000 feet, basically five miles up in the sky, the greatest height we were allowed to jump from, you could die within 40 seconds of coming off oxygen. At this height it would take you ten seconds to fall the first 1,000 feet and then you would have reached Terminal Velocity – 120 feet every second. This gave us just under three minutes flying time. HALO is a very hazardous means of parachuting so I was well switched on at our final brief for the first HALO descent.

We started with a clean fatigue jump, then progressed to jumping with equipment; with equipment at night; with equipment at night following a large bundle which we had to run off the ramp of the Herc and chase after. We all felt good as a team. It had been a good course so far and we had made up the shortfall in our jump quota caused by the UK's weather.

It was pitch black as we loaded our gear into the back of the Herc. The bundle was secured onto its rollers and Cyalume snap lights were masking-taped on all its sides. These were to be snapped on just before we pushed it out, so we could at least see their green fluorescent glow. We also taped one on the back of each of our helmets, so we could follow each other. The process of checking and rechecking oneself and each other began almost immediately. I sat with my legs resting over the top of my bergen. My parachute was on, my oxygen mask firmly clipped onto the inner helmet, and my personal oxygen cylinder was on my chest. The aircraft roared into life and within minutes we were steadily climbing to a height of 28,000 feet above the Pyrenees. We all had our AODs set to open at 3,500 feet. (The Automatic Opening Device opens your main parachute should any thing go wrong in the air, such as getting into such a spin that might black you out, or a collision that might concuss you. Since they worked on barometric pressure, they had to be recalibrated every day, adjusted to changes in the weather.)

The interior of the Herc was dark, noisy and very cold. Only the red tactical lighting was on, so the instructors gave their orders on large pieces of card. The order was given: get ready. I began to strap my bergen on to the back of my legs, at the same time going through all the safety checks in my mind. Moments later, we were told to go on to the aircraft's main oxygen supply, another drill. We sat and waited, looking at each other to spot any problems. The aircraft was still climbing. Another card from the instructors: 'ten minutes'. Then the order came to come off the main oxygen supply and to go on to our own personal supply. This was a dangerous move because by now all of us had been in the aircraft for about 30 minutes and the fatigue and pressure were beginning to increase. Fortunately I switched over with no problem.

The tailgate was released, letting in welcome fresh air, and the noise greatly increased. At this height the tailgate sometimes does not lock open properly so the pilot has to drop the aircraft about 500 feet and quickly come up again. He did this now, and we tried to jump up as he brought the aircraft back to the correct height, to experience weightlessness – difficult with a weighty bergen strapped to the back of our legs, but we did it just the same.

That bit of fun over, the tailgate was locked into position. Cyalume sticks were snapped and we made sure that they were glowing on our helmets. Then we waited for the green light. Noise, sweat, adrenalin, fear, all were building up. It was black and minus 60 outside, and we were about to jump into it. My goggles were now misted up and I could hardly see what was in front of me. Red light on! We moved forward towards the rear of the tailgate, and into the dark, like penguins. Green on! The front two men launched the bundle and I followed, but Buster slipped on the tailgate, and I accidentally stamped on him as I went out. He crawled to the edge and just flopped over the side – with a little help from one of the instructors.

As I fell I managed to keep the bundle in my sights, though my goggles began to freeze up. It was spinning so violently, all I could see were its little green lights flickering. My goggles were not the only problem. My bergen had shifted as soon as I jumped and I was now falling on my side, trying to keep stable. Both my legs were wide apart in an attempt to stop the bergen from whipping me around into a spin. What I was doing felt like lying face down on top of a huge beach ball, trying to balance yourself with an 80-pound sack of potatoes strapped to the back of your legs and a ten-pound yard broom shoved down one side of your body. And there was the effect of someone constantly spraying iced water in your face. I was trussed up like a Christmas turkey in a 120 mph wind!

My AOD popped off, not before time, and before I knew it I was under the canopy, drifting slowly earthward. My landing was good, but I was covered in sleet and my goggles were now filmed with ice. I spotted the rest of the guys and started to look for the bundle, then I realised I was bleeding from my mouth. I spat; out came a piece of tooth the size of the tip of my little finger – half a wisdom tooth! The pressure of the jump had reopened my wound and ejected this piece which the dentist had obviously missed. My mouth tasted disgusting because of the pus, but I was too happy to worry about that; I had passed the HALO course!

When I returned to the Troop, I felt I was finally part of the team, now that I was a qualified freefaller and HALO jumper. Actually I had only done 43 jumps, whereas most of the guys in 16 troop had done well over the 200 mark. Some, like Gaz, had jumped 2000 times. I still had a lot to learn.

As a troop and as individuals we jumped as often as we could. It became a drug to me – the more I did, the more I wanted to do it. I got onto the Pilgrims Freefall display team, which was made up of guys who were around at the time when requests came from locals who wanted us to jump into garden fêtes or for charity causes. This did two things. One, it gave me the opportunity to jump and learn what is known in freefaller terminology as RW and CRW skills (Relative Work and Canopy Relative Work. RW is where you build a formation of two or more jumpers when you are in freefall. A civilian term, it also has a tactical use, teaching a patrol to stay together in the air so that on landing you are not widely scattered. By contrast, CRW, the skill of forming a 'stack' of freefallers whilst they are under the canopy, has no tactical function but looks good for displays.) Two, it cemented 'hearts and minds' with the local people of Hereford, who are very much pro the Regiment and staunchly proud of it.

On one occasion, I was asked to jump into the Regimental Wives' Club annual sportsday and to present the winner with a box of Cadbury's Milk Tray. The winds were up that afternoon, and it was a bit tricky on the best of days to land on the camp sports field. The 109 helicopter took us up to six grand, then we pulled the pins out of our smoke canisters which we had bungee'd to our ankles. We got out, formed into a four-man circle and were under the canopies a few seconds later. The box of chocolates, stuffed up under my jump suit and chest strap, had moved down when I was in freefall and was now resting on my leg straps. As I was coming into land, I lined up with a makeshift stage. My intention was to get as close to it as possible, when all of a sudden, as I was just about to land, a cross wind came from my left and blew me sideways just enough to knock me off my feet. I felt the box of Milk Tray bend under my weight, and when I stood up and took it out I presented the winning lady with the most mangled box of chocolates ever!

CHAPTER TEN

The Libyan Embassy Siege

THE CHINOOK LANDED with a bit of a thud and the wind kicked up by its rotors made us all turn backwards. The Puma dropped down just beside it. These SF (Special Forces) pilots could land their machines almost anywhere. We respected them and in turn I reckon they trusted us. Not once had they refused to land on any of our landing points since they trusted us to pick a safe landing zone.

Past experiences with regular pilots, with their strict adherence to doing everything by the book, had made training seem so unrealistic it tended to take the purpose out of the whole exercise. Timing in a contact is vitally important. Timings on a hot extraction, or time taken to get to a particular incident such as a QRF (Quick Reaction Force), were often delayed while troops were told to 'buckle up', so a blinkered following of 'the book' was nonsensical. These pilots were different. They knew how to fit into the way the Regiment trains and they knew what corners to cut if the task required it, without compromising the safety of their aircraft, its passengers or the operation.

As the Chinook shut down its engines, the boss man ran over to the Puma, exchanged a few words with the loadie and took off again. He was off to pick up some kit in Hereford. It was the big beast we wanted, so we performed the ritual of sweet talking the pilot into letting us have a couple of jumps at lunch time. In fact this was the norm but, as ever, etiquette played a part. Tom's priority task of the morning, as Red Team IC, was to sort out the blokes' freefall programme. He knew most of the SF pilots and most of them knew *him* all too well. When the Pumas were flying into Stirling Lines (as they now were) on a particular task (mostly for a brew stop and chat), Tom would appear out of nowhere with a rig on his back and challenge the pilot to let him have a lift up when he was to take off again. Reluctantly the pilots would agree, but only if Tom agreed not to fuck up their careers by letting us all pile in after him. Tom would jump from *anything*. 'I need a fix of the old slipstream,' or 'I can feel one coming on!' he would say every time he heard a chopper. Most of the time a chopper would stay for a couple of hours. That would give us time to get our rigs together and butt in on his solo boogie. As blokes would say to him, 'Are we on then?' meaning, Had the pilot agreed to give us a flight? 'Nah, the pilot's got a bit of trouble with linkage or something,' He'd make up some plausible excuse and we'd all forget about it. Then, a couple of hours later, someone would see a lone freefaller land on the camp playing fields – Tom.

The aim of this particular day's training was to practise loading all the team kit and certain vehicles for a fast move to wherever. We would use the Chinook while the Puma flew in support. Out of the back of the Chinook came two blokes I already knew: 'Gungy' Gaz, and Wally. Wally was from 3 Para; both were attached to JATE (the Joint Aircraft and Transport Establishment). Their job, apart from swanking around the world freefalling, was to test, assess and sometimes devise all sorts of new flight equipment, from new-style parachutes and underslung cargo nets through to fast ropes and jungle extraction devices.

Old acquaintances were revived. As ever, Gaz had a brew in his hand.

'How you doing Gaz, you old scrote?' I said.

'Pretty good, young Devs, bet you didn't think you'd see us today!'

Oh no, I thought. The last time he came down with Wally they had just developed this new jungle extraction device for us to try, to extract men from jungles with high canopies. It was a means of exit

189

when a chopper could not land, mainly used for medivac in peacetime.

Last time I took this system up for a test, myself and three others were hooked up to it – 300 feet of climbing rope, enough to clear the tallest jungle trees – with a large hook for attaching to the side of a chopper. The other end had four lengths of what were basically webbing straps, and attached to each was a karabiner. Each man would clip a karabiner to his body harness, and when everyone was ready, a thumbs to the loadie (by now hanging outside the chopper so he could see) would tell the pilot to heave ho upwards. Meanwhile the loadie would be directing the pilot to go left, go right, steady, until the package had cleared the canopy.

Prior to this earlier test, Gaz's answer to the obvious question any sane man would ask was,

'Yeah, we've tested it, both me and Wally have, haven't we Wally?'

Concern was still being voiced when Gaz said, 'Come on then, Devs, what's up, lost your bottle?'

That was enough for me, so along with three others from the Troop, I picked up the rope and walked over to the chopper. A quick thumbs to the pilot and then we were up and away, twisting around the Hereford countryside, suspended from the Puma by 300 feet of rope, two grand up. There was no way to stop ourselves from spinning, and the rope was kinking so much that it gave out a creaking noise at each full rotation, which at a speed of 50 or so knots was about once every two seconds.

We had no comms with the pilot and I was getting dizzy but we just had to hang there. Our hands were free so I took a few happy snaps of the kinking rope and surrounding area. I couldn't help looking at the webbing strap which I was attached to, and for no apparent reason, stared at its stitching. It was double-stitched, as on any parachute harness, which was a good thing, but what worried me was that it was only double-stitched on one side – that was all that kept us from 'death by impact'. My horror was interrupted when the bloke to my right said, to no one in particular,

'Did you see the size of that axe the loadie's got up there? Maybe he's going to cut some buckshee wood at lunch time.' It was a nervous, stupid comment; we all knew what the axe was used for. If, for some unfortunate reason, the pilot got us snagged in some trees or something, he would order the loadie to cut loose the snag – us!

One of the blokes wasn't sure about the banter. He'd just passed selection and all this was new to him. 'Hey!' I said. 'Don't worry about that fucking axe, mate. Have a good look at the stitching on the webbing strap. It looks like Gungy Gaz's just tacked it.'

The ground was getting close and the pilot put us down with ease. We looked like four puppets who had just had their strings let go. We later found out that during that 15-minute flight the rope had stretched 30 feet and that the webbing strap was indeed just a double-stitch tack. Knowledge might dispel fear in the RAF, but a little knowledge that day scared the shit out of me.

'What load of bollocks you got for us today then Gaz?' Tom said, snapping me back from my recollections.

'A fast rope you might want to test at lunch time.'

'What's special about it that it warrants testing then?'

'Well, it's 120 feet,' Gaz replied.

'You're fucking pissed, aren't you? Well, that can stay on the frigging chopper then,' Tom joked.

'It's not us you want. Give it to the SBS to test. They like long thin things.'

Fast roping was a method of getting out of a chopper quickly without it having to land. This involves a three-inch diameter hairy-type rope hooked up to the outside of a chopper. You slide down it like you would a fireman's pole. No safety. It was a rapid way of getting on the decks of a ship without the pilot having to worry about the sway of the vessel in bad seas. It was pioneered by the SBS, but the Regiment perfected it.

But that day, in mid-April 1984, there was to be no testing of the 120-foot rope which lay by the Chinook like a huge coiled serpent. Someone got paged: we all had to return to camp for a brief. There was an incident in London, and as the half-hour team, we were now on stand-by. Maybe it was connected with the Libyan Embassy we had been hearing about over the past couple of days.

We screeched out of Trechlais training area, giving Gaz and Wally the usual, all good fun, hand gestures from the back of the

Range Rovers. As we drew into the hangars we saw frenzied activity. All the hangar doors were open, even those for the Blue Team, the three-hour team. We all knew what to do. The drill for a call out was well rehearsed.

The thing about the blokes in the Regiment is that everyone knows their job and, most of the time, everyone knows their place in the pecking order. The 'load up' usually runs like clockwork.

Tom jumped out of our Range Rover as it slowed down to take its place in the queue at the ammo bunker, to get a brief from the Int on what the position was.

I was loading up the Team's MOE (Method of Entry) gear. I was 'junior' to Trev, the Team's main MOE man, but he was away on a course. The van carried all sorts of equipment, from premade explosive charges for blowing doors and windows, through to a complete tool kit of which any keen DIYer would have been proud.

'Right, Devs. Tell everyone to be in the briefing room in three minutes,' Tom said, and disappeared.

'Briefing room in three minutes,' I shouted with no real commitment as I continued to load my vehicle.

All the blokes knew the drill and understood the urgency of the situation, but we also knew the 'on the wagon and off the wagon' syndrome (being told to do one thing, then being told to do the exact opposite a few moments later). We just hung around, knowing that a briefing was imminent.

Within three minutes most of us were ready. The urgency intensified. Tom popped back: 'Right, everyone in the Briefing Room,' and without waiting for a reply he carried on.

In these situations timings were of the greatest importance. Tom was a past master at giving snap briefings. He took a full set of orders, giving us just what we needed to know; nothing more, nothing less. Too much info usually starts the old 'rumour control' network. He was 100 per cent behind the blokes, and in turn the blokes were 100 per cent behind him. To fuck Tom up with higher authorities was to fuck the Team up as a whole, and then we all suffered.

He started the briefing in his own style:

'Right. In no particular order, you are all probably aware it's the

Libyan Embassy in London. Yesterday, WPC Yvonne Fletcher was shot dead, possibly from the Libyan Embassy, number 5, St James Square, London, by one of its occupants. At this stage we know that there are 30 people in the embassy, 22 of them diplomats, the other eight are unknown to us at the moment. The building is on the east side of the square and is set into the corner. It has four floors and a typical Georgian front.'

He moved to a large picture of the embassy pinned up on a briefing board. He went on:

'Nothing more is known. All we have been told is to deploy ASAP. No questions.' Tom didn't wait for questions that would take him valuable time to answer. 'A chopper's en route. The OC, Int, myself and Colin will fly to the holding area. You got that, Colin?'

'Yep.'

'Delta One, Delta Two, and Delta Three to leave here and we'll meet you at the Holding Area.'

There were people coming in and out of the briefing room all the time. There was no time for anyone to give a full set of orders. Maps were being put up behind Tom, tables were moved around; we stood taking notes and drinking our brews. Everyone knew exactly what to do, though to an outsider it would have seemed total chaos. These are the conditions in which the Regiment often finds itself operating, in theatres all over the world. It's the ability of each man within the Regiment to work under these conditions that makes it the best in the world.

Tom continued. 'Get your route sorted and get going immediately after this briefing. There will be a Police escort to meet you at the end of the M40. You all got that? Tosh, Jake, Devs?'

He called out the drivers of the three vehicles to confirm; we answered. Then the OC interrupted.

'Tom, let's wind it up. The chopper's here.'

'OK, guys, the rest of you get going, ASAP. Ben! [Ben was the 2IC of the Team] You follow up when you're ready, but don't leave it too late.' We all had our jobs to do and we all knew where we had to be. That was all we needed to know until we got to the incident.

Phase one, the move, was now in motion.

193

I checked with Tosh and Jake about the route. We checked the radios, we confirmed our anti-ambush drills, in case there should be a contact on route. It would be not an uncommon practice for a terrorist organisation to put in an incident en route, an ambush of sorts. It's always uppermost in our minds so we took serious measures to avoid them, or to deal with them should they occur. I was to be middle vehicle, being the slowest and heaviest laden. The three vehicles roared into life. I loaded my pistol, cocked it, put the safety catch on and stuck it under my right thigh, also placing four loaded mags in the top pockets of my jacket. The chopper to take Tom and his team to London from Hereford landed.

In Blue Team's hangars there was another flurry of activity. Because of the urgency of the situation, they, the three-hour team were bleeped in at the same time. The last thing I heard as we left the hanger was Tom shouting to Colin, straining to be heard over the noise of the chopper:

'Don't you fucking stitch me up and forget to load my doss bag.' Colin pretended not to hear. In times like this you have to rely on your mates to sort out your own bits and pieces, while you deal with more immediate concerns.

In the Regiment you never go anywhere without the green maggot (sleeping bag) even if it seems it's not required. The old sweats carry them everywhere, because although you may be told that 'You're out for a couple of hours', life's learning curve tells you that two hours in the Regiment often means two or three days. So I never left the camp gates on operations or exercises without the old faithful doss bag.

We were now travelling at speed. The lead vehicle was four up. I was by myself. The rear vehicle, vehicle 3, was also four up. I thought, What if, by the time we reach the incident, things have turned nasty? I reckoned the IA would be to drive straight at the front door of the stronghold.

Incidents have a habit of passing the negotiation stage within hours, quite often catching out the Police who have had control over the situation from the outset. Higher command are good at pre-empting this situation and generally call us well before the point where the Police feel they cannot contain the situation any further and hand over responsibility to the Regiment. As we drove to

London, I thought that if control was handed over to us, there might only be just a few of us to carry out an assault on the building. I thought through the options available to us should this scenario actually be thrown at us. I had enough Rosette charges to breach most walls and doors already made up. Ammunition and weapon availability were not a problem.

Did we have enough CR gas, flash-bangs? Did I have abseil rope? Would we need to use the small sets of ladders that have never been taken out of the back of the wagon since I took it over from the last team? Had I checked to see if they were even there? Quickly I turned around to see if I could see them. Yes, I saw them sticking out from under the pile of ropes and demolition stores. My wagon was fully loaded. It used to take a full day to hand over the equipment to the oncoming MOE team member. The equipment check list was twice as long as the opening credits on *Bonanza*, and that's frigging long!

Other things ran through my mind. What if we needed to do a covert approach? Did we have enough suppressed weapons to go round? If we didn't, who the fuck would go without? It certainly wouldn't be me, I thought, because I carried two on board my wagon. Of course, everybody had everything they should have. These were well rehearsed drills, brought about through years of experience in anti-terrorism work. Our equipment was the best available, and we had trained, trained and trained again for all sorts of incidents: aircraft hijackings, ships under way, any number of buildings and vehicle assaults. Any structure or thing that was a potential target we had trained on, working out our SOPs (Standard Operating Procedures).

Things were going well. We were in constant radio contact with each vehicle, and had comms with Police controls when we passed through their areas. It was about 10 miles east of Gloucester that something happened to cause us all concern. Travelling uphill slowed the two Range Rovers down, so a gap appeared between my vehicle and the lead. The third vehicle closed up when all of a sudden a dark red saloon came shooting up, passed the rear Range Rover and tucked itself in between my vehicle and the lead, causing us to brake heavily. All my heavy gear shifted forward, nearly joining me in the front seat. The saloon's driver was obviously a total fuckhead. We didn't know why he was driving like that, but one thing was sure, no way was Tosh going to let him pass, as he told me on the radio. So the driver was flashing his lights and tooting his horn all the way to the end of the M40. As we raced towards London, the lead vehicle radioed through to the police, giving them the essentials: we had 'unwanted baggage' with us. We described it and gave them its registration number. The police promised to intercept. We had been travelling on the outside of the motorway while the police directed all other traffic over to the two nearside lanes. I could see about a mile in front that the traffic had come to a standstill, and the road was cordoned off for our approach. It was crazy of the saloon's driver not to notice this and I was beginning to think that the dickhead, three feet from my front bumper, was indeed a suicide merchant from the terrorist group holding the embassy, trying to do his bit.

Just then the police response vehicle came speeding up and drew level with the 'baggage'. The police car was four up; unusual, I thought. The policeman in the front passenger's seat started a rapid series of hand gestures to the driver. Something on the lines of, Pull over! You're fucking nicked. I thought, Fuck, these intercept boys know how to drive! Then I smiled, thinking about the mad driver's fate. Although I never heard what happened to him, the look on his face convinced me that He Who Gets Caught Gets Fucked Up, Big Time.

Braking heavily, we arrived at the police RV. A few quick words were exchanged, then we were off again, this time with a full police escort, motorcycle outriders and all. Sixteen outriders and four patrol cars escorted us into London to the holding area. I imagined how the Queen must have felt on her first ride in a motorcade. It was a bit over the top though, I thought. We turned off the main road and were escorted into an old airbase on the outskirts of London. Tom was standing at the side of the hangar doors dressed in his assault kit, MP5 slung to one side, a Mars bar in one hand and a brew in the other. It transpired, after talking to one of the police outriders later, that they thought we were the main convoy and that was his excuse for the apparent overkill in escort numbers, but I got a different story from another cop. He said that they knew that we were just the advance party, but they all went along for the crack.

seemed these blokes really enjoyed themselves every time they went out in a large formation.

We were shown where to park and told to get into our assault kit. This must be serious, I thought. Fuck, only ten of us, great! A nice little assault team. Tom stood around us while he gave us a quick Int update. Nothing seemed to have changed much from the initial brief we had got back in Hereford, only that the police negotiating team had managed to talk the terrorists out of their fanatical state for the time being. However, a deadline they had set was fast approaching. It was now 17.35 hrs and the deadline was less than three and a half hours' time.

Tom was a decision maker. I admired him for that, and for the way he conducted himself in general. We had to have an IA ready to stand to at any moment, and it was his job to format it for agreement with the OC. On carrying out an area study of the map and plans of the building, we, the assault team, would add our ten bob's worth, to either have it accepted or rejected by the other members. Then we would agree on what was left, get the relevant pieces of specialist kit from the appropriate wagon: weapons, explosive charges and 'Barclaycards' (a sawn off shotgun, so called because, like a Barclaycard, it gets you in anywhere), load up and return to the tea urn, which was near the negotiator's loudspeaker. We could then hear what was being said between the negotiators and the terrorists, real time. If there was a sudden deterioration of the situation, then we would all stand by to carry out the IA procedure.

About two hours later the main Red Team and Blue Team parties arrived. They made home on the other side of the hangar, started to debus and got their kit on almost immediately. Nine o'clock: the deadline came and went, and there was a lull in the proceedings as daytime turned into night. The requests of the terrorists were agreed to and acted on. Generally they wanted a certain type of food delivered. This was what the negotiators wanted. They had struck up a good rapport with one of the main players and the conversations became more genial. It seemed odd that a few hours previously the terrorists were threatening to kill a hostage, so threatening that we were stood to – at 30-minute intervals. Now conversations between negotiator and terrorist sounded like an order from the local take away. It was crazy, but it was down to the good negotiating skill of the police. The talk of food made me feel quite hungry. All we had were plates of the old Airborne stew to keep us alive and kicking.

The first night was the longest. None of us got much sleep. We were all under the constant apprehension that we might be called out at any moment. This was the first embassy incident since the Iranian Embassy siege at Princes Gate of 1980. There was, of course, some street cred to be gained by the blokes on both teams and it was interesting to see the rest of the support arms come into play. It was also interesting to see all the old brass come out from behind their desks, just to cut a piece of the action if everything actually went right.

The second day saw another deadline come and go without incident. As time goes by on such incidents, the teams are able to formulate and rehearse a more definite plan of attack and a more deliberate attitude can be adopted. Before the real use of computer software, we were solely reliant on floor plans and recent and past architectural drawings to tell us the lay out. Which rooms have which doors, and where? Which way do they open? What type of handles did they have? The air-conditioning system, in which direction did the vents and ducts run? We even had an engineer who had recently installed the latest air-conditioning unit in the embassy. This was a bit of luck, as every detail was still fresh in his mind. One option was to fill the building with CR gas through this system. We had everything we needed at our disposal to formulate an attack plan. We had all this technology available to us and yet we were kept in pretty much the most uncomfortable of places you could imagine: a dirty old hangar smelling of cats' piss and spent AVGAS (Aviation gasoline) in which to prepare for an attack which, if it failed, might even bring the Government down. It was always the case, in my experience, that those dealing with the Regiment had an attitude which implied, 'Keep the boys in shit, they're used to it.'

We had now been kept under wraps in the hangar on London's outskirts for over a week, only ever venturing out to be driven to the cordoned-off St James's Square to observe the target. My team was to go through its top righthand window. One evening, I was so close

198

to the window that I had to be careful not to be seen by those inside and, equally, those on the outside, the world's press. My aim was to confirm the size and type of material that the window was made out of, and to recce the most tactical approach. In all such incidents nowadays the press like to get in and dominate the area; the Libyan Embassy was no exception. They had, without any authorisation, taken over all the high buildings around the embassy, and their brilliant TV lights would penetrate it as they hoped to catch a sight of the occupants. It was a big problem for us. We all had to physically recce our external points of entry. One small slip-up from the shadows where we were lurking could instantly project us all around the world on the TV and, in particular, on to the screens of the terrorists, who just might see live pictures of their embassy window.

All routes were checked constantly. Plans on points of entry were upgraded and modified according to the movements of those inside. If the main section of occupants moved down onto the lower floors assault positions would then have to change to account for these movements. Through our sources, we worked out the general living pattern of life in the Embassy. During certain times of day the occupants would gather on the ground floor, around about scoff time, leaving only one man guarding the building's main points of entry. During the evening, most of them would congregate on the first floor because there was a TV there. At night they would almost all sleep in one large room on the second floor, leaving only eight men, two on each floor, as guards. Their daily routine was becoming predictable, which in turn allowed us to rearrange our tactics once again, for the better. As the days went on we were in the stronger position from an assault point of view. As for the Government, they had to do some fast talking.

It dragged into week two, and now all the blokes were sure that the attack would go in. It was exciting to be part of this operation, listening to the negotiators talk to the terrorists every day, knowing that it was really a game of cat and mouse. All the blokes were hoping that the negotiators would agitate those inside so we could go in. It's not just a macho thing to say. Like all soldiers, and in particular, blokes in the Regiment, we were keen for the challenge. Being scared was not what it was about. We train in very hard circumstances and it's a one-off to get on an operation like this. We were all secretly wishing, 'Let's do it now, fuck all this talking. We've been here for almost two weeks now. For fuck sake will someone please make a decision?'

The Prime Minister had obviously had enough. On day 15 there was a more of a rush around the hangar. More unfamiliar faces were seen about. Who they were I don't know, but they were obviously Army/Government people who had got wind that an attack was imminent. Still, it was not one of my priorities to make small talk with some high-ranking officer. If someone on our side didn't have the decency to tell us who these people were, cutting around our bed spaces, then fuck them. The hangar was, after all, like a large bedroom to us, we all had imaginary areas and a limit of exploitation to adhere to, even amongst ourselves.

We hung around for the best part of the morning. Nervous tension was thick in the hangar as blokes were checking and rechecking their kit, a routine which I had carried out time and time again. I found myself going over and over again in my mind the approach route, the placement of the window charge. Had I made the charge strong enough to blast through the double sash window? Did I have enough PE4 to take it out? What would be the secondary fragmentation effect of the blast on the occupants of the room? Hell, if it was full of the terrorists, then hopefully they would be looking like pincushions when we got through the window. Intelligence people would, of course, keep us fully up to date as to movements in each room. Hopefully all the hostages would be located in the same room, which had been the case up to now; none was expected where our initial entry point was. The third floor contained the master bedroom which was to be our LOE (Limit of Exploration) and we could almost guarantee that someone would be there on guard. This bedroom also had a large domed glass ceiling. Plans were evolved to blast the dome and come abseiling down but, unlike in the movies where visual effect is uppermost in the mind of the director, common sense dictated that going through the sash window would be quicker and a lot safer. Also, the route across the roof to the dome was in direct view of the TV cameras, so the risk of being compromised was far greater.

Intelligence updates were coming almost by the minute, and all the support elements were running around making sure that their tasks were well in hand. Vehicles, straps on the ladders, radios, were all constantly checked. It seemed the only people looking relaxed were us. Some were standing, some lying on the bonnet of the Range Rovers, all tooled up in the black kit and ready to do the business, others sitting in front of the TV, drinking brews and listening to the negotiator's running commentary. We were all deep in thought. Would this Op go as well as the Princes Gate one? Or would something happen out of our control which would make our well rehearsed plan turn to a bag of rat shit in front of the world's media?

People in the UK have such high expectations from the Regiment. Everyone always expects us to win. It's partly the media's fault and partly that the Regiment is very good at what it does. It had, until this incident, basically done itself out of a job since the Iranian Embassy. That had gone so well that I reckoned all budding terrorist groups around the world thought, Fuck the UK for a game of hostage taking, let's check out the US, don't fancy being carried out in a bin liner on day one of the siege. If we were to fuck up there would be no excuse. In the eyes of everyone we were the business. We had to perform and win, even against horrendous odds; it was expected. Many times I have overheard people talking in general about a particular drug problem or urban hostage siege and they would say, 'Send in the SAS and let's stop fucking around,' not knowing that I was a member of that Regiment.

I guess to some people, the SAS is called out to sort the fuck ups made by governments. Sometimes I felt like that.

A lot of the public are ignorant of the role of the SAS and sometimes even the blokes themselves felt so, too. Summed up quite aptly I thought, by a question from one of the blokes, Tosh, to the boss man at the end of one of the many briefing updates: 'Who the fuck are all these people cutting about the hangar?'

'They are just people from Group HQ. Need to know basis, Tosh,' the boss man said.

'We're just like fucking mushrooms. Fed on shit and kept in the dark,' Tosh chuntered to no one in particular.

Keeping the blokes in confinement for such a long period at the highest state of readiness was not a good thing, as the head sheds plainly understood.

The siege was not going anywhere and it seemed that no side would give way. Then, totally out of the blue, the British Government backed down from the firm attitude it had adopted during the whole of the siege and gave in to the terrorists. They allowed the 'terrorists' and the possible killers of WPC Fletcher to walk free and travel under escort to Heathrow, from where they flew to Libya to a heroes' welcome. It was a total loss of face for us, the blokes who had been giving it our all for the past two weeks. We felt angry, let down. In our view we had done our job. We had fulfilled our role, so why the hell did the Government back down? Did they not have confidence in us, was that it? The Government had done a deal with the terrorists, that's what it seemed to us. No one gave us an explanation.*

We loaded up the wagons and went back to Hereford. It was as simple as that.

*In 1996 the TV documentary series *Dispatches* screened a programme called *Murder In St James's*. This proposed that the shot that killed WPC Fletcher came from a direction other than that of the Libyan Embassy. This may have been the reason for the Government's backing down, and our quick departure from the scene.

CHAPTER ELEVEN

Her Majesty's Killing House

ONE OF THE less risky tasks that we had to perform whilst the Squadron was on the team was to play host to all sorts of dignitaries, from Heads of State downwards, giving a full demonstration of just exactly what the Anti-Terrorist team could do. One was for the Queen and the Duke of Edinburgh. They came to visit us and wanted the full Monty – from the Anti-Terrorist demo through to seeing all four troops carry out their entry skills. It was to be a big two days for the Regiment and we were all keen to perform well.

The demo would start in the Killing House on the lines. The Queen and party would be shown a series of well rehearsed entry techniques and live shooting skills. The Killing House is a large single-storey building split up into several rooms for practising all aspects of assault techniques. For example, one room would have a live hostage plus two head targets, representing the terrorists. The guests would be ushered into this room, about 20 feet by 20 feet, and told to stand behind a line of masking tape. Unbeknown to the guests, the boss, who was their host, was to be a hostage. He would start explaining a particular assault technique to them, when, on the command 'Stand by, Stand by, GO!' the door would slam open and three of us would burst in in black kit! Two would double tap the heads whilst the other man would snatch the boss, then all four of us would disappear as quickly as we had entered, the whole exercise taking no more than three or four seconds, leaving the guests in stunned silence. The four of us would then re-enter the room, take our hoods and gas masks off and the boss would introduce us and take any questions the guests might have.

Other demos within the Killing House were similar. One would be a multi-room clearance, another would be a covert entry in the dark with the team wearing Passive Night Goggles (PNGs) armed with Suppressed MP5s (SDs); they would creep up to the guests and fire a double tap into targets that had been placed very close to them. Because all the guests were asked to wear ear defenders they wouldn't even hear the 'tap tap' of the silenced weapons being fired. All they might feel would be the hot, empty cases hitting them.

After two demos the Queen and the Duke were led into the mock train carriage and asked to sit down, one either side of the aisle. The Brigadier, CO and entourage would stand by me at the back of the 20-foot carriage. The Queen decided to sit on the right, just near the entrance, but the Duke chose to sit in the first seat in the front row, on the left. My aim was to demonstrate to the Queen and the Duke how accurately I could shoot the targets that would appear on the screen in front by way of slides. These would come up at random, anywhere on the 15 by 10 foot screen. The slides might show a terrorist holding a hostage around the neck in an aircraft, or a woman and baby in front of a terrorist.

The projectionist started the demo and I double-tapped the slides as they appeared, every three seconds or so. I was concentrating like mad because I didn't want to fuck this up, in front of the Queen. I was doing fine, I was putting two neat holes in every terrorist's head. When the fourth slide came up it half covered the Duke's back and head. He was sitting upright and because he's a tall man, I had to do a 'double take' of the slide. Instinctively, and lucky for me, I spotted the terrorist just off to the right of the Duke's head. It was close but I fired two rounds and hit the terrorist. The rounds winged past the right hand side of the Duke's head, missing by inches. He didn't bat an eyelid. I knew it was a tight shot, but I made the decision to fire anyway. After all, that's what I had been trained for. I caught movement out of my right eye. I sensed that the

Brigadier had quietly nudged the CO and murmured something. The CO came over and whispered into my ear,

'Very good shooting Devs, but Jesus Christ, take it a bit easy. I don't want the Duke slotted, OK.'

When I had finished the demo, the Queen and the Duke came up to me and thanked me for 'an excellent display'. As they left to go to the next room, the Duke turned and gave me one hell of a vacant look. His right ear must have been buzzing like a bastard!

I bumped into the Queen and Duke later that day when we had just finished a helicopter house-assault down at Trechlais. We were all lined up outside the Embassy (the main assault building) and once again the Queen and the Duke went down the line and thanked us personally, stopping off every now and then for a quick chat. When the Duke saw me he still had that vacant look on his face.

One Friday afternoon, I had just returned home from camp. I had planned to take Lynn out for a meal that evening and then, on Saturday, get cracking on with the garden. The garden was mainly Lynn's responsibility and she enjoyed it, but this weekend I was to buy and erect a garden shed and fill it with whatever she wanted – one of those domestic chores which more often than not, I seemed to slide out of. This was no exception. My bleeper went off as we were perusing the gardening section of the local paper. A call out – I had to leave ASAP. I gave Lynn a big hug, kissed her goodbye and told her not to worry, I'd be back soon as I could. I had a big grin on my face as I raced into camp.

It was a call out for four of us to go across the water – NI. An unexpected job had come up and we were to go over in support of the troop which was in the process of being deployed. It was SOPs on the team, to have our NI call-out kit packed and ready. There had been no requests to bring over special weapons so I just grabbed the usual assortment. The chopper was already waiting for us. It took a couple of minutes to get into the thick red survival suits, then we were off. Less than two hours after considering the difference between tongue and groove or featherboard sheds, I was on the ranges in NI zeroing the Kite sight to my rifle. Thirty minutes later we were back in the troop hangar for a quick set of orders, then out in a chopper, heading for our drop-off point.

The weather had been foul since Hereford and the ride over was horrendous. We flew as high as possible from UK but as soon as we got to the coastline of NI, the pilot started go into a tactical flying mode. We didn't know what the hell was happening, until the loadie said, 'There have been reports that the PIRA have just got their hands on their first delivery of American SAMs [Surface to Air Missiles] and the Int reckon they're going to use them as soon as they're out of their packing crates – any time now!'

Fucking brilliant, I thought. If the pilot doesn't kill us there's always the chance of getting blown out of the sky by 50 pounds of heat-seeking HE.

Our drop-off point was one of the 'Magistrates' – a line of static Army look-out towers dotted all along the border with the Republic. We then had a long tab to an ambush site by a small road T-junction somewhere on the border where there was going to be an exchange of one of these SAMs. Half the troop had been deployed at other probable hand-over sites, the rest were on a long ongoing surveillance job.

We landed at the Magistrate's tower. It was not unusual for choppers to be flying around at this time of night, so our arrival would not alert PIRA lookouts of troops in the area. We ran through torrential rain to the Magistrate's bunker. The men who manned it, from the Green Jackets, worked a month rotation. We got our shit sorted out, one of the Green Jackets made us a brew and a sandwich and then we left. We had a lot of ground to cover in the remaining hours of darkness. It was still pissing down when we sneaked out of the Magistrate's defences and tabbed through bogs and marshland. The night was completely black and all we had to go on was the compass bearing. The landscape was featureless apart from the fading glow from the tower behind us.

We had to be back in the tower before first light, 12 hours away. It took us six hours to get to the T-junction. As I went forward with Chas, the patrol IC, to check out we were at the right place, I caught the sound of a metallic clink just above the wind and the rain which seemed to have come from my front. We both froze. Tensed up, I didn't dare move an inch. My rifle was pointing in the right direction with the safety catch off and my finger on the trigger, but no way was I going to risk bringing it up to the aim. It was that tense.

Chas, just off to my left, did the same. Absolutely nothing. When you're in a situation like that, your senses become electrified. The only thing you think about is when to move, when to pull the trigger. Nothing was said. The two guys behind us had seen that we were standing still and instinctively knew something was up. I pictured in my mind what they would be doing. One would be picking a spot either side of me and Chas just in case we were to be fired at, and the other would be watching our backs. All four of us just waited for one of us to spot something that would make us react. We would then go into automatic mode and carry out our patrol contact drills, just as we had practised hundreds of times before.

Fifteen minutes had passed, a short time in one's life when you consider what the consequences would be if one of us moved or made a noise and compromised ourselves. I was not sure what I really had heard, but it was definitely a metallic sound. I tried to look into the dark. I could make out the start of a dry stone wall some five metres in front and reckoned that the road was the other side of it and the T-junction was another 15 metres ahead.

My mind was racing. Had they heard our approach? Were they now looking at us? I doubted that, because the wind was blowing in our favour. Did they have a man forward on the road to act as an early warning trigger? If so, had he seen or heard us coming, and run off to warn the others? If someone was there, maybe they didn't know we were just standing in the field behind them, waiting for their drop-off to take place. I was hoping that this was the case. I wanted him, or them, to make one more distinctive noise to confirm that something was going to happen. After all, why the hell would anybody be out on a night like this, in the early hours of the morning, if they weren't up to no good?

Thirty minutes had gone by; not a sound. Had I got it wrong? Had I mistaken the sound of a snapping twig caused by the wind for something sinister? I was sure I hadn't. Time was not on our side, and if we did not make a move within the next five minutes, we would be caught out moving back into the Magistrate in daylight, and that would compromise our position. The last thing any of us wanted was to let the local PIRA know that troops were patrolling from the tower, as that would cause them to plant IEDs all around the area.

Still no noise, no movement, no nothing. I slowly turned to face Chas, still keeping my weapon facing the threat. He turned and did the same. He slowly moved off back and I followed, looking back all the time. Because of the motionless waiting my joints had almost seized up. I had cramp all along my shoulders and down my right leg, and it was to take me some time before I got any feeling back in my feet.

By the time we got back to the Magistrate we were totally bollocked. We had not eaten since the sandwiches the evening before, and we were not going to eat until we got back to the troop hangar, because the helicopter was inbound and due in two minutes. That was how close our timings had been. Had we not made the chopper, we would have had to sit it out for another 12 or so hours in the bunker, sodden wet, tired and pissed off, ready to do a similar task that night. It would have been a complete nightmare.

When I got back to the hangar, we had a quick debrief, and Chas finished by saying that the whole operation was a total waste of space, manpower and energy and that the time appreciation of the operation was shite. Because of the terrain and the distance we had to tab, we had had 30 minutes on target; what good was that? Unfortunately, Chas's words were not sufficiently heeded, despite the fact that he was an experienced soldier, with a few tours of NI under his belt. We were told to be back in the briefing room for 16.00hrs for the same thing that evening.

I cleaned and pulled my weapon through, sorted out some dry kit, hung my webbing up at the end of my bed, stripped off and got my head down, too tired even to have a shower. My body was gopping, but I would have to address my personal hygiene problem later.

That evening, as we repeated the operation, the weather was not only shitty, it was freezing. We tabbed all night to an ambush and tabbed all the way back. Once again, 12 hard hours out on the ground for nothing.

I got back home on Monday morning. My head was spinning from the last three nights' excitement and my mind was still back in NI when I walked into the cottage. Lynn was there to greet me, but I fucked the welcome home bit up, just as I always did. I had said to myself time and time again, that when I next came home after a job, I would switch off and try and act like a normal civilised man. But I forgot. Lynn wanted to know if I had noticed anything different about the place, but I just complained about what a load of bollocks the past few days had been, not even listening to her. I was in a selfish world of my own. She then disappeared upstairs crying and I was left standing in the kitchen looking out of the window. Then I saw what she had done whilst I was away: we now had a shed. I felt a completely selfish twat, too bound up in my own SAS world, not giving a shit about anyone else. Later, when things had settled down, she told me how she had arranged it all and even put it up, all by herself. That made me feel even worse. After that incident I thought, I must try harder to act normal. But what was normal? I had never experienced a normal life; it was not something you could learn from a book!

After the team, the next two months were taken up with courses. I was to do the Demolitions course, then if I was successful, move on to the MOE course and then on to an Advanced Demolitions course, so that after about a year I would be fully trained to blow up or enter into any target with the least amount of PE. That was because the way the Regiment operates, everything I was to use I had to carry, or it had to be carried into the job by another member of the patrol. It was to be a challenging year. It also meant that it gave me a lot of time with Lynn, which was definitely needed, otherwise things were going to go tits up.

CHAPTER TWELVE

Desert Heat

IT HAD BEEN a long time since I had used my brain to its fullest capacity. I have never really been considered as an academic, but I passed all my exams and qualified as an all-singing, all-dancing bomb maker and bomb blaster.

It was during this time that Lynn told me that she was pregnant. That was a shock to the system. Once reality had sunk in I was over the moon, so I did the decent thing and asked her to marry me. She said yes. The baby was due on 6 June 1986, the anniversary of the D Day Landings, very apt I thought. We arranged to get married in March because I had a six-week Squadron trip to the Middle East in April. At least I would be home for the birth.

We had a no-nonsense wedding. We didn't invite parents, we just wanted a quickie, so two friends came and acted as witnesses, then we went off for dinner and that was that. Short and sweet with no pomp or circumstance. For a long time I had felt that there was something missing in my life, but now I had something more than the job to worry about. I had a family. It was a lovely feeling I had inside that day. I had married the woman I loved who was carrying our baby.

Jordan is a beautiful country, as with most of the Middle East.

warmed to it as I did to the Arabs. There is something strange and mystical about the whole of the Middle East and its people. Lawrence of Arabia and all that. I also liked the ex-pat's way of life – a good, warm climate, excellent food and a healthy lifestyle. So when I left Jordan, I said to myself I would be back very shortly, if not to Jordan, certainly to the Emirates or Kuwait.

We had a new OC and the Regiment also had a new CO. The trip turned out to be my best, but not lacking in life-threatening incidents. On one occasion, half my troop was located in an OP up in the mountains for two weeks. We had to survive under tactical conditions. We could not take all our water in with us, so at the end of the first week, we had to tab miles to a prearranged DZ in order to pick up our water ration which was to be air-dropped by C130. Trouble was, the trip to the DZ was to take up the last of our water. As you can imagine, it's thirsty work tabbing around the desert, even at night. We made the DZ and recovered the water with ease, but, because it was so heavy, we were dehydrating under its weight so we had to drink a third of it on our tab back. It was either that or tip it away, just to reduce the weight. So we spent the next week in temperatures way above 120° on less than half our recommended water ration.

Our task was to observe the twin-engined freight train which carried phosphate on a single track from the desert mines down to Aqaba on the coast. We had to log every time the train came up and down and how many wagons it was pulling; very tedious. When it came time to move out, we were given a second task – go and search for an enemy camp, do a recce and then attack it. The enemy camp was 20 men from the Jordanian Special Forces, all part of the exercise, who knew that at some stage we would attack them. It was rather a low-key exercise, but we took the job as seriously as we would have done in a real-life situation.

Having discovered the camp, we formed up just before first light, ready to attack. We set up a couple of loud bangs as distractions, then put in the attack. The two guys who had carried out the recce had come back and said that the enemy seemed to be pretty switched on. They had actually got sentries out, who were awake.

The explosions were our signal to attack. It was still pretty dark. All of us were up and running, firing our blank ammunition, when all of a sudden, *live* rounds started to be returned by the Jordanians! They were shooting everywhere, and within 30 seconds of the distractions going off, 20 of them were firing real bullets at us, thinking they were getting attacked by an Israeli hit squad or something. We lay low as our Jordanian SF liaison officer screamed out in Arabic something like, 'IT'S YOUR CAPTAIN YOU SONS OF BITCHES, STOP FIRING!'

His orders got through and warily we raised ourselves up from our fire positions. We were pretty much OK about the whole incident. Hands were shaken and heads were bowed in a vain Arabic attempt to apologise without losing face. But the Jordanian captain went ballistic with his men, kicking them all over the place. What happened was that the Arabs always carried live magazines on their weapons when they are out in the desert, just in case they met the Israelis, or more than likely, roaming bands of desert pirates, and since they had been expecting us to attack several days ago, they thought that we were not coming, so they changed their blank ammunition back to live. That was their excuse, but some of us thought that maybe one or two of their grandfathers had been slotted by Lawrence of Arabia and were getting their own back.

CHAPTER THIRTEEN

Anti-Terrorist Team

I GOT BACK from Jordan two weeks before our child was born and was there at the birth. It was not something I wanted to attend, but as I was on leave I could hardly refuse Lynn's request. I could have made an attempt to get out of it, and say that I had been called out but I think Lynn would have found out sooner or later, through her own sources, had I pulled a fast one. Emma was born two days late. She was a healthy seven pound three ounces.

The cottage was not really convenient for Lynn and Emma to cut about in, especially with all those extra runs into town for more nappies and all the rest of the baby business, so while I was away, Lynn had been very busy trying to sell her own house and the cottage and also negotiate the purchase of a new house on one of Hereford's latest building programmes. This she had done all on her own. It was because of the woman she was that I let her make all the key decisions to do with the household. We were compatible, we had to be because it was generally Lynn's choice of car, wallpaper and furniture. I thought that was OK because I was a away a lot of the time, and it was she who had to live in the house, day in, day out.

When I used to come home from trips she would have re-wallpapered the lounge or rearranged a bedroom. Trying to find something like a pair of scissors was a nightmare. If I had left something out and disappeared for an hour, she would have picked it up and stuffed it into any drawer or cupboard that she might be passing. Although the house was always very clean and tidy, it would have been nice to see a couple of the sofa cushions squashed flat as if someone had sat on them, but they would always be puffed out and put back in their rightful position.

The new house had a study where I could throw all my crap and have it stacked around my desk within arm's reach, but she even used to sneak in there and give it a once-over with a tin of Sparkle. Sometimes I felt a bit of a stranger in my own home, but I guess that's how Lynn subconsciously coped with the separation and, to some extent, the boredom that most of the guy's wives and girl-friends experienced.

Our new CO changed the policy on the Squadron's 18-month plan put in place by the last CO. This meant that my squadron would now go back onto the Anti-Terrorist Team for another six or nine months. Six or nine months, it didn't bother me either way. At least Lynn would know I would be around to help out with Emma and all those early feeds. I wasn't so sure!

I was part of the Red Team Assault Group again, but this tour I was the Team's MOE man, in charge of all aspects of gaining entry into any location or object we had to assault, whether it was explosive or non-explosive. That was my specific job, as well as being a part of a four-man assault team.

Most of the time, Squadrons have a incident-free tour. Nothing operational happens unless there is a call out to go across the water, so life could get pretty boring. There are only so many ways to assault through a window and only so many entry points into an aircraft. We tried to vary the training as often as we could. Looking at new kit that had come onto the market and going out and testing it helped split up the routine. Sometimes CRW (the Counter-Revolutionary Warfare Wing, those in charge of the overall training of the Team), would arrange with other agencies to conduct a training programme on a civilian site, for example a disused railway yard or an old aircraft. This at least gave the team the chance to get out for a couple of days.

On one such occasion, I took the Team down to Southampton

214

to practise explosive entry on two old council tower blocks that were due for demolition. We had two days of live blowing. A police cordon secured the area and we were left very much to get on with whatever took our fancy. I made Rosette charges (shaped charges set into a two-inch thick piece of polystyrene, usually round in shape and segmented a bit like a dart board, but three times as big and containing CLC (Charge Linear Cutting), thin strips of explosive filling (RDX) enclosed in a lead sheath, with an inverted V running along its length to direct the blast to make a clean cut.) With these strapped to us we would abseil off the top of the tower blocks, place the charges against the concrete in between two floors, rope off out of the way and detonate the charges, then abseil through the nice neat hole to practise high-rise entry techniques. We did this all over the outsides and insides of the towers. It was real good 'live' training. God knows what the locals thought we were up to!

When we left to go back to Hereford, every other floor down the sides of the towers had nice neat round holes blown into them. The insides weren't so tidy. We had physically smashed, with sledge hammers, and blown through, large sections of walling. My only hope was that when the civvy demolition contractors came in to drop the towers, they didn't use their standard level of explosives, and that they would take into account the fact that half the main charge-placement areas had already been blown.

On our way back, one of the guys wanted to stop off and see his family so he and one other Range Rover shot off for 'family' brew. We were tuned into the police radio, so that every time we crossed into another police area, we would inform them that we were coming through, really a matter of courtesy.

Heading west along the M4, still tuned into the police net, we heard of a shooting incident that had 'kicked off' in a place called Hungerford. I didn't think much of it, but after a quick map study, I was now aware that the two 'brew stop' Range Rovers were innocently heading for a village somewhere near Hungerford. There was obviously a major problem there because of the heavy police radio traffic. Soon after, the radio went quiet. I had gone out of range and into another police area. I had to retune, and once again make my movements known to them.

Those of us who travelled straight back didn't worry about the incident. We just went about our usual task of unloading the wagons and getting cleaned up. It wasn't until the other two Range Rovers returned some hours later that the guys explained what had happened. They were heading north for Marlborough along the A338, when they heard, just like the rest of us, that there seemed to be trouble at Hungerford, so using a bit of ABI (Airborne Initiative) they cut across to Hungerford. As they drove into the town, the police were only just getting their act together and starting to seal the place off. It was apparent that someone had gone berserk with a gun – people and police were running everywhere. The commander of the two Range Rovers stopped and spoke to one of the police who seemed to be in charge, and offered his assistance, not to put in a full live attack on the lone gunman, but to 'gas and bag him' – meaning that they would work out a plan to fire instant CR gas at him, which would totally incapacitate him. Then the police could go pick him up with a bin liner and make their arrest. The offer was refused. No more prompting by the guys was going to change the situation, so they left and headed back up the road.

Later that evening in the hangar, all of us sat by the TV and learned the extent of the body count: 16 murders.

It had turned into a massacre. When I went home that night, I recalled what my instructor had said to me one day on the MOE course about CR gas: 'You know these CR flash-bangs, Devs?' He was holding one up to me and pointing to its rubber-covered casing. 'One of these little babies carries 24 grams of CR gas. Do you know what that means?' I remember shaking my head and recalling that CR was a shit load worse than CS.

'Well, if you were in a room 20 by 20 and I put one gram into it, your eyes and nose would tell you to get the fuck out of it. So imagine what 24 grams of this shit would do to you.' Before I could answer he had pulled the pin and thrown a grenade straight at me, and was out of the bunker like a rat up a drain pipe. The grenade exploded almost instantly, but even though I was up and half out of the bunker I had been totally incapacitated. I lay down helpless for five minutes before I could even get my senses back, spewing up all over the place and when I could spew no more, retching and coughing my lungs out. My eyes streamed with water. Lynn had to wash my kit several times before the gas particles eventually dissipated.

216

Two guys throwing a couple of CR grenades each, one guy on the Arwen firing CR dust rounds, and one guy on the pump-action shot gun firing CR liquid rounds, would have gassed Michael Ryan back to the Stone Age.

CHAPTER FOURTEEN

Fast Ball Operation

LIFE IN THE Regiment had always been non-stop. Time spent away from the UK was increasing every year, but I didn't mind at all. I was having a hell of a time and enjoying it. Nevertheless, sometimes, when I was away, I found myself – as a lot of the guys did – wishing great chunks of my life away. Sometimes it would be for only a couple of weeks, other times it would be for longer. Wishing I was back doing something else, where I did not have to wish life away so much. It was not that the tasks we had to do were more dangerous than the last, it was the fact that 95 per cent of my time was spent lying up in some situation, watching and waiting. Then, if the gods were on your side, there would be 5 per cent action. But then nothing more, for months.

On other occasions time flew by so fast it worried me. Those times were when the troop went on the freefalling trips to America, where, for four weeks at a time, I jumped my balls off out of anything that could fly. I jumped loads of different types of 'rigs' and got to know their capabilities, how they flew and how we could use them in certain operational environments. I learnt the skill of jumping onto roofs of high-rise buildings, a skill which the Americans had pioneered. It had a tactical use as it was another way of getting to an incident where, for example, terrorists had seized a office block, or where an approach to a target could only be made by air. Landing on a ten-foot ringed circle in a field in front of a crowd of people was not a problem. It required skill, but you knew that if you 'over cooked' your approach, you could easily find another place to land outside it. By contrast, jumping onto the roof of a office block, even though it might only be three storeys high, took a *lot* of nerve. Even if you had lined up and come in on a good approach, you still had to contend with the little thermals which could arise from the roof and sides of the building and blow you off course. Once you were over the building, another problem had to be faced – where to land. Often the roofs were covered in air-conditioning units, heater pipes or just rubbish that had been put there out of the way. And then, getting safely on top was only phase one. You then had to go and deal with the problem of the terrorists.

Jumping jets was another skill that was taught. You had to identify them for suitability, because you could not just pick any jet and jump it; you might get a face full of a tail wing. Jumping suitable jets was 'high adrenalin', because, unlike the Herc and other prop aircraft, jets didn't have a low stalling speed. Certainly in the ones I jumped from, the lowest was about 170–200 mph, which was a lot faster than Terminal Velocity which is 120 mph. The exhilaration of exiting the aircraft and *slowing down* to 120 mph was incredible, in some cases better than sex!

In early 1988 the Squadron was called out on a 'fast ball' to a military air base in the Mediterranean. We loaded onto two Hercs which were waiting for us at RAF Lyneham and took off, less than four hours after the call out.

On landing we were ushered to an isolated place across the airfield. Our accommodation for the duration was to be a series of old aircraft hangars. Only when we had off loaded all the equipment were we told of our mission: to storm a civilian airliner which was carrying two British university lecturers who had been held hostage by extremists in Lebanon, and we were due to be flown out of that country to Libya. We were also told that one of the world's most wanted terrorists was travelling on this same flight.

The RAF, who still had a squadron of Lightnings stationed in the Eastern Mediterranean, were to intercept the flight and force it to land at the air base, where we would be ready in black kit, to storm it, rescue the hostages and, if need be, take out the international terrorist. A mid-air hijack by the RAF, then an aircraft assault by the Anti-Terrorist Team.

The intelligence we were given was very much open-ended about when the aircraft might fly. All we really knew was that the aircraft was likely to be a Boeing 737. So we practised our entry and assault drills on an imaginary one of those. It was not a case of not being able to get hold of an aircraft to train on; rather, that nobody knew we were here and it had to stay that way. Any sign of a 737 landing at the far end of the runway would have aroused suspicion. We couldn't even go to the nearby civilian airport to carry out familiarisation, it was that secret.

We were kept in the hangars and the immediate outside area, and for two weeks carried our drills on an area the same dimensions as a 737, drawn out on the ground with chalk, and a series of step ladders to simulate the entry points each Assault Group was to attack from. This must have looked really strange. Men dressed in the black kit all huddled up in small groups, some standing on step ladders, some crouching down under the invisible 'aircraft fuselage', surrounded by a ring of men acting as the sniper cordon.

We spent two weeks at a high state of readiness. It could happen any day. Every day intelligence said that the flight was coming, so every day we had to stand to. Our assault plan was arranged, within limited intelligence, to be adapted at any moment should things not go according to plan. This is why the Regiment differs from most other Armed Forces. It can easily adapt to a rapid change in an operation, and then put in the best attack at that time. The men who carry out these operations are the rankers – *not* the officers, as the media might think. It's the guys' own individuality and sense of professionalism which make them the world's best.

We could not know whether, once the aircraft had been forced to land, the pilot had depressurised it or not, so we had to plan our tactics on the worst case that it was still pressurised. That would make the assault more difficult, slowing up the momentum of the attack. We simulated firing a special round into one of the windows. Selecting a window could only be done once the plane had landed, because of the risk of killing one of the hostages, or exploding the on-board fuel. There were many different factors to dictate who fired the shot and when.

Another major problem would be now to get into the fuselage if we could not open the doors for whatever reason. Would an explosive entry be the best option, or, as we also practised, entry by disc cutter? That sounded ridiculous, because it would take too much time, something you do not have when assaulting any strong-hold, so the disc cutter option was ruled out, for the time being. But we practised it, just the same. Two men on top of the step ladders at the correct height for where we thought the best place would be, one supporting whilst the other cut.

Two weeks went by. Still no sign of anything happening. Most of us were very bored by now. Physical training was obviously restricted, so none of us could get out for a run just to loosen up and get rid of any nervousness. At the beginning of week three, someone back in London made a command decision. Thank Christ for that! I thought. But the decision was that we were to be extracted immediately and flown back to UK. (As luck would have it, the two British lecturers were eventually released by their captors unharmed.) The operation never happened and I think Whitehall had the commonsense to see that a mid-air hijack of a foreign aircraft by the Brits in international airspace was, in essence, a terrorist activity, which would have gone down as well as a 'death at a birthday party' with our allies and other countries who abhorred the use of fighting terrorists with their own methods. I was not so sure. I thought, Play them at their own game, when it suits us, and keep them guessing all the time: 'Are they going to play this one or are they going to play it dirty?'

CHAPTER FIFTEEN

Supertanker Patrol

AFTER THE AIRLINER incident, I went on the Regimental Body Guard course: six weeks of fun. I also attended the Malay language course as I wanted to develop linguistic skills, and this was the only such course on offer. It was really the first period when I had spent any length of time at home with Lynn and Emma. I lived the life of an office worker, up at seven, in the classroom at nine and back home with slippers on at five. It was at that time I started to evaluate just what I actually wanted to do in life. I had a wife and a young daughter and had to think of them. After all, we were a team, a family, a bit like the Regiment. I had passed the SAS selection at a very young age, I was still only 29. Most guys were just coming into the Regiment at that age. I reckoned I had peaked early, if that was the case. At times, I thought of being in the Regiment as resembling the work of a Hollywood stunt man. Doing all sorts of dangerous acts for someone else to get the glory. Sometimes I felt honoured to be part of this élite band of men, at other times I felt like a cornered rat, hidden underneath a bucket, all fired up, ready to kill and being released do nothing. And then having to deal with those emotions, most of my time, on my own.

During my time, I had been scared within the operations I had been involved in. I had been bored with the monotonous red tape which governed us, in 'real time' situations, but now I was getting bored with being scared. I had begun to realise that there was a big world outside the Regiment. I had travelled more than most people were ever likely to do in a lifetime, I had experienced a lot of what it had to offer. Now it excited me to think that if I left, I could be out into the big world within a month. I got a real buzz from thinking, Well, I've passed the most physically and mentally challenging soldier's course in the world. What sort of a challenge would I face if I gave up all this financial and personal security? I came home one day and said to Lynn, 'I'm a civilian in one month's time.'

She went ballistic. She immediately wanted to know why I had not consulted with her, she then went on about Emma; and what about the mortgage and the bills? What was I going to do for a job? She was really furious. I thought that was what she had wanted, for me to leave the Regiment so that we could both bring up our daughter together instead of me being away all the time. I listened to what she was saying. She was right, I should have consulted her. She was also right about money. We had some savings but that would only keep us going for a couple of months at the most. I had made another really selfish move without even testing the water as to what she thought. I had fucked up, big style.

It took Lynn a couple of weeks to get over the thought that I might be around her and Emma a lot more than she was used to, and also the thought of not having the sense of security the Army had provided. But she calmed down, and I sensed that she was quite looking forward to the future. After all she was a bit of traveller as well, so she had ideas of being able to travel all over the place. We were not restricted any more. We could both do and live what and where we wanted to, and I didn't have the Army to answer to. We were now free agents.

One Friday, two weeks before I was due to be discharged, I got a call from Ses, the new Squadron Quarter Master (SQM). It was a Friday night. Lynn and I were cuddled up on the sofa, just about to crack open a bottle of wine, when I was told to report to camp ASAP. I told Ses that I was due to get out in two weeks, but he insisted. Lynn was none too pleased. As usual, a call had interrupted our intimacy.

I hastily grabbed an overnight bag together and rushed into

camp, for no other reason than that it was just instinctive, as if I was still in the Army. I was, of course, but only on paper.

Ses gave a quick brief. 'A Middle-Eastern Boeing 747 had been hijacked and was en route to an airport in the Mediterranean. You guys, because you have just come off the Team and are current on 747 assault procedures, are to make up the "Third Team" and act in support of A Squadron. If negotiations go tits up, you guys will more than likely find yourselves as part of the Assault Group ... ' Was I therefore going to end my Army career as a hero going up the ladder on the port side of a 747, guns blazing? No. The operation was cancelled, and a few days later, I handed in all my weapons, black kit and specialist equipment. I walked through the Regiment lines and out of the main gate for the very last time, and promised myself there would be no looking back.

Quite by chance I was walking through Hereford city centre on my way to check my bank account when I bumped into Archie, the guy I got badged with. He asked me what I was going to do now that I had left. I told him that I really had no idea. I don't think he believed me, but that was the truth. I had not even begun to address the problem of work. I wanted to experience what I had not had during my entire adult life – the taste of freedom.

He gave me a telephone number to call should I get bored with life. It was to one of his old mates from the Marines, involved in supplying ex-SBS men to act as Security Advisers to merchant ships that were due to sail up the Persian Gulf and into the Iran/Iraq war. He said that the operation was well run and that the pay was very good. I talked it over with Lynn and she agreed that I should give it a go, so the following morning I rang the number, introduced myself and arranged an interview for two days' time.

The background was this: war had spilled over into the Gulf, Iranian oil tankers were being targeted as they sailed up and down the Gulf. Some acted as floating oil storage platforms for smaller oil tankers to fill up from. Also, in order for Iran to keep the war effort going, it had to sell its oil, but there weren't many tankers who would risk sailing up the Gulf; that's why Iran brought the oil down into a relatively safe area. Meanwhile Kuwait and Saudi Arabia were also getting pissed off, because container vessels bound for them were constantly getting boarded, or even worse, attacked, mainly by the

Iranian Navy, thinking these ships were bound for Iraq.

Since I had come to them with good references, the guys interviewing me decided to give me a go. I walked out of their office that day thinking, I've got a job that's paying me twice as much as I would get if I was still in the Regiment and what's more, I was going into a war zone!

A week later, I was picked up at Dubai Airport by two of the team members, both ex-SBS, Gaz and Titch, and driven to our hotel, where I was going to stay until a ship became available. They filled me in on the operation, how many recent attacks there had been, when I was getting my first ship and all the meaty points which I had not been told of, back in UK.

Within a day of arriving, I was told that there was a tanker waiting off the coast of Dubai, requiring our services. Gaz was to come along on this trip to show me the ropes, and after that, I was on my own. I was excited by this new challenge. I knew very little about the sea and all the naval terminology. Gaz had written out a list of what everything on board was called, and told me to learn them ASAP, because the quickest way to lose credibility with the crew was to call the 'the heads' the toilet or 'the galley' the kitchen.

It took us three hours in a small motor launch to get to the ship, at anchor in a place which looked just like a ship park: about 50 medium sized oil tankers all at anchor, just waiting for their orders to sail up the Gulf and load up. As we approached her the crew slowly let the gangway down the side of the ship. To me it looked huge, but at 100,000 tons Gaz said it was quite small compared to others he had sailed on. Still, as I made my way up the gangway and eventually to the bridge, I was absolutely amazed that such a vessel actually floated.

Once all the introductions had been made, Gaz and I set about briefing the crew on the event of a possible attack from the sea or from the air. We also started to put in place physical protection measures should any of the crew get caught out on deck. Gaz was very good at putting over the main points to the crew. Most of them spoke and understood good English and were keen listeners. They accepted us as their personal protection, as indeed we were.

The ship's only port of call on the Saudi Arabian coast was to load up with naphtha. As Gaz told me later, we would be like a floating Molotov cocktail, should we get hit on our outward bound journey. That cheered me up, knowing that in four days' time I was going to be sitting on 100,000 tons of highly combustible liquid, between two countries constantly throwing missiles at each other. This fact made me switch on even more as to what Gaz's plan was to prepare the ship for war.

There was not a lot of preparation to get the ship ready, luckily. She had been up the Gulf only six months ago, so a lot of the protective measures were still in place, but we still checked them for serviceability. On the bridge, we issued body armour and ballistic helmets to those on duty, we welded steel plated shields all around it to stop small arms, and to decrease the effects of an exploding RPG7 attack. We hung anti-blast curtains and safety film to all windows in the ship, to cut down on secondary fragmentation caused by explosions, and with the crew's help we filled countless sandbags to build small bunkers out on the ship's deck and around the wheelhouse. We steel-plated the ship's steering gear and checked that all the fire-fighting equipment and breathing apparatus was in good working order. We also laid out extra water hoses on the deck and tested them, so when we were sailing, there would be a constant flow of water on the deck to decrease the effect of possible flash fires.

After we had prepared the ship, Gaz and I got the crew together again and gave them an Intelligence update: what to do before, during and after an attack; then finished off with Gaz's special one-hour lecture on combat medical procedures, where he used all sorts of props, such as a bottle of tomato ketchup and half-a dozen field dressings to simulate the effects of having your leg blown off by a RPG7. After this lecture, we were all well prepared to set sail for the six-day journey into the war.

Over the next two months I sailed with several ships. I had learnt a lot from Gaz during my first trip, even to the point of plotting the ship's course and advising the skipper on where to anchor up at night and where not to sail, if at all possible, because of recent Iranian attacks. The crew were really good people to work with. All the skippers I sailed with were seasoned sea dogs, and they listened to and carried out all my requests to do with securing their ship. It was one of the few times in my life that I had a management responsibility. In the Regiment you had to wait years for some decent command task. All the guys wanted responsibility, but there were very few opportunities to be had, so now I seized this chance with both hands.

I never spent more than four days R&R, back at the hotel. Our services were in constant demand as the war escalated. On one occasion I was sailing inbound on a 350,000 ton supertanker. She was enormous, almost a quarter of a mile long, the bridge sat 200 feet off the water. Because of her size she had to sail in the middle of the Gulf, meaning she would be a lot closer to Iran than most of the other ships, which were small enough to stay as close to the Saudi coast as possible. Hence she was an easy target for the Iranians. They would attack in small ridged inflatables which we called 'Boghammers', carrying six heavily armed men at speeds of well over 45 knots, assuming the sea was calm, which it usually was. They would strike from their bases along the Iranian coast, riddle a vessel with small arms fire and RPG7 rockets, hoping to set it ablaze, and within an hour be back home. It also made it easier for the larger ships of the Iranian Navy to board us, out of range of the British and American warships; the Iranians would check that we were not bound for Iraq. There was nothing I or any of the crew could do when this happened. I was not armed, I had to be a merchant seaman for the purpose of the visits. It was unnerving, because the Iranians could arrest me for no reason, they were the ones with the guns, and take me back to Tehran and give me a good kicking, or even worse, kill me. That was very much at the forefront of my mind as I was sailing.

We sailed up to Saudi Arabia at night and spent two days at a loop terminal offshore oil port filling up with crude oil. We had not encountered any Iranians on our inward journey, and had not heard of any other ships sailing through the night having a 'close encounter'. This was a good sign, as it probably meant that the outward bound journey, if we sailed at night, would be Iranian-free. That was the pattern evolved over the past few months. There would be a series of daylight attacks over a four or five day period, then nothing for two days and then the attacks would resume, this time at night. Because of this, it was relatively easy to avoid making contact with the Iranians. You couldn't set your watch to it, but it was the rule of thumb that I used to tell the captain.

Whilst at the loop terminal we were relatively safe from a sea attack, but in the skies above me, the Iraq and Iran airforces were in a constant dog fight with each other. There was not much for me to do when we were at anchor, so a lot of the time I used to take my Walkman up onto the bridge and listen to a U2 tape and watch in amazement a multi-million pound aircraft getting shot out of the skies above me.

The evening we sat sail, an American warship had, some hours before, shot down an Iranian 767, a commercial airliner, killing all those on board. This was bound to have rattled the Iranians, big style, so I was well aware that we might be sailing into problems. I was wearing my armoured vest and helmet and I advised the rest of the crew to do the same. I also told them to keep away from the port side of the ship, where the threat of attack was most likely, and if any of them had cabins on that side, they should move to cabins to starboard until we were out of the danger zone. They did this without question, because on my initial brief I had reminded them of an unfortunate colleague of theirs who, two months earlier, had had his body splattered about his cabin by a visiting RPG7 round. He had refused to take advice from one of our team and had paid the ultimate price, death by HE.

At around 20.00hrs the First Officer picked up a small craft on the radar heading our way, from the east at a rapid rate of knots. He lost it soon after, and it was not until 30 minutes later that one of the crew screamed down the ship's intercom that he thought that we were under attack, because he had seen and heard small arms fire. I ran out onto the bridge wing and looked to stern to try and see or hear something. It was pitch black and the noise from the wind did not help, then all of a sudden I heard two muffled pops one after another. Were we under attack or not? The ship was so enormous it was like shooting a whale with a 9mm. I ran back onto the bridge, where the skipper was back on the intercom ordering the crew into attack routine; he was not taking any chances and neither was I. A complete search of the ship revealed nothing. I stayed aft for some time in one of the sandbag hangars we had built, hoping to hear or catch sight of any nasties which might be lurking behind us. But all was quiet. I went back up to the bridge. An hour later, the Emergency Channel, Channel 16, burst into life with Gaz's voice. He had set sail 24 hours before us on board another supertanker. It was his Mayday call which sent a shiver down my spine. A US warship responded, and after the preliminaries, Gaz gave the essence of the situation: 'We have one gun boat on our stern who has just fired two, repeat two RPG7 rounds at us. No hits, no casualties, as yet. Over.'

The transmissions between Gaz and the radio operator on the US warship went on for an hour. There was nothing I could do apart from listen in and make sure that if we got attacked, I could respond accordingly. Gaz's ship was attacked a second time, taking a series of small arms and RPG7 rounds. There were no casualties but the ship's bridge and the port side had been raked with fire. As for our incident, when daylight came, a full inspection revealed no signs of an attack. Possibly we had come under attack but they had missed us; possibly they had been preparing for another attack and had been scared off by one of the many small coastguard boats that operated up and down the Gulf.

The United States warship, the frigate *USS Elmer Montgomery*, came to the assistance of Gaz's supertanker, attacked the three Iranian gunboats and escorted her out of the Gulf and into safe waters; the first time during this war that an allied warship had come to the aid of a merchant ship. It was also to be one of the last, because shortly after that engagement, Iran accepted the United Nations Security Council's Resolution 598, which demanded that they cease hostilities against all shipping in the Gulf and bring about the end of the war between themselves and Iraq. This they did some weeks later. So I said goodbye to the sun and sand of the Middle East and goodbye to a sackload of money each month.

Epilogue

FOLLOWING THAT PERSIAN Gulf stint I had done a few surveillance and BG (Bodyguard) jobs. It had kept me in the country but away from home. Lynn and Emma were very much a team of their own, and I was aware that I was beginning to be a stranger to both of them. It was the classic story of a man who loved his wife and child, and because of that, would chase the job opportunities all the time, earning money to give them a decent standard of living, while forgetting the basics of life: love, affection and sharing.

One day I was standing on the platform of Reading station waiting for my connection to Heathrow Airport. I was flying out to a troubled Third World country with a team of ex-Regiment guys on a contract. We were to train Special Forces in their war against a powerful terrorist group backed by an external power. I was debating whether to give Lynn a quick call. Things had been a bit strained before I left. In some sense she did not want me to go on this job, but didn't go out of her way to try and stop me. I wanted to go. I was keen to get back in the field of fire and get operational again. I had five minutes before my train arrived, so I called. I knew immediately there was something wrong, it was that slightly sinister pause in our conversation that made me think the worst. As the train pulled into

230

the station she said that our marriage was over. I didn't have time to ask the obvious questions: why? what? when?

I was stunned. But there was no time to chat. I told her that I would call her back later, and put the phone down with only one thing in mind, to catch that flight. I had a head full of 'theme tunes' on the flight, but I put them out of my mind. The last thing I wanted was to carry a load of emotional baggage into a contact situation. This could quite easily get me killed.

Being a single guy back in Hereford had its advantages. The city is full of beautiful women and I was enjoying my new enforced freedom. All I had to worry about was how many beer tokens I had to play with once all my bills had been taken care of. Work was coming in from everywhere. There seemed to be no shortage of BG work or surveillance projects. I used to go away for a couple of weeks and generally the pay on these jobs was such that I only had to work three days to cover all my outgoings.

One time I was asked to go and work for Sir David Stirling, the founder member of the SAS back in 1941. He was an elderly gent by now and on my first meeting with him I was struck by his gentle voice and his very modest manner. Here was the man that Rommel had called 'The Phantom Major.' On the weekly visits I used to make to his flat in Chelsea he would often like to talk about past SAS operations he or I had been involved in, before any of the company's business.

In the true traditions of the SAS, rank did not mean a lot to him; what mattered was the ability of the man himself: how he could adapt to certain situations in life, not necessarily in theatres of war, and how he got on with the men around him. He would always have time for a chat with one of his own, be they officer or trooper. During the months I got to know David Stirling, he was knighted by the Queen, but he did not want to be addressed as Sir David. It struck me that he had been a bit of a rebel all his life and was one still. He was an ex-Scots Guards Officer, whose private army, born on paper when he found himself in a Cairo hospital, used totally unconventional methods of operating to run rings around Rommel's Army, and which in turn formed the basis of the most élite fighting force in the world today, the British Special Air Service, whose skills are still very much in demand, as they had been back in the Second World War. I can only guess as to why the Establishment had not honoured the mighty warrior with a knighthood earlier than this, instead of leaving it until six months before his death.

During this time David Stirling introduced me to another ex-Scots Guardsman, who was also working for him at the time, Tony Mac. It was suggested that Tony take me along to visit the HQ of the Household Division, in particular the Scots Guards at Wellington Barracks near Buckingham Palace, to walk around their museum. I did. It was all an education for me because having only ever been part of the two most recently formed Regiments in the British Army, I had been somewhat blinkered in my view of the rest of the Army: 'If it wasn't part of the Maroon Machine then it was craphat.' Walking down the corridors of the barracks to get to the museum, I could not help but feel unashamedly humble at the rows upon rows of medals, in between old oil paintings and etchings depicting scenes of past conflicts, which had been awarded to the Guards over the centuries when they had fought for this country. From Waterloo and the Somme through to Tumbledown in the Falklands, men had laid down their lives for their mates and their Regiment, and, quite possibly, for Queen and country as well. That visit reminded me of the feeling I get when I hear the bagpipes play on Armistice Day and I give a thought to all those mates I have lost too.

After Sir David's death, another operation took me to the Middle East at the start of the most recent Gulf War. The war kicked off when I was flying over Saudi Arabia so the aircraft had to do a one-eighty and we were diverted to Nairobi International Airport in Kenya. It was a bit of luck because the 747 I was on was the first to land and so we got a decent hotel, the Intercontinental Hotel, where I watched the TV news reports of the war getting up momentum. It was then I realised that there was more to life than killing. I felt slightly uneasy about my friends from the Regiment who were over there doing their bit. Part of me wished I was over there with them and the other part of me said, 'It's the same shit, different day.'

Some weeks later, I was in a bar in downtown Hereford having a drink with a couple of the returning 'Gulf Warriors' when I was slapped so hard on the back that I almost ended up with a face full of glass. I turned around to see Ches, my mate who I had met in Port Stanley when he had just missed the Falklands War. He gripped me in a bear hug. He was a bit of a big lump and obviously glad to see me, even though he was two-thirds full of Hereford's Best, and said, 'Fuck me, Devs, you've just missed a war!' – trying to make me feel a bit guilty and getting his own back for my comments all those years ago.

'Oh, is that right, big man? Did you fix bayonets?'

'No, but we fixed a shit load of Scuds.'

All of us laughed and went on to get absolutely shitfaced.

'Do you swe outrageously and dine ther

Amusement glimmered in his eyes. 'I don't wine them and dine them.'

Questions clamoured in her brain. The evidence pointed another way. She needed to get things straight. Was she dining with him as a woman, or as his PA? 'But here you are,' she persevered, 'wining and dining *me*, sweet-talking me—'

'*Kissing* you.' His eyes darkened and he leaned forward, making her gasp as he traced her lower lip with a sensual fingertip. The bold desire in his eyes threatened to send her insides into melt-down all over again. 'How else am I to get to know you?' He sat back, a small frown creasing his brow. 'I know what's worrying you. It's tricky when office rules get tangled up with a genuine attraction. The important thing is not to let it get in the way.'

Her breath caught. 'The—the attraction?'

'No. The office.'

Dear Reader

Some time ago, I saw a television programme in which a number of charming, talented women, all highly successful in their different professions, revealed to an interviewer their deep disappointment at not having found loving long-term partnerships, and their sadness at missing out on the joys of motherhood.

While to many people the glorious gifts of love, marriage and children come easily, and as a matter of course, Fate is not always so beneficent. It seemed to me those women's stories needed to be told—from the loneliness and grief they experienced, to the anxiety and sense of shame their separateness caused them to suffer and conceal.

Those lovely women all deserved to find their happy endings, and now I can share one with you—the story of Ellie and her darkly gorgeous true love Sam.

Ellie has despaired of finding love—Sam has been wounded in the past. Though when they meet their instant chemistry triggers a relationship fraught with sensual passion, their journey to finding soul-deep, satisfying love and happiness is not an easy course.

Please, dear reader, step into their shoes and go with them on their quest. I sincerely hope you enjoy their emotional roller-coaster ride.

With warmest good wishes

Anna

MY TALL DARK GREEK BOSS

BY
ANNA CLEARY

⊙™ MILLS & BOON®
Pure reading pleasure

All the characters in this book have no existence outside the imagination of the author, and have no relation whatsoever to anyone bearing the same name or names. They are not even distantly inspired by any individual known or unknown to the author, and all the incidents are pure invention.

First published in Great Britain 2007
Harlequin Mills & Boon Limited,
Eton House, 18-24 Paradise Road, Richmond, Surrey TW9 1SR

© Anna Cleary 2007

ISBN: 978 0 263 85403 9

Set in Times Roman 10¾ on 12¾ pt
171-1207-57584

Printed and bound in Spain
by Litografia Rosés, S.A., Barcelona

As a child, **Anna Cleary** loved reading so much that during the midnight hours she was forced to read with a torch under the bedcovers, to lull the suspicions of her sleep-obsessed parents. From an early age she dreamed of writing her own books in a stone cottage by the sea, wearing a velvet smoking jacket and sipping sherry, like Somerset Maugham.

In real life she became a school teacher, and her greatest pleasure was teaching children to write beautiful stories.

A little while ago, she and one of her friends made a pact to each write the first chapter of a romance novel in their school holidays. From writing her very first line Anna was hooked, and she gave up teaching to become a full-time writer. She now lives in Brisbane, with her daughter and a deeply sensitive and intelligent cat. She prefers champagne to sherry, and loves music, books, four-legged people, trees, movies and restaurants.

This is Anna Cleary's first novel for Modern Extra!

For Jenny

PROLOGUE

SAMOS STILAKOS leaned his tall frame against the bar. Displeasure darkened his stern, handsome face. Why, he wondered, had he allowed himself to be persuaded into attending the Sirius Bank's Annual Masked Ball? He was a financier, not some show-business scout. And where the hell was this woman who was supposed to be his hostess?

Nothing they showed him now could save them, anyway, he thought, strafing the throng of colourful characters with his dark gaze. Least of all a staff function at a beach hotel.

As often at celebrations, the urge came over him to stride from the room, head for the airport and fly. Somewhere. *Any*where. Some deserted isle, or a snow-capped mountain in Peru, where the only music was the rush of wind. Anywhere free from this noise.

He glowered at the ballroom's lavish decorations. For a bank about to plunge straight to the bottom of Sydney Harbour, no expense had been spared. Under the glitter of the chandeliers, the Sirius staff were switched into party mode, and seethed with an excitement bordering on delirium.

Exactly what his ex-wife would have loved, Sam

brooded, watching a scarlet-cloaked Romeo cavorting with a laughing, shrieking woman on the dance floor. His sensuous mouth hardened.

A pity they weren't tuned into the reality facing their bank.

An adventurous Catwoman swayed out of the mêlée and reached up to put her hands on his shoulders. 'Dance, gorgeous?' Through the slits in her mask her eyes gleamed with allure.

Sexy, he had to admit, but did the bank's directors really think he'd succumb to such a ploy? 'I don't dance,' he said, politely removing her clinging hands. She murmured something about Greek gods *any time* before she undulated her way back into the party crowd, but Sam didn't catch it.

He wondered if that had been the purpose of the courtesy suite they'd pressed on him. Was this woman they'd told him to expect intended as a sweetener? It wouldn't be the first time he'd been offered such an enticement.

They should have done their homework, he grimaced. If he did decide to rescue the ailing bank, they'd learn.

In the Stilakos Organisation ethics were everything.

'Sorry. Sorry about that, Mr Stilakos.' Stephen Fletcher, Sirius's portly Senior HR Executive, was unconvincingly attired as a gangster. 'I don't know what can be keeping Ellie.' He flashed Sam a quick, nervous grin. 'Are you enjoying the party?'

Sam stared incredulously at the rotund executive. 'Is this how you usually do business at Sirius? You invite potential investors to your staff parties?'

Fletcher gazed up at him with an earnest intensity. 'No, no. Not at all. Only you. We wanted you to see for yourself… We wanted you to *understand* the Sirius Staff Policy. At Sirius we want our team to *work*.' He thumped the bar to make the word stick. 'That, we firmly believe, means giving our folk ample opportunity to *play*.'

Sam's mouth twisted with sudden humour. 'Seriously? You thought this—' he swept one lean, bronzed hand towards the exuberant throng of assorted harem girls and Ned Kellys '—this would convince me to bail out your bank?'

'Well, not me alone. It was someone else who suggested showing you the *human face* of the Sirius Bank.' Fletcher's fist connected emphatically with the bar. 'She thought that your seeing the *actual people* involved—' thump, thump '—in a *personal* sense… The wonderful men and women whose livelihoods are *on the line*—' For an alarming second his hyperactive fist came close to seizing Sam's lapel. 'If you could only key into the real issues of *sincere human beings*, and try to *forget* the bottom line…'

Sam listened in thunderstruck amazement. No wonder the Sirius Bank was in trouble. What bank tried to operate with this folksy creed?

He lifted his brows in amusement. 'And whose was the great brain who thought I might be overwhelmed by the personal charms of your workforce?'

Fletcher saw unexpected warmth lightening the forbidding expression of the bank's rich suitor, as if the sun had been there all the time and was about to break through. For the first time since he'd met Samos Stilakos, he knew a ray of hope.

'Ellie,' he replied eagerly. 'Ellie O'Dea. Your hostess. She's one of my staff. You'll like her, I'm sure. Charming.

Charming girl. And a real looker, too. You won't be disappointed, I asssure you. She's been briefed and she's all prepared for you. She must be here by now. Ellie's not usually late— Hang on!'

He stood on tiptoe to scan the milling crowd, trying to pick Ellie out from among the fancifully garbed women, then turned and collided with black ice in Sam Stilakos's eyes. He felt the very breath freeze in his lungs.

Stilakos looked down at him from his considerable height, the essence of polished courtesy, though his smile chilled Fletcher to the core. 'I appreciate your assistance.' The clipped precision of his deep, cool voice injected an icy sliver between Fletcher's ribs. 'Fletcher, wasn't it? I've seen all I need. Don't let me keep you from your celebration.'

Fletcher shook his head in consternation. 'But—but I hoped I could introduce you—' With the cold realisation of defeat he met Samos Stilakos's unforgiving gaze. He hovered for a moment, then, his shoulders slumped, edged away.

Sam watched him go, then turned to survey the ball, disillusion in his heart.

Once the challenge of the Sirius Bank would have appealed to him. Its sad market performance and falling profits made it as attractive a proposition for the Stilakos Organisation as he could remember. He could buy it for a song, give it a drastic structural shake-up, and, with an exhilarating measure of risk, take it straight to the top of the tree. If its indulgent staff culture didn't hold it back. And if—

Face it. If he weren't so *bored*.

Lately his zest for winning against the odds seemed to have blunted. What he needed, he mused, was one damned good reason to buy the bank beyond making money.

A voluptuous Cleopatra spotted him and started an unsteady progress towards him. Not tonight, sweetheart, Sam thought grimly. What he wanted, what he needed…

An indefinable longing surged through him, reminding him of the nights of his youth. Nights when there'd been magic in the air, and mystery in a woman's face. Where had it all gone? All at once the noise, heat and activity reached an unbearable pitch. He loosened his tie and looked about for the nearest exit.

In the hall beyond the ballroom heavy curtains beckoned. He shoved some unsecured balloons aside, and threaded his way through the throng. If he could just get away from the relentless carnival atmosphere…

Thank God the doors weren't locked. He stepped out into the soft dark, onto a long balcony, and was met with a wave of fresh, salty air. The door closed behind him, and instantly the hullabaloo was cut.

It took him a moment to adjust. Still early in the season, the night was cool, but the promise of summer carried on the breeze like a woman's perfume.

He strolled over to the rail. Across the street from the hotel was the beach walk, and beyond it the vast, black heaving space of the sea. A gentle susurration spoke caressingly to him of the surf, curling itself up on the dark beach below the sea wall.

Flexing the muscles in his powerful arms and shoulders, he breathed in deeply, as if to inhale some energising essence from the brilliant night sky. He watched the moon's flickering progress under a few wispy clouds, then started as a small sound alerted him to a presence.

Something. Or someone.

He stiffened, every muscle on the alert, and searched

the dim balcony. In the furthest corner he thought he could make out a figure. He strained his eyes against the dark. The moon chose that moment to peep through, and something took shape that resembled a human form.

'Hello?' he said, taking a few steps that way.

At the sound of his voice the figure stilled, as though frozen to the wall. Intrigued, he began to walk towards the mysterious presence. Who would be lurking outside in the dark at this hour, unless they were up to no good?

'Whoever you are,' he said firmly, 'you'd better come forward and introduce yourself.'

The form moved, and at once he recognised it as being female. 'Don't come any closer,' a feminine voice said sharply.

He stopped in his tracks. 'Why not?'

There was a moment of silence, then she said in a strangled voice, 'Because you're invading my personal space. Now back off.'

He grinned to himself. 'Oh, come on. You can't claim an entire public balcony as your personal space.' Curiosity aroused, he strained his eyes to make her out. There was something strangely unearthly about the woman's pale form, like a wraith seen through a mist.

At that moment the moon burst from behind a cloud, drenching the balcony in its silvery glow. The breath caught in his throat, halting him to the spot.

She was an ethereal vision, gowned in shimmering white. An angel. A moon nymph. Beneath some glittery ornament, her long hair fell almost to her waist, and her face was strangely shadowed. A sensation of unreality, almost of magic, swept through him, as if he'd stepped into some childhood fairy tale.

'There's no need to come any closer,' she flung at him, a repressive note in her voice. 'I'm not in the mood for a chat, so you might as well stay right where you are.'

Sam laughed, his blood quickening. 'I'm not much of a one for small talk, myself.'

He felt rather than saw the glare from her shadowed eyes, and as he moved closer realised that of course she was wearing a mask.

'Now let me see…' He smiled as he took in the full extent of her slender, moonlit form, deliciously outlined in clinging satin. She held her hands folded at her breast, while on the ground beside her feet a couple of large, silver-trimmed wings reposed limply against the wall. 'What are you? An angel?' he enquired, smiling, then, recognising her crown, 'Ah, of course. You must be the Fairy Queen. What's her name? Titania, isn't it?'

Trapped in her worst nightmare, Ellie O'Dea clung tightly to her frail bodice. As her big, masculine discoverer drew nearer, she racked her brains for a way to get rid of him without betraying her gown's fragile coverage of her vulnerable breasts.

'Well done,' she said. 'Anyway, it was great to meet you. My boyfriend will be back soon, so don't feel you have to wait.'

She held her breath. The mention of her boyfriend—just supposing she still had one and he hadn't dumped her in favour of Antarctica—might have worked, as for the moment the stranger remained where he was. He was tall, at least six-three, she guessed, *big*, and though in the dark his face was shadowy, its lean planes and angles, tipped by the moonlight, suggested flaring cheekbones and chiselled male beauty.

At twenty-nine, she knew enough of the score about gorgeous men. Too gorgeous, she thought, noting his brilliant dark eyes and the flash of his white teeth. Too spoilt. Lethal.

Sam drank her in from head to toe. She was nearly tall enough to reach his shoulder. He couldn't determine the exact colour of her bright waterfall of hair, but with its lustrous sheen every slight movement of her head was an invitation to touch.

His eyes had accustomed to the light now, and he could see her more clearly. It was as if the moon had picked up the shimmer in the dress and somehow transferred it to her white, pearlescent skin. The slinky, ankle-length satin seemed moulded to her, revealing with her movements the supple slenderness of her waist, sweetly rounded hips and long slim thighs. The dress's bodice was supported by a silver chain that hung from her neck. Though she kept her hands folded at her breasts, it was easy to guess at their ripe, tip-tilted lusciousness. He tried not to stare, but it was an effort to drag his eyes from her bare satin shoulders and the creamy swells just visible beneath her sheltering hands.

He was overwhelmed by such perfect female beauty; his blood stirred, and a huskiness deepened his voice. 'Isn't your boyfriend concerned about leaving you alone out here?'

She drew a sharp, quivering breath. 'But I'm not alone, am I? Though I would be if I could be. If you hadn't *insisted* on intruding on my privacy.'

'Oh. Oh, I am sorry,' he said at once, turning half away. He felt a twinge of guilt, almost as if he'd stumbled onto sacred ground. 'I'll go away.' As he turned his back he threw over his shoulder, 'Enjoy the night air.'

He took a few easy strides in the direction he'd come, but with every step away the vision lured him back with a siren's power.

'Look…Wait—just a moment, will you?'

At the sound of her sweet, low voice a pleasurable sensation he'd almost forgotten could exist shot through him. He paused, and half turned in her direction. With a casual hitch of his shoulder he said, 'Are you sure? I don't want to cause you trouble with your boyfriend.'

'Oh, don't worry about him,' she said hastily. 'He isn't… He won't cause any… Did you happen to see anyone in there dressed as Scarlett O'Hara?'

He sauntered back, as cool as if the thrill weren't gathering in his blood like a wave. 'I'm not sure I know what Scarlett O'Hara looks like.'

In an excited burst of realisation, he didn't believe the boyfriend was coming back. What man would leave this beauty out here to be accosted by strangers?

He longed to see her face, but the mask frustrated him. From what he could make out, her lips looked soft and kissable, curling up with an enticing sensitivity, as if they'd respond to the lightest tongue-flick. Her chin was delicate, with a piquancy he was sure would apply to the whole of her face.

'My moonlight fantasy,' he exclaimed with a low laugh. 'At last I've found you.'

Her eyes glittered at him through the mask, and his hand twitched with the desire to tear it away. He reached for it, but she backed away and, as though unable to free her hand from her bodice, used her elbow to gesture.

He frowned. 'Is there something wrong with your

dress?' He leaned forward, his eyes narrowed for a closer look, and she stepped sharply away from him.

With the purest amusement he realised that she was holding the bodice and chain together with her hand. 'Oh, no!' he said. 'Has there been an accident? I think I can see why you're in hiding.' Instinctive thoughts of seduction crept in to colour his voice, and he added softly, 'I do hope you're wearing something under that.'

There was a tense silence. It dawned on him at last that she was embarrassed.

She surveyed him from behind her mask with glittering eyes. 'Laugh by all means.' Her lips curved in a proud smile. 'I've no doubt this does seem very amusing to one of the *heartless* species.' Despite her brave front, some strong emotion caught at her voice, and he felt chastised.

'I'm sorry,' he said with velvet remorse. 'You're right. It's no laughing matter. But can't something be done to fix it? Some pins or something?'

She was silent for a moment, as though struggling with herself to trust his good intentions.

After a while she said stiffly, 'I tried that, but it's no good. The taffeta has started to fray now.' She eyed him through her mask for a second, then indicated one side of the bodice. 'This here is only hanging by a few threads. It was these stupid wings that did it. Whoever designed the costume—! They're far too heavy for the fabric. They were supposed to hook into the clasp at the neck, here, and here. Look…'

She half turned to give him a rear view. The dress was charmingly draped across her lower back, and as she twisted to indicate the mid-point where the wings had hooked and

ANNA CLEARY   17

further damaged the fabric her hair swished a little aside to
reveal an alluring glimpse of smooth white back.

His mouth dried. He imagined seeking out the ridge of
her spine, tracing the bumps with his fingers, grazing all the
little hollows with his lips, tasting her white satin flesh...

'We pinned this back seam as well as we could where
the hook was, but it's still unravelling, and the halter
chain has started to separate from the bodice.' She
straightened to face him, sighing, 'It's only a matter of
time before the whole thing falls apart.' After a moment
she added, 'One of my girlfriends is going home to get
some clothes for me.'

He supposed he deserved to have been called heartless.
The woman was in an embarrassing situation, yet all his
thoughts had been about caressing her. Kissing her.

The breeze picked up, teasing the hair on her neck. She
gave a little shiver, and at once his imagination flew him
to a parallel universe, one where he could take her with
him across to that moonlit beach, lay her down beside him
on the cool sand, and...

But she was cold. 'Here,' he said, and in a swift fluid
movement slipped off his jacket and stepped close enough
to wrap it around her shoulders.

'Oh!' She received it with a surprised jerk of her head,
and the sweet summery scent of raspberries rose to his
nostrils in an intoxicating cloud. 'Thanks,' she said in a
soft, appealing voice that wound its way into his blood-
stream like an aphrodisiac. 'Thank you very much. I
really didn't expect— You're very kind.'

To his regret she drew the lapels together across her
breasts, though she still held onto her bodice. The jacket
swam on her feminine form, and his loins stirred at the sight.

He had to rescue her from this, he thought with urgency. Take her somewhere safe. And private. 'You can't stay out here all night,' he said. 'Why don't I take you home?'

Ellie heard the warmth in his deep voice and her sexual antennae zinged as from a high-voltage charge. This charming devil, with his smiling assurance and desire in his dark eyes, had more than rescue on his mind. As if she'd let herself be picked up! Although, in his shirt-sleeves, with the power of his lean, well-made frame clearly defined, he was frankly gorgeous. And he seemed civilised, sophisticated...

When was the last time a high-powered man like him had come her way? He was a far cry from a geography teacher with the mountaineering bug.

She could see no wedding ring, though that didn't make him eligible. Hadn't she learned the hard way? The world was full of heartbreakingly attractive men who had no intention of settling down and raising families. Why else were women forced to go it alone? But—there was kindness in him. He *had* sacrificed his jacket.

His dark, sensual gaze drew hers and heat shivered through her. Unable to keep her consciousness of the pinging vibrations from her voice while she argued the pros and cons with herself, she said, 'Charmaine—I mean, Scarlett—should be back soon.'

He lifted his eyebrows. 'How long have you been waiting?'

'An hour. Maybe two.' She smiled and gave a shrug to cover her growing sense of dilemma. 'It's not my night.'

'It's not over yet.' Through the dark lashes his eyes lit with a sinful gleam, and her insides plunged into chaos. 'Come, fantasy girl. I'll take you home.'

She hesitated. 'I shouldn't really go home. I'm supposed to be in there helping to co-ordinate the programme.' And meeting Samos someone, the old Greek tycoon who was the bank's last chance. 'Are you—are you with the bank?'

'No.' His dark eyes ran over her, and she felt her flesh thrill like the breeze whispering in her hair. 'Maybe you can find some clothes here. Are any of your friends staying in the hotel overnight?'

'No. That's only for the big cheeses so they don't have to drive home afterwards.'

His brows snapped together, as though he didn't approve of that, then he gave a shrug and stood thinking.

'I'd—I'd better give you back this.' With reluctance she started to take off the jacket, but he held up his hand.

'No, no. Keep it.' His sensuous mouth edged up at the corners in a smile. 'I have a suggestion. To save you waiting for Charmaine, what if I ask the hotel to find you something to wear? You can change in my room.' He held out his hand, persuasion in his voice, smiling seduction in his eyes. 'What do you think? All right?'

This was it, she thought, her heart skipping. Just because she'd given up falling in love didn't mean she had to become a nun. It was a long time since she'd been held in a man's arms. She fingered the jacket's luxurious fabric, and inhaled its faint scent of expensive, sophisticated *man*.

He angled away slightly, as if he might walk off and leave her, while she struggled to make up her mind to do something daring for once.

He cast her back a deep, gleaming glance beneath his lashes. It was quietly, intimately sexual, a look between adults. Man to woman, it stirred her to her feminine soul.

What mature, twenty-nine-year-old career woman in charge of her life would hesitate?

'All right,' she breathed.

She allowed him to usher her through the doors, conscious of every touch, his wrist brushing hers, his hand light on her back. And for once she was lucky. There was a lift waiting, and none of the stragglers spilling from the ballroom even glanced her way.

In the light of the lift he looked to be in his late thirties. Blue highlights danced off his pitch-black hair, and there was a sardonic lilt to his black eyebrows that gave him a devilish look. Below his cheekbones, a shadow underlay his bronzed cheeks and jaw. He was a Greek god made flesh. She met the naked sensuality in his midnight eyes, and her blood surged.

'Are you staying here long?' she said, trying to keep her voice from betraying her.

He shook his head. 'I suppose you'd say I'm a guest of your bank. I hadn't intended to use the suite, but as it happens…I now have a reason.' A smile illuminated his face and shimmered in his dark eyes. 'I'm Sam.' He held out his hand.

When her ravished insides had settled back into place, the name filtered through.

Sam. An unusual name for a Greek Australian. Then realisation hit her. Not *that* Sam! As in Samos Stilakos. But of course it had to be. How many rich Greeks would be visiting this hotel on this night of nights?

She put her hand into his strong, warm grip, and as their palms met skin cells all along her forearm shivered with electric pleasure. 'Lovely—lovely to meet you.'

He didn't try to keep hold of her hand, as some men

would have, though her flesh yearned for it. He just waited for her to respond, his eyebrows raised. The lift stopped and the doors opened before she could muster a reply.

Her brain whirred rapidly. Samos Stilakos's awesome reputation had dominated gossip in the staff canteen for the past six weeks—his daunting standards, his uncompromising stance on ethics. According to the grapevine, he'd struck terror into the department heads. She felt an extreme reluctance to tell him her name. He might end up being the big boss of the entire bank.

In the corridor she gave a light, embarrassed laugh. 'I'd rather not tell you my name, if you don't mind.'

He frowned a little, his eyes glinting.

With a pounding heart she realised he probably thought she did this sort of thing all the time. Went to hotel rooms with perfect strangers. But then, how often did *he* do it? Quite often, judging by how smoothly this little operation had gone. How would it go down for her future in the bank, if she knew he seduced vulnerable employees?

For her job's sake she should leave now. Thrust the jacket back at him, ignore the risks, and risk walking out to the taxi rank. At least she'd have the mask.

She should. But she let him guide her down the hall to Room 525, and, with her adrenaline flowing, watched his smooth, olive-tanned fingers slide in the key.

The room was pleasantly furnished in the impersonal style of hotel rooms. The counterpane on the king-sized bed had been turned down, and lamps on either side cast a soft apricot glow.

The door closed behind her and she turned to face him. The room sprang alive with sexual possibilities.

He nodded to her, 'Make yourself comfortable.' He

strolled to the desk and picked up the phone, murmured a few words into it, then covered the receiver. 'How does a maid's uniform sound?' She nodded and he spoke again, appraising her, his black lashes half lowered over his dark, sensual gaze. 'About five-seven. Size ten. Thank you.'

He strolled back to her with an easy, hospitable smile. 'It will take a few minutes. Would you like a drink after your ordeal?' He made a lazy gesture towards the mini-bar.

'No. No, thanks.' She tried to sound casual, to match his relaxed demeanour, but her senses were in uproar.

He said abruptly, 'Would you feel better if I went away?'

He was giving her an option, she realised, relieved her instincts about his essential decency had been right. She raised her chin. 'No, don't. Don't go.' Despite her bravado her voice sounded croaky, as if it was about to dry up.

Samos Stilakos didn't look ill at ease, however. He pulled off his tie and tossed it to a chair, the shimmer back in his dark eyes. 'Won't you take off your mask?'

'I'd rather not,' she said with a careless smile, knowing how rude and ungrateful and insanely weird it sounded, after he'd so kindly rescued her. 'Not yet.'

He moved closer, his gaze warm and compelling, and said softly, 'But I think I'll feel uncomfortable kissing a woman without knowing her eyes and face.'

She closed her eyes. The blood was thundering in her ears. 'Who—who said anything about kissing?'

Almost lazily he reached out to curve his lean, smooth fingers under her chin, tilted up her face, and bent to brush her mouth with his.

At the first touch, excitement ignited in her blood. He drew away, leaving her breathless, fire dancing along her lips. He frowned down at her, a flame in the depths of his eyes, then drew her firmly against his hard body, and kissed her properly, while her breasts swelled and her lips parted.

With sensual artistry he took first her upper lip, then the lower lip between his, to tease and tantalise until her knees gave way. Then he captured both lips firmly, and slipped his tongue inside her mouth, inflaming the delicate tissues while her bones liquefied and she nearly swooned.

Wildfire rose in her blood.

It was nothing, nothing like she'd ever experienced. So tender, so wildly, thrillingly arousing. It was as if he knew how to kiss a woman as a woman dreamed of being kissed.

A raw sound came from her throat, and she thrust her soft curves into the lean angles of his muscular frame. Forgetting her fragile dress, she linked her arms around his neck and clutched at his hair, aware with excitement of his big, vibrant body's charged response to her. Eagerly she helped him push the jacket from her shoulders, and let it slide.

He deepened the sizzling intensity of the kiss. In some way liberated by the mask, she threw aside constraint, and, instead of her usual polite co-operation, matched him tongue for tongue, caress for caress, without inhibition.

She was hardly aware that the weak threads of her satin bodice had given way, removing one of the barriers between his iron-hard body and her sensitised skin. Grazed by the friction of his clothes and belt buckle, her bare nipples thrilled to the delicious contact.

She'd never experienced such instant desire. Hotly aroused, she felt one of his seductive hands close over her breast, while the other slid to her nape, trailed tinglingly over her scalp, then snaked through her hair to pluck at the string of her mask.

At once her survivor instinct clicked in. In a lightning reflex, her hands shot up to secure the mask, and she broke from him. 'No,' she panted hoarsely. 'Don't take it off.'

He stared back, fire in his eyes as they devoured her naked breasts. His voice was rough and gravelly. 'Why not? Why does it matter? Are you married?'

'No. I just don't want you to see my face.'

'Why not? I need to know who you are.' He gestured with his hands. 'Don't get me wrong. It's erotic making love to a mystery woman, in a kinky sort of way. I might even get a taste for it. But if you stay with me tonight…'

His voice thickened with the words, and she sensed how much he wanted it. Wanted *her*. Somehow, it strengthened her instinct to keep her face covered. She said in a low, firm voice, 'I won't stay unless I can leave the mask on.'

He stared at her. 'You're not serious.'

'I am serious. I am.'

Calculation glimmered in his eyes, as if he was recognising the real possibility of his moonlit fantasy slipping away from him, then his lashes lowered.

'Try to see it my way.' His deep voice was almost a purr. He held out his hands and advanced to back her gently against the wall, his long muscular thighs grazing hers, melting her with his devastating sexual power. 'I don't want to feel I'm taking advantage of you.' With one long, tanned finger he trailed fire down her throat to the valley between her breasts, fanning her sweet erotic craving, and she burned for him to go further.

'Love-making shouldn't be an impersonal thing,' he said persuasively. 'If I can't see into your eyes it feels— soulless. Can't you understand?'

He was so meltingly, mouth-wateringly sexy, so honourably, she wavered. But just as his mouth began to tease her ear, turning her veins to liquid fire, some cool little internal voice piped up to remind her that the last time she'd believed a man was honourable she'd given him two years of her life, and he'd left her without a word.

His lips blazed a scorching trail down her throat and she shuddered with pleasure. 'I do see, and I do want to stay,' she panted when she could speak, 'but only if you agree not to snatch the mask off. And not—not to ask me my name.'

'But how will I find you again if I don't know your name?'

Even in her state of arousal she knew the smooth words for a ploy. 'You won't want to.' Wry cynicism deepened her huskiness. 'And I won't want you to.'

He drew back, a frown in his eyes. 'But you want me. You can't deny it.'

'Yes, yes. I admit it.' She leaned back against the wall and sighed, and stretched her arms voluptuously over her head, unable to keep her hungry gaze from his shirt-opening with its dark, sultry promise of chest hair. 'I do want you,' she said with throaty conviction, imagining the salt taste of that bronzed, hair-roughened skin. 'But only tonight.'

He gave a sexy, disbelieving laugh. 'Isn't that my line?' Then his brows drew together and he stared at her in bemusement. She could see how used he was to women falling at his feet. He took a deep breath, reefed his hand through his black hair. 'Why do you say that? Why only tonight?'

An amused, sophisticated little smile played about his mouth, but she could tell he was piqued. She supposed with his assets it was natural. She could hardly explain that, since the end of her romantic dreams, her job security was of critical importance. She wasn't one of those women who could face down gossip about their sexual antics with the bosses. If he took over the bank and news of this got out, she'd have to leave, if he didn't sack her first.

She touched his hand. 'You're very attractive, but I don't want an affair. Affairs use a woman up. If I stay with you tonight it will only be this one time, and you'll have to agree not to take off my mask.'

He shook his head. 'If I see you again,' he said, his tone charming but insistent, 'I'll know you, with or without the mask. I'd know the shape of you and the way you hold your head. Your mouth…' His voice deepened. The flame smouldered in his dark eyes, and she was tempted, *how* she was tempted, to wrap herself around his hard body. 'And that red hair is—unforgettable.'

'It's strawberry,' she corrected huskily. But she could see his point. He might recognise her again. If she stayed with him, she had little choice but to appeal to his gentlemanly instincts not to blab about her all over the building. And she wanted to stay, she realised, with an upsurge of desire.

'All right.' She could almost see the flat nipples under his shirt, and wantonness dripped from her voice like honey. 'If I ever did meet you again, and you recognised me, you would have to promise that you'd never, ever refer to what happens between us this night. To anyone.'

He gave a sharp, disbelieving laugh. 'As if I would—' He took a couple of impatient strides away and flung out his arms. 'Why should I? I don't bargain, and I don't make promises to get a woman into my bed.' He paused, his shoulders tense, and said with a cool shrug, 'The only promise I can make to you, sweetheart, is the one of giving you pleasure. If that isn't enough, we'd better both forget it.' He smiled, but there was an edge to his voice, his dark eyes glinting, his face suddenly proud and unrelenting, like the uncompromising Samos Stilakos she'd heard so much about.

It made him even more wildly desirable, if possible, and when the rejection had sunk in her disappointment was potent, but she said with dignity, 'Then I'll leave.'

He looked incredulous, and was about to speak when there was a discreet knock.

He tucked in his shirt and went to open the door. After a few murmured words he came back with a package, and thrust it to her with a burning, sardonic look. 'Your dress.'

She accepted it, her hands trembling, and with a muttered 'thank you' took it into the bathroom.

The maid's uniform was a white zip-up dress. She dragged off the ruined costume and threw it in the bin. Goodbye fantasy woman, she grimaced as she zipped the uniform. It was tightish, and only covered her to mid-thigh. But at least it was decent.

She raised the mask for a glimpse of her face, and met a stranger in the mirror. Her mouth was swollen from kissing, her blue eyes heavy-lidded, languorous with unfulfilled passion. Like his beautiful, expressive eyes. If only…

Images of the pleasures she'd turned down rose to torment her. She'd never met anyone like him before, or experienced such chemistry. But it was too late now, she reflected regretfully. She'd insulted him, and now he could hardly wait to get rid of her. She braced herself, and, with the mask back in place, opened the door.

Samos Stilakos stood waiting, brooding tension in the set of his powerful shoulders, his thick black lashes downcast.

He looked ready to leave, his jacket slung over his shoulder. He'd rolled his sleeves back a little, and she could see the dusky hairs curling on his bronzed, sinewy forearms.

He looked up. His dark eyes riveted to her, intent and smoulderingly sexual.

Her blood started to boom in her ears with a heavy, sensual beat.

'Come here,' he said thickly.

The fierce fire in his eyes compelled her. She felt a burning, primeval urgency to run into his arms and press her lips to his throat, but some stronger part of her forced her to her resolve and clamped her feet to the floor. 'Only if you promise…'

She held her breath.

The deep voice, when it came, was harsh. 'I promise.'

She allowed herself to advance a step, desire torching through her like a fever. Dared she risk pushing him further? She breathed, 'And do you agree, even if we should meet again, never to refer to this night, or to anything that happens between us here?'

The silence simmered while his dark, molten eyes raked her from head to toe. Her yearning for him reached a torrid pitch. She imagined his hard, virile length thrusting and thrusting to fill her. The sublime, delicious pleasure…

His mouth quivered. 'I agree,' he said rawly, then threw away his jacket, and in one long stride covered the distance between them and pulled her into his arms.

CHAPTER ONE

FOUR months later, Ellie sat at her desk, settling into the precarious role as latest in a string of PAs to the most ruthless and exacting boss the Sirius Bank had ever known. It was twenty-six days since she'd landed the job, and how she'd done it she still wasn't sure. But there was one thing she was sure of.

Sam Stilakos had a very poor memory.

Or a seriously overcrowded sex-life. How else could he have forgotten the night that blazed in her memory like an inferno? Not that she wanted him to remember, she hastened to reflect. If he did she'd be out on her twenty-nine-year-old ear with her life's plan shot to pieces.

Even so, it was distinctly lowering for a woman to discover how completely forgettable she was.

For a while she'd wondered if he was just a very good actor, but she'd stopped thinking that now. Not once in the weeks of seeing him every day, working with him in the tense atmosphere of his office, meeting his deep, inscrutable gaze across the table at board meetings, melting to his dark chocolate voice on the intercom—and he buzzed her constantly for the most finicky reasons—had

he shown the merest flicker of recognition. Or flirtatious-
ness. Just scrupulous politeness.

No wonder his ex-wife had issues with him.

A crash from inside his office jolted Ellie from her
reverie. The wife's visit wasn't going well. At almost the
same moment she glanced around to see an elegantly
groomed older lady appear at the outer door. The woman
approached the desk, and, with the assured charm of her
years, introduced herself as Irene Stilakos.

Ellie concealed her intense fascination behind her
professional face. So this was Sam's mother. But she
wasn't Greek!

'He's had an unexpected visitor.' Ellie smiled up into
shrewd grey eyes, wondering if Irene had heard the crash.
'He shouldn't be long. Would you like a coffee while you
wait?' She indicated the plush armchairs in the small
lounge area by the window.

Irene Stilakos smiled a refusal, and selected a chair.
Behind her, Sydney glittered in the morning sun like a jewel,
but oblivious to the scene, she bypassed the pile of recent
glossies and picked up a copy of Sirius's annual report.

She looks friendly, Ellie thought, covertly searching for
a resemblance to Sam's stunning chiselled features and
imperious dark eyes. With her softly waved hair and lively,
pleasant face, you'd never believe she had a son so—

The door to Sam's inner office burst open. Ellie
jumped, and Sam's mother looked up as a shrill, impassioned voice rent the air. 'Anyone can make a mistake,
Sam! Haven't you ever heard the concept of forgiveness?'

There was a deep, curt response, then the pert rear
view of Natalie, television soap star and Sam's ex-wife,
appeared in the doorway, arms flailing. 'You know why

you're scared to come to my **wedding**, lover?' she screeched. 'Because you haven't been able to find another woman in four years. And do you know why that is, Sam? Do you know why? I'll tell you why. Because you can't replace *me*! And you never—ever—*will*.'

She slammed the door so hard Ellie's filing cabinet shuddered. Then midway in storming across the room she halted, muttering, to feverishly rifle her bag.

She wore impossibly high heels Ellie had no trouble in identifying as Jimmy Choos, and a minuscule leather dress with peep-holes that showed her fabulous all-over tan. A flick of her ragged blonde designer hair, with its fashionable black roots, revealed the obligatory tattoo on her shoulder.

She looked like trouble. *Sexy* trouble, exactly the sort men went mad for.

Unconsciously Ellie patted the smooth coil at her nape. No wonder she'd made no lasting impression. She'd considered going completely blonde herself when Sam had taken over as boss, but had gone the other way instead, choosing a deep, rich, camouflaging red. It seemed to have worked well. Too well, she sometimes thought.

She watched as Natalie pulled out a handful of tissues to dab at her professionally modelled nose. All at once the blonde's eye fell on Sam's mother, and she froze rigid.

Her fashionable pout grew puffier and more defensive. 'Well?'

Irene Stilakos started, and sat straighter in her chair. 'Oh,' she said hurriedly. 'Don't mind me, Natalie. I was just thinking you should be careful in those heels. You need to look after those bones in your lower spine. Think ahead, dear, to when you'll be bearing children.'

Natalie hissed in an outraged breath, then to Ellie's alarm she whipped around to her. 'And what are you staring at, Miss Mouse? Hoping you might have a chance with him? It's what you've been hanging out for, isn't it?'

Ellie felt her face flame scarlet. Her lips parted in stunned denial, but there was no silencing her accuser.

'Don't try to deny it.' Natalie's rather high-pitched voice vibrated with passion. 'I've heard you talk to him in that drooly-drooly voice. You're after him. You all are. Don't you think a woman knows?'

Ellie scrabbled for her professional poise and drew herself up, searingly conscious of Sam's *mother* sitting there. And Sam himself was very sharp of hearing. 'That may just be the way I talk,' she retorted as coolly as humanly possible, in her low, admittedly quite husky voice. 'I don't have the luxury of screaming or throwing things. And I have too much work to do to go after anyone.'

'Yeah, right.' Natalie's brittle laugh rang out in the quiet room. 'Just look at her, will you? It's written all over her face.' She shrugged and started for the exit. 'You're welcome to the cold-blooded brute, if you think you can measure up to him.' Her eyes filled up with tears. 'Try living with a perfectionist.' Out in the corridor she flung rawly over her shoulder, 'See what's it like to be dispensable.' With a despairing hair-flick she stalked off in the direction of the lifts.

Ellie gathered her shell-shocked self together to find Sam's mother piercing her with her penetrating grey gaze, intensified by the lenses of her glasses.

'It isn't true,' Ellie said quickly. 'I don't like him at all.' Then, recollecting who she was talking to, she rushed to add, 'I mean—he's very good-looking, and brilliant and

everything, but he's not at all my type. He's far too demanding, and arrogant, and bossy. Not that that's a bad
thing, of course, when he's the boss.' She made a weak
attempt at a laugh. 'Please don't be offended—'

Sam's mother gave her a worried smile, as if she
needed convincing.

'—but I actually prefer less high-powered men. You
know—friendlier.' Her recurring vision of herself
enfolded in Sam's strong arms, his stirringly sexy mouth,
his midnight satin eyes slumbrous with desire, swam into
her mind, but she forced herself to stay on course. 'I like
men who are more—accessible. Emotionally. Do you
know what I mean?'

This was, in fact, a bare-faced lie. She only ever fell
madly in love with inappropriate men who were totally
*in*accessible.

Sam's mother seemed to know it, because she frowned
at Ellie and gave her head a very slight shake. Ellie
thought she must have gone too far and had better back-
track, and lowered her voice confidentially. 'I don't mean
he isn't good to work for. He is, he's wonderful, and he
can be so-o-o charming to people who don't irritate him,
but in a personal, or—or *sexual* sense I could never find
him attractive at—'

She broke off. Sam's mother's gaze had shifted to a point
somewhere above and to the right of Ellie, and Ellie had a
horrible sinking feeling that someone was standing at Sam's
door. She glanced down and saw a pair of handmade leather
shoes, polished to a very high gloss, trouser legs of the finest
fabric, and knew immediately who.

Her dismayed gaze travelled the lean, powerful length
of Samos Stilakos, and connected with his intelligent

dark eyes, brimming with an expression she couldn't quite read. There was a sardonic quirk to his sensuous mouth, and his black eyebrows were drawn.

Her heart jarred to a halt.

'Come in,' he said, holding the door wide for Irene without taking his eyes from Ellie. Irene gave her a warm glance as she went past, and Sam said in deep, clipped tones, 'I'll talk to you later, Eleanor.'

He closed the door.

Ellie plunged into turmoil. How long had he been standing there? She covered her burning cheeks. There was no chance he hadn't heard some of it.

What if Irene told Sam of Natalie's accusation? Wasn't it only natural she would? She would. Of course she would. She'd be telling him even now.

Sam absently steered his mother through some scattered shards of antique vase and across the luxurious expanse of his office. While she settled herself on the deep red leather chesterfield, he wandered over to stare moodily at the view from his wall-sized window. Curious how a couple of smudgy little clouds could take the shine off Sydney Harbour. That bridge could look bloody grim.

'She seems like a lovely girl, Sam,' his mother commented, crossing her ankles.

Sam gave a shrug, but something like a skewer slid through his intestines. *Why* had she said she didn't like him? Could he have offended her in some way?

He scrolled back through their exchanges about work. Her mouth was often grave—intriguingly so, for a woman whose blue eyes could actually glitter at times with mischief—but she'd seemed happy enough, calm and competent. She'd coped with all the projects he'd thrust her into with cool efficiency, surprising him at times with her instinctive grasp of the big picture.

She was a little too inclined to try injecting her feminine viewpoint into his careful strategies for the bank's recovery, but he could easily keep that under control. In all other ways he still found her—pleasing.

He'd honoured his agreement with her, and would continue to do so, although it had been extracted under duress. Her total rejection of an affair was impressive. Although…what more tantalising challenge had ever been given a man?

Not that he condoned personal relationships in the workplace. Purists might argue that he shouldn't have placed her so close to him. It had been a business decision, no more, no less, to keep his eye on her. In fact, once or twice he had actually fantasised having a section of the wall removed so he could see her face.

That face. For an instant his eyes drifted shut. The curious breathless feeling he experienced whenever she entered the room came over him. It was amazing how, once a woman's face had been forbidden to a man, that face could become so infinitely more alluring and desirable than any other.

But… He knew the rules and there was no risk. That invisible line she'd drawn around herself was as definite as a castle moat, and in twenty-six days he'd never tried to cross it. Not once.

So if she was unhappy… He felt a skidding sensation inside his chest. Could it be something to do with *that night*?

His mother cut in on his thoughts. She was studying him with a thoughtful gaze, her head a little on one side. 'I don't think you should take the things she said personally, dear. She assured me she only meant it in the sexual sense.'

He gave a careless laugh. 'Is that what she said?' Nevertheless the skewer made a savage twist. Women *always* found him attractive in the sexual sense. If Eleanor O'Dea was the woman he thought she was, whom his instincts told him she must be, she had every reason to find him sexually attractive.

Unless…unless he was mistaken.

He thought back to the first time he'd laid eyes on her after he'd taken on the bank. Wasn't it the Christmas party—?

He frowned, recalling how once again he'd been taken aback by the scale of it. Mature men and women carousing, hugging each other in boozy camaraderie at the company's expense, some far-gone woman from Sales actually performing a dreamy, inebriated dance on a table-top. When he'd enquired as to who had been responsible for organising this latest orgiastic extravaganza, someone had pointed out Ellie.

The name.

His lungs had momentarily seized, for there she'd been, a tallish slender woman standing quietly in the middle of the scene of riotous debauchery, in the thick of it, but in some strange way alone, as if she occupied her own small pool of serenity.

It was *her*, he was certain. Straight away he'd noticed her soft, curly lips. And her skin. How incredibly pure and satin-white he'd remembered it being, in contrast with her bright hair, and looked to be still under the revolving strobe light. But it was seeing her eyes for the first time that had affected him most. Luminous, sapphire eyes,

with long curled lashes, sparkling at the antics of her colleagues like some laughing female devil's.

She'd been wearing very high heels and some brown
thing—or was it beige?—with what looked like a strange
glitch in its neckline. As he recalled, it had been quite
shapeless. In fact most of the things she wore failed to
make the most of her shape. The moonlit shape that
haunted him.

His frown deepened. He hadn't been able to take his eyes
off her, but when she'd glanced across at him, unbelievably
those lovely eyes had looked straight through him.

It had shaken him. Could he have been mistaken?

His mother hastened to soothe him. 'It's not that she
doesn't like you for yourself, dear, I'm sure. I think she's
exactly what you need out there.' She gazed earnestly at
him and added, her eyes as innocent as the dawn, 'Natalie
didn't like her one bit.'

Natalie. A grenade lodged in his vitals, but he didn't
move a muscle. 'Didn't she?' he said without expression.
'When did Natalie ever like another woman?'

'That's true,' Irene conceded, sending him a quick,
searching glance. 'Natalie can be very threatened by the
sort of woman she can't compete with.' She clasped her
hands. 'That was what I wanted to talk to you about.'

Sam saw the anxiety in his mother's face, and shelved
the mystery of his enigmatic PA. A woman who could so
easily dismiss the most torrid sex he'd ever experienced was
either an actress or a fool. And why a woman so lusciously
endowed with feminine charms felt no need to display
them to advantage was frustrating, but hardly important. As
for her claiming not to *like* him— From what he could
gather, Ellie O'Dea was one of the more popular staff

members. She seemed to like everyone else, so why not him? As he recalled, she'd certainly liked him on that night.

'Sam?'

He snapped into focus. 'All right.' He dropped into the chair facing her. 'Go on, then.' Resignedly, he raised a hand to motion her on. 'Let's hear it—the wedding.'

Irene sat on the sofa's edge, the better to make her pitch. Her son's face was patient, but wary, his dark eyes watchful beneath their black lashes. She would have to tread carefully. After Natalie and the divorce she'd seen a tougher layer of cynicism added to his sophistication. His resemblance to his proud father ran deeper than his Greek colouring and hard male beauty. His handsome, urbane surface concealed a well of feelings that wouldn't easily be touched a second time.

'I'll be honest with you, Sam,' she began. 'I'm a little nervous about going to the wedding on my own. My being there is bound to upset Natalie, and she's such a volatile girl, who knows what might happen?' Her hand stole to her heart.

Sam noted the unconscious gesture with a frown.

'If your father were still alive—'

He leaned forward and took her lined hands in his strong, smooth ones. 'If Papa were alive he wouldn't let you go.' He made the effort to gentle his voice. 'You don't have to, you know. You could decline.'

'And then this horrible feud would go on! No, dear, whatever your father would have thought, I can't be cut off from my family for the rest of my life. For all his faults I miss my brother, and, although you'll never admit it to yourself, you must miss Michael. He's not only your cousin, he's still the closest friend you ever had.'

A blistering retort rose to Sam's lips but he suppressed it. Her frail heart wasn't up to the savage passions generated by the betrayal of his honour. It was clear enough what she was about to ask for. His attendance at his cousin's wedding.

To his ex-wife.

Smooth it all over, as though it had never happened. His fractured life patched together under a coat of gloss.

It had been a while, he mused, since he'd wanted to cut out both their hearts. Now he only wanted to wipe them from the universe, but he'd never mention it to Irene. She was a woman—essentially not even Greek. His father would have understood, if the strain of the dishonour hadn't killed him.

'I won't go to their wedding.' The intensity of the quiet words resonated in the silence for seconds.

His mother nodded. 'No one could blame you, Sam, but if you don't go, this myth Natalie's spreading around—that you can't get over her—will seem to be confirmed. Even my brother seems convinced you can't look at another woman.' She rolled her eyes. 'He wrote me such a sympathetic note, asking about your state of mind. "If Sam doesn't want to come we'll understand," he said. "Has poor Sam made any progress?" I have to admit, dear, I found it quite galling.'

Sam broke into a sardonic laugh. Though it was true he hadn't looked for a replacement. There'd been no woman in his life since the divorce. Perhaps lately his apartment had begun to seem quiet, tomb-like even, but one Natalie was enough for a lifetime. In the beginning he'd thought their differences would soon be ironed out, but they had only seemed to widen with time. There'd

been no meeting of minds, no shared humour. The charmingly volatile young woman he'd married was too often
a spoilt, destructive child. Too much of a child herself to
be prepared for the responsibilities of parenthood.

His gut clenched at the memory of the unforgivable
thing she'd done in the name of her career. Eventually
she'd dragged his cousin into an affair, scandalised his
family, and ended by splitting it in halves.

It occurred to him then, as he listened to his mother discussing the arrangements for Natalie's next wedding, that
if he ever sought another woman she would be different.
More subtle and elusive. The sort of woman who could
inspire a man's imagination.

As it often had since the night of the masked ball, a
vision surfaced in his mind. And the more he saw of Ellie
O'Dea, the more he listened to her low, husky voice on
the intercom—sometimes he called her just to make her
talk—the more he was convinced that his first overwhelming instinct about her had been correct.

She was the fantasy woman. At least, he thought so.
Since acquiring the bank, he'd examined several possible
candidates, but it was amazing how many tallish, slim,
red-haired women there were working in the building.
Though none of the others had had her curious power of
dislocating his lungs, he wanted to be absolutely sure.
What he really needed was to see more of that fascinating arrangement of curves.

If only he could see her in different clothes, outside the
office context. Perhaps he could arrange a conference, or
a business dinner where she'd be obliged to wear something more revealing. Clinging, even. Satin.

And he was damned if he wouldn't break down that

barrier of reserve. The very idea of her not finding him attractive was laughable. He could enjoy watching her eat those words. In fact, it wasn't too much of a stretch to say that she'd flung him the challenge all over again.

At the possibilities this conjured his red blood cells stirred to the music and sprang to the salute. Dammit, if he couldn't find a way to rediscover the awe-inspiring flexibility of that slim, willowy body his name wasn't Sam Stilakos!

But…

He drummed his fingers morosely on the chair arms. The promise. It always came back to that bloody promise. Whilever he was bound by that ridiculous verbal contract he could see no way forward. With her gloriously passionate nature so cunningly hidden beneath her demure office persona, she was as maddeningly distant from him as some mediaeval princess in an ivory tower. Unless she could somehow be encouraged to break the embargo herself…

His mother's voice, still on about weddings and grandchildren, finally filtered through. 'I don't know why you can't find a nice girl, Sam. It's a pity you're so choosy.'

He stirred himself to reach over to his desk for his diary. 'It is,' he agreed, flipping it open to the day's schedule.

'If you could only find some lovely girl to take, it would shut them all up. I'd love to wipe the smug grins off their faces.' She heaved a sigh. 'If only I had a daughter to go with. Some nice, sensible girl I could rely on. Don't you have anyone here you could ask?' Her eyes flitted over his face, and beyond him to the view. She clutched at her heart and said, a brave little quaver in her voice, 'I suppose I'll just have to go it alone, and hope I don't drop dead in a strange place.' Dejectedly, she dragged herself to her feet.

Sam got up with her and gave her a bracing hug. 'Don't worry. I'm sure they have medical facilities in Queensland.'

Despite her talent as an actress, he knew her anxiety was well-founded. Natalie could be a hellcat, and the wedding would be stressful, not a good situation for Irene's health. Wild horses wouldn't get him there, but if she had to go it was up to him to find a means to protect her. Perhaps, he mused, he could send someone to support her in his absence.

It would take some calm, sensible person. Someone with exceptional interpersonal skills. Preferably someone who could stand parties.

An inspiration seized him then that was so fantastically brilliant, such sheer, diabolical genius, he was nearly swept away. Someone—*someone*—who'd need the appropriate clothes.

Suddenly energised, he planted a kiss on his mother's soft cheek. 'Leave it with me,' he said, the old thrill rising in his veins like an elixir. 'I'll find someone to go with you.'

Ellie sat slumped in her chair. A month in the job and she was finished. She wouldn't even have lasted as long as Sasha, Sam's first PA when he'd taken over as CEO.

Her thoughts flew back to the staff Christmas party, delegated, as usual, to her. The festivities had been in full swing before Sam had finished meeting with Gary, the finance manager, and descended from his alpine heights on the fifty-fifth floor for a brief chilly drink with the staff.

She'd done her best for Gary, writing out in detail exactly what he had to say to Sam in defence of the functions budget. A pity she'd had to leave it to Gary to deliver himself.

She hadn't spotted Sam at the party straight away. She'd been far too busy negotiating with Gary to come in off the ledge, but when she *had* seen Sam she'd been rocked by the sheer physical impact of once more being in the same room as him.

In the living, breathing flesh, in a suit cut by a master's hand to celebrate his wide shoulders, narrow hips and long powerful limbs, he was even more stunning than she'd remembered, his brilliant dark eyes more stirring. But the sight of him surrounded by all the executives eager to defer to him had made her realise how inaccessible he was to the likes of her.

That was when she'd noticed Sasha, enticing him to dance. She'd been flirting with him, swishing her long burgundy hair around in an obvious attempt to captivate him.

He'd declined, but by the time Ellie had recovered from her frozen shock she'd done the only possible thing, and pretended not to know him.

Rumour had it that poor, besotted Sasha had later draped herself around Sam's neck in the corridor and attempted to seduce him. Whether or not it was true was unclear, but what *was* clear was that when the office had reopened after the Christmas break Sasha had gone. Transferred to one of the Brisbane branches, someone had said. They'd all shuddered.

After Sasha there'd been an astonishingly rapid series of PAs who hadn't lasted the first week of their probation. Occasional glimpses of them had been caught on the lower floors as Samos Stilakos strode through the departments on snap inspections. They had followed along two-steps behind, gazing at him in adoration like Sasha, or blatant lust like auburn-haired Vanessa, but as quickly as they had seemed to snaffle the job, they had disappeared.

Ellie wouldn't even have dreamed of drawing attention to herself by applying, if it hadn't been for a fateful encounter with the man himself.

It had been after the staff farewell to Prue in HR. Poor Prue, still a beauty at forty-seven, had sacrificed the possibility of motherhood in search of a long-term relationship, and had ended up missing out on both.

Ellie had gone to great lengths to make the party one of her best. Afterwards, she'd been directing the caterers' tidy-up in the dishevelled function room, when a sudden fall in the noise level had alerted her to the presence of The Boss.

Her heart had gone into a series of crazed spins as he'd paused at the entrance, all six-three of commanding masculinity, his hair so black it was nearly blue, dark, lean and sternly handsome in a well-cut navy suit, with a crisp blue shirt and purple silk tie.

Her midnight lover.

He'd cast an appraising eye over the suddenly frozen activity in the room, then strolled the entire length of it to her.

Her heart had nearly stopped. Had he recognised her?

Once more he'd captured her in his dark, mesmeric gaze. 'Ellie O'Dea, isn't it?'

Somehow, hearing her name wrapped for the first time in that deep chocolaty timbre transported her straight back to that sizzling hotel room. Or maybe it had been the faint, tantalising spiciness of his aftershave. Or the controlled self-possession of his sensual, severely sculpted mouth.

Whatever, the flame he'd ignited in her blood that night flared back to intoxicated life.

'Yes,' she admitted breathlessly, once she'd recalled it. 'It is. Eleanor.' Automatically she held out her hand. The instant he took it in his firm, warm grasp, ninety thousand volts of electricity thrilled in recognition along her arm.

Did he want to thank her for the party? Perhaps, as she'd so often fantasised, with just the hint of a twinkle in his eye?

But his deep dark eyes were merely as cool and searching as any boss's meeting a prospective employee for the first time. 'Are you ambitious, Eleanor?'

Eleanor. Now why on earth had she told him to call her that? No one had called her Eleanor since she was five. 'I am, yes,' she tried to respond with the poise appropriate to a twenty-nine-year-old career woman with supremely marketable skills. Although, to be honest, she was confused. She knew he'd promised not to refer to that night, but he could have at least smiled.

'A vacancy has arisen in Executive Management for a PA,' he said with impersonal calm. 'It will be gazetted in tomorrow's Staff Bulletin before it goes out on the net. You might consider applying for it.'

She stared at him. A *job*? she might have said if she weren't in shock, but by the time she recovered he'd already walked away, detachment in every brisk, autocratic stride. The reality slowly sank through.

He hadn't recognised her.

At home that evening she drew the tattered mask from the satin box where she kept it, along with the postcards Mark had sent from remote locations around the globe, and other romantic memorabilia. She tried it on, and studied herself in the mirror from every angle.

To be fair, it covered quite a lot of her face, and gave

her nose an entirely different shape. In her suit and with her hair severely pulled back, she supposed she bore little resemblance to the woman at the ball. But shouldn't there still be something—some indefinable thing that was unique to her?

She couldn't wait to get her hands on the bulletin, and was at work even earlier than usual next morning to comb her pigeon-hole. As she'd hoped, the PA advertised for was his. His latest—experienced Schanelle with her sleek coppery bob, and, it had been wildly rumoured, references from Donald Trump—hadn't survived the week.

Someone in HR must have recommended her. Looking on the bright side, it was exciting, even flattering, to be included in the selection list out of a thousand employees. Professional recognition was something. She'd certainly done enough study over the years to give her the academic qualifications. And, despite the risk of him eventually realising who she was and despatching her to the back of beyond, the salary was strongly tempting. It would bring the goal she'd set for herself into view as a distinct possibility.

And she knew better than to follow the example of her predecessors, who hadn't been able to resist advertising their wares to him.

But underneath she was disappointed. Maybe it was irrational, but she wanted him to have guessed who she was. She'd had a sneaking little hope that he had, in fact, recognised her, but was honouring the promise she'd extracted from him by pretending not to.

The job offer wrote off that hope, though. Samos Stilakos would never allow her to work near him if he knew who she was. Unless…unless she'd meant more to him on that tumultuous night than just another one-night stand. Unless the job was a means of getting to know her!

What a laugh. There she was again, backsliding into fruitless romanticism.

'It's like being chosen by Henry the Eighth,' Beth, her friend, said, wrinkling her brow. 'Are you sure you want to risk it? What if he does eventually recognise you? God knows where you might be transferred. And what are your chances of not falling in love with him? At the Staff Appreciation Breakfast I even saw Schanelle ogling him with her mouth open.'

Ellie wondered how she could have missed that. She'd probably been occupied with settling the blood-feud that had arisen between the hired chef and the wait staff.

'If I keep my professional distance I should be safe,' she argued. 'And there's no chance I could fall in love with a man so—*spoiled* by women he can't tell one from another.' Indignation nearly got the better of her. 'Anyway. I told you. I've given up falling in love.' She noted Beth's unconvinced frown. No doubt mentally leafing back through the notorious O'Dea files.

All right, so once or twice she'd had her heart broken and her dreams shattered. It had cost her a few sleepless nights to be thrown over in favour of an ice-field, she could now freely admit. But that was the old Ellie O'Dea. She was stronger now, and in charge of her own life. Her heart was still there, large as life, but she'd locked it in an armour-plated box and it would never betray her again. If it showed any signs of weakening to the charms of some smiling predator, she had only to think of Mark.

'I have to think what the salary would mean,' she told

Beth firmly. 'Samos Stilakos doesn't recognise me, it's a great job, and I need the money. End of story.'

Beth eyed Ellie's suit with the knowledgeable air securely married women used for their less fortunate friends. 'You could get some new clothes. Brand-new. Like from real shops. In fact, I think you'd have to, in that position.'

'Possibly,' Ellie allowed stiffly. 'But I'm thinking of more important things. I'm not getting any younger. With the salary hike I could reach my target a year earlier.'

'Oh,' Beth muttered. 'Right. Your target.' She straightened the flowers in the vase she kept on her desk, replenished at least twice daily by her adoring husband. 'Look, Ellie, you don't have to give up yet. You're not even thirty, for goodness' sake.'

'When should I give up? Thirty-two? Thirty-three? Or wait till thirty-six when my poor brave little ovary buckles under the strain?'

Beth knew her ovary saga, and what the doctors had warned. 'Don't waste too much time to have your children,' they'd told Ellie back in her late teens after the painful cyst had been removed. 'There's no predicting how long your egg production will continue.'

It wasn't just the damaging scar tissue that had been left behind. It was the distinct possibility that it could happen again, and ruin the other ovary's chances as well.

She hadn't thought twice about children until Isabella, her sister, had given birth to her first little girl. Ellie would never forget the day. It had been just one week after Mark had left her.

She could still see Isabella gazing radiantly at the newborn in her arms, while her awed sisters crowded around the hospital bed, exclaiming over the baby's tiny pink perfections. 'Every woman should have a daughter,' Isabella had crooned on high from her cloud.

Ellie had been stabbed then with such a sickening bolt of fear, she could still feel the pain of it. What if she'd left it too late already? What if she *never had a child*?

She had driven from the hospital with a growing certainty that she shouldn't waste any more time. Waiting and hoping for the next man to come along was a fool's game. Recent events had proven something she had long suspected. Though men might desire her, she was not a woman who could inspire a man to love her.

If she wanted a child, she'd have to go it alone. And she should do it while she still could, even if she had to break rules.

She knew Beth didn't approve. Thousands wouldn't. She could hardly bear to think of it herself when she tried to imagine herself actually going to an IVF clinic, and admitting to some professional that she was forced to resort to a clinical procedure.

It was all very well for happily married people who were secure in their egg supply. Beth thought she should rush down to David Jones and splurge her savings on a chic little suit. But Ellie had made sacrifices, and now her money had begun to mount up, especially since she'd let go the Kirribilli flat she'd shared with Mark, and moved further out of the city. Skipping lunch and forgoing drinks with friends after work had helped. She'd even given up the major vice that had driven Mark crazy of constantly buying new shoes with very high heels.

A quick costing from some infant catalogues had shown her just how expensive raising a child was likely to be, even without the childcare. Even if she was very frugal—and with Mark she'd learned to be *extremely* frugal—a safer car, as well as all the baby paraphernalia, would stretch her resources to the limit. The childcare would be the most difficult thing. It would all be much easier if she could bring the baby to work. Somehow, she would have to find a way to wangle that.

So, she reasoned, *plan*-wise, the advantages attached to becoming PA to Samos Stilakos far outweighed the risks.

She made practical preparations for the interview, determined to keep her reactions under control. If he gave her cool and impersonal, she'd give him super-efficient and remote. A man who couldn't remember her voice, or have any sense of her unique spiritual essence even after he'd slept with her, didn't deserve a drop of the Ellie O'Dea brand of personal warmth.

She rejected the idea of an expensive new suit, and chose a navy blue pinstripe her sister could no longer fit into. Tried and true, it looked dignified, even if the jacket was a little bulky on her and the skirt long. At least her last remaining pair of three-inch heels gave it some semblance of style. She rejected the sexy-camisole look for a crisp white shirt, loosely braided her hair into her nape, and was more than usually sparing with her perfume. If Samos Stilakos disliked secretaries who made their attraction to him obvious, she would give him nothing to complain of.

The interview got off to a disconcerting start. No other candidates waited with her in the outer office. After a lengthy wait, Caroline from HR—Caroline had waited too long and now had golden retrievers instead—emerged and gave her the nod.

With a pounding heart Ellie entered.

As tall, autocratic and darkly handsome as ever, Samos Stilakos was standing at his window, hands in his pockets, staring out. At the quiet sound of the door closing he turned, and her feet slowed to a halt. His dark eyes locked with hers across time and space, and she felt a dizzying whoosh, as though all the air were being sucked from the room.

The world held its breath, then Samos Stilakos moved, gesturing politely towards a chair with one lean, elegant hand, and she realised it was just that her lungs had forgotten to breathe.

The chair he'd indicated looked out on his Chief Executive view of the harbour. He chose the chair opposite, so the light fell on her face, while his was in shadow. He murmured a few crisp words of greeting, then for a long, drawn-out minute scrutinised her, his dark eyes cool and impenetrable.

She waited, her nervous pulse ticking along until the sound of it swelled to fill the room.

After an eternity he said very softly, 'You have a piquant chin, Eleanor.'

The blood rushed to her cheeks. 'Really?' she said, struggling not to be thrown by a weird personal comment that had no place in a job interview. 'I hadn't noticed.'

What had he meant by it? Was it a criticism, or a compliment? Could a chin even *be* piquant?

He flicked her an enigmatic glance, then opened her CV and got down to the task of rigorously grilling her. She managed to answer his questions coolly and pleasantly, and hardly noticed his lean hands leafing through her personnel file.

Only once did she feel herself begin to slip into the mad craving she could have for him if she let herself go.

It was during his line of questioning about her role on the Social Committee.

'I need my PA to be flexible, and not be afraid to show initiative,' he said in his deep, quiet voice. 'And you must realise, should you be successful in your application, that you won't have time to continue organising the staff parties.' He added drily, 'Of course, in the future there won't be so many to distract you.'

She gave a stiff nod. The stringent cuts to entertainment and the little luxuries of working life were sore points with the staff.

At that moment Samos Stilakos made a slight shift in position. She saw his trouser-leg ride up to expose a black sock. Beyond that black sock, her wanton imagination raced to envisage the hairy, muscular leg she knew resided inside the expensive fabric, and went on to roll out the whole, mouth-watering picture of bronzed, virile masculinity she remembered with such vivid power.

Without warning heat curled through her. Involuntarily her armpits and the palms of her hands moistened, and she felt her ears and other, more sensitive points grow hot.

'Are you finding it warm in here, Eleanor?' The deep polite voice cut through the steam of her flashback. 'Would you like some water?'

She met his cool enquiring glance and her flush deepened. 'No. No, thanks,' she said jerkily.

'Please,' he said, leaning forward, a dark gleam lighting his eyes, 'feel free to take off your jacket.'

She resisted that invitation, and somehow floundered the rest of the way through the interview, managing to keep all her clothes on, and to avoid any dangerous references to the masked ball.

She wasn't quite sure why, but a day later she had the job.

It was a tightrope, but not in the way Beth had predicted. Though Sam was always courteous and professional, a tension existed between them. When he was discussing projects with her, his deep, dark gaze intent on her face, sometimes she wondered if they were really talking about something else. Sometimes she felt his eyes dwelling on her face when he thought she wasn't aware.

At night she couldn't stop thinking about him, analysing everything that had happened between them during the day, even though she knew it was a dangerous weakness, and a path she mustn't travel.

And sometimes, right on the edge of sleep, at that moment when she had least control, she'd allow her mind to drift into wildly romantic fantasies, like the swooningly delicious one in which he'd acquired the bank solely because he'd fallen in love with her on the Night of Nights.

At work he smiled rarely, but when he did her insides were wrung. His deep, seductive voice swayed her concentration, and she had to fight to conceal her awareness of him behind a bland smile.

Though obviously she hadn't succeeded, she now realised with a sinking heart. And he would be sure to have heard by now what Natalie had accused her of. Alice Springs beckoned, possibly even New Zealand.

She bent to search her bottom desk-drawer for the photo of Mark camping in the Pyrenees. Even after fourteen months she hadn't been ruthless enough to throw it away. At least he'd come in handy for something, even if it was only camouflage.

She sat it upright on her desk just as Sam's office door opened and his mother came out. She bid Ellie a friendly farewell, although Ellie thought she could read sympathy in the older woman's eyes.

The advice she always gave to juniors in trouble with their bosses was to never apologise, only explain. And to justify, justify, justify. But how would she ever explain this without giving everything away?

With a growing sense of dread, she made an attempt to get on with doing some strategic tweaking of Sam's latest presentation for the board. There was nothing wrong with his basic ideas, just that they were heavily weighted towards the bank's profits. Usually time just flew when she was editing one of her boss's projects. Now it was the longest ten minutes in history before the intercom buzzed.

'Come in, will you, Eleanor?' the deep, cool voice said.

With trembling hands Ellie whipped out her compact and made a quick inspection. Paler even than usual, and not at all mouse-like, but outwardly under control, apart from her hands and the slight dilation of her pupils. Her neck suddenly felt very sensitive, but if Anne Boleyn could face it, so could she.

A little unsteadily she rose, corrected the slight left-wards list of her Country Chic suit jacket—bought brand-new from a last season's seconds shop in Chinatown—and, head high, entered the office.

CHAPTER TWO

SAM at work was nothing like the Sam in a hotel bedroom.

Usually when Ellie came in he would be at his desk, writing, or frowning at spreadsheets. He would look up and watch her approach with that brooding, inscrutable gaze, then return to his work, silently motioning her to be seated.

This time she saw with foreboding that he was upright, his lean hips resting negligently against the massive rosewood desk, arms folded, waiting. He looked taller, his powerful shoulders wider. From across the room she saw his eyelids half lowered over watchful eyes as unreadable as the night.

She waded across the rich crimson carpet to him, conscious that his deep gaze was measuring every centimetre of her progress. She came to a halt a few metres short, her heart thumping against her ribs.

The silence thundered with her disgrace, though even in her suspense she couldn't help noticing the outline of his long powerful thighs, highlighted as his posture tugged on the fabric of his trousers.

'Ah, Eleanor,' he said with sinister, velvet charm. 'Please sit down.' He swept one bronzed, lean hand to indicate her usual chair.

'Thank you,' she said, shaky but resolute, 'but I'd prefer to stand.'

His black eyebrows twitched up. His eyes lit with a disquieting gleam. He shrugged. 'As you wish.' He straightened, strolled a few paces to the right, swung round to shoot a look at her, then strolled a few paces back.

Searching for the words, she supposed. He should have been good at it by now, with all his experience.

His foot crunched on something, and he kicked it aside and came to a halt. Ellie shifted nervously as his gaze seared down her vulnerable throat, to the fragment of lace revealed by her disobedient jacket, down to her brave but slightly tatty heels.

Sam felt an overwhelming desire to reach out and unbutton that jacket, but he repressed it. He wished he had X-ray vision to see the curves under the demure clothes, but at least the skin of her throat was the satin-white he remembered. He noted the small, betraying pulse there with a quick surge of satisfaction. It wasn't just him. Miss Ellie O'Dea wasn't quite as cucumber-cool as she pretended.

He lanced her with a glance that held just the right degree of professional sternness. 'I may have mentioned during your interview, Eleanor, the need in your job for absolute discretion.'

His deep voice sliced through the silence as easily as a sword through a tender neck.

Ellie's lashes fluttered down. This was it. The chop.

'Of course. You did mention it.' She braced herself, and plunged bravely in with, 'Is there something you want to say to me, Mr Stilakos? Because if there is something I need to explain, I'm sure I can satisfy you.'

He gazed meditatively at her for long seconds, his eyes

narrowed, then said, 'I have no doubt of that, Eleanor. And, yes, there is something I want to say to you.' He strolled over to sit on the edge of his desk, and captured her eyes with his compelling glance. 'Until now things between us have been a little formal. I think you'll agree that the time has come for us to remove our masks.'

'Our—' The breath choked in Ellie's throat. 'What do you mean?'

The perceptive dark eyes scrutinising her face glinted. 'I think you know exactly what I mean.' Her blood had just started a panicked rush to her head when he added in measured tones, 'A personal assistant has to be just that. *Personal*. If we're to work as a team our relationship needs to be closer. That means us getting to know each other. Being open with each other. I'm sure you have issues with me I know nothing about.'

Relief he was only using *masks* as a figure of speech made her so giddy she was seized with a rush of generosity. 'No, no, I don't. Well, not that many.' The attentive tilt of his dark head made her conscious of her soft words seeming to crash around the walls. 'I dare say everyone has his or her own management style.'

He grimaced. 'Good— I *think*. I hardly dare to ask, but are there some suggestions you'd like to offer? To help me improve my—performance?'

His eyebrows made an ironic twitch and the sternness of his beautiful, sexy mouth relaxed. Instantly her imagination flew her back to that lamp-lit bed where he reclined, bronzed, naked and wickedly intent on giving her the ultimate in pleasure, and a tidal surge of warmth swelled her breasts inside her cut-price bra.

'No, no,' she said, shaking her head to crush any suggestion of sexual innuendo. 'Of course not. I'm sure your performance—I mean your performance as a *boss*—is very good.'

He smiled. It was a rare event and she wished he hadn't. His eyes crinkled at the corners and seemed to lengthen charmingly. It made him devastatingly like the Sam of the hotel bedroom.

'Of course I knew you meant my performance as a boss,' he said softly. 'What else would I have thought you meant?' A shadow of the smile lingered as he contemplated her with a shimmering, intent gaze.

The suspicion crept into her head that he knew very well who she was and was toying with her. She twisted her boneless hands behind her back. Was he tempting her to flirt?

He began to pace again, only this time, to her intense confusion, *around* her. He circled, inspecting her as if she were a slave girl in some biblical market-place.

He prowled behind her and paused, and she stared straight ahead, embarrassment warring with her overwhelming physical awareness of him. What was he looking at? Suddenly she remembered a little fault she'd forgotten to fix in the pleat at the back of her skirt, and felt herself grow hot. She whipped around to face him, concealing her discomfiture with a touch of hauteur. 'Was there something else?'

'Tell me, Eleanor,' he said. 'Are you finding your salary adequate?'

'My salary?'

She nearly gasped. Her feminine pride was stung, though she knew there were those who would say she deserved to feel some shame. She was earning more than she'd even dreamed, and could easily have bought a new suit. Her bank balance had received such a boost that her savings fund was becoming quite healthy, but, she'd reasoned, in extreme circumstances a woman was forced to take extreme measures to protect herself.

'It's more than adequate, thanks,' she admitted. 'It's generous.'

He stood looking thoughtful for a second, then strode across to the desk and picked up the phone.

He dialled, unnerving her with a keen, meaningful glance. 'There is something of a deeply personal nature I need to discuss with you, but this isn't the place for it. I'm taking you to lunch. Payroll?' he said into the phone, then covered the mouthpiece with his hand and said, 'You'd better warn the restaurant upstairs we want a quiet table. And cancel our appointments for the afternoon.' With a brisk nod he turned back to his call. 'Jenkins? What do we pay Eleanor O'Dea?'

He waved her away, but as she headed for the door she had the sensation that his eyes were burning through the back of her suit.

'No,' she heard him tell Jenkins. 'Yes. No. No. Take it up. Make it twenty-five per cent. Better still, thirty.'

Outside the office door, Ellie stood for a moment, her mind in a whirl.

Something—*everything*—had changed. It appeared she wasn't getting the sack.

But what personal thing did he want to discuss? Surely not the night of the masked ball?

She dialled the penthouse restaurant, then stood rapidly reviewing their conversation. She still had her job, which suggested he hadn't remembered her. Though some of the things he'd said…

And there had been a definite buzz in the atmosphere. Whether he'd intended it or not his behaviour had been seductive. Charming, even. Although, if she was to be honest with herself, she always felt that zing in the air when she was near him. The question was whether it was all generated by her.

It was highly unlikely he'd flirt with her. Still, did a sophisticated man like Samos Stilakos use the word *relationship* accidentally? Somehow she doubted it.

Although…although…

This was the man who'd transferred four assistants for falling in lust with him, *and* sacked his Advertising Manager for conducting staff performance appraisals in the Honeymoon Suite at the Crown Regis, one of Sydney's most salubrious hotels. He'd never risk starting an affair with his PA after setting his workforce such an uncompromising example.

And what was this about her salary? Unless she'd misinterpreted that phone call, he intended giving her a raise. She thought back to that unsettling moment when he'd been prowling around her, and nearly groaned aloud. Beth had been right. She should have upgraded her wardrobe. What if the deeply personal thing he wanted to discuss with her was her suit?

Though anxiety gnawed at her vitals, she still made an effort to concentrate on the booklet she was preparing to support Sam's strategy for bringing the department heads around. Should she, or shouldn't she, include that fascinating research she'd uncovered about childcare in the workplace? Surely it was a prime opportunity to inform them of what they truly needed to know.

Sam's door opened and he strode out with his firm, energetic step. 'Ready?' His glance shifted past her and he halted. His eyes narrowed, and he strolled over to her desk and picked up Mark's photo. 'Who's this?' He turned a veiled glance on her face. 'Your boyfriend?'

'No, no. He's—a friend.' She supposed Mark could still be called a friend, even after fourteen months without a word. Certainly he hadn't wanted to be called a husband, or the father of her children.

Sam held up the photo to examine under the light, tilted it this way and that. 'There's something about him,' he commented, frowning. 'Reminds me of someone. Yes, I know. The woodsman in that story—what's it called?' He clicked his fingers. '*Hansel and Gretel*—that's the one. Does he always keep that beard?'

'He's a mountain climber. An—adventurer.'

He'd made Mark sound so ridiculous she couldn't help feeling a bit defensive. Although why should she? Mark had never been into haut couture. Her yearning for beautiful, elegant clothes had been one of the contentious issues between them, and she'd long since learned to suppress it. But there was nothing so ridiculous about a checked flannelette shirt, was there? Millions of men wore them.

'He likes—a challenge.' She'd been going to say *wide open spaces*, but the truth of that could still hit a nerve.

'Ah.' He shot her an inscrutable dark glance. 'Don't we all,' he said softly, and gave the photo a careful wipe with his immaculate Armani sleeve, before placing it on the desk directly in front of her chair. He flashed her a wicked smile. 'There. Now you can see him clearly. Ready now?'

He curved his arm around her back to escort her to the lift.

The revolving restaurant on the top floor was packed

with the lunch-time crowd of executives and members of the public who wanted to enjoy spectacular views with their meals. She spotted several of Sirius's management staff, gossiping over their dry whites.

The news would be out in a flash, she thought, noting some curious heads turning their way as she made her entrance with Samos Stilakos. She could just hear them in the canteen—*Ellie is making it with the boss*. At least, though, with members of staff present he wasn't likely to spring any major surprises on her.

The *maître d'* swept all before him to lead them to a table in a discreet corner, magnificently set in white linen and crystal. 'Champagne, sir? Madam?' he said, after he'd seated them with a superb flourish of starched napery.

She was relieved when Sam said, his deep, quiet voice polite but commanding, 'Mineral water. This is a business meeting.'

Executives all over the restaurant hastened to conceal their wineglasses.

Sam gazed at her across the table, golden depths shimmering in his dark eyes, and her relief began to wane a little as her susceptible pulse picked up speed. 'Eleanor,' he said softly, ravishing her with a gleaming white smile. 'That's a Greek name. Did you know that?'

If only the smile didn't linger in his eyes like a caress. 'I thought it was French,' she answered, unable to prevent her own giddy smile from breaking out. 'You know, Eleanor of Aquitane and all that.'

'Eleanor of Aquitane was almost certainly of Greek descent,' he said. 'And I believe she also had strawberry hair.'

Strawberry. The word hit her like a thunderbolt and the smile was wiped from her face. If ever she'd needed proof of this man's pathetic memory here it was. Hadn't she provided him with a shining example of strawberry-blonde hair at the masked ball? On that occasion he'd displayed a passionate enthusiasm for plunging his hands into it, even burying his face in it. Having experienced it to the utmost, it was one colour he should have remembered.

It was glaringly apparent that to him all shades of red hair were the same. As no doubt all *women* looked the same.

'What is it?' His eyes lit with amusement and his thick black brows lifted. 'Have I said something?'

She concealed her chagrin behind the self-possessed demeanour she'd perfected for bosses over the years. 'I believe Eleanor of Aquitane was one-hundred-per-cent French,' she replied coolly. 'And my hair colour is usually described as Titian.'

His lean, handsome face betrayed no expression. 'Oh, is it? Titian. I must remember that.' He looked so solemn she had the strongest suspicion that for some reason he was pleased with himself, and trying not to show it. He motioned to her to open her menu, and perused his while she made a pretence of reading.

Food words danced meaninglessly in front of her eyes. Why were they discussing her personal attributes? Next he'd be bringing up her piquant chin. If she didn't know better, at any minute now she'd be expecting a sexy little après-lunch invitation down to the Crown Regis.

A nasty suspicion occurred to her. Perhaps he always seduced his PAs over lunch. Maybe that was why he then had to banish them to the ends of the earth.

She hated to believe it, but it fitted. Why hadn't she realised? For months the staff had speculated about those transfers. No one had had any doubt that the women had earned them with their unprofessional behaviour. But what if *he* had been the seducer? When he turned on his devilish charm he was impossible to resist, as she could testify only too well.

With growing disappointment she surveyed the handsome, inscrutable face absorbed in reading the menu. A serial sacker was one thing, but a serial womaniser quite another. For some reason she'd needed to believe in his integrity. What did it say about her, that she'd spent the night with someone like him?

'A lovely name,' he murmured. 'And yet—' He looked up to capture her gaze. 'You invite people to call you Ellie.'

She looked enquiringly at him over the top of her menu.

'Your friends.'

'Yes?'

'But not your boss.'

She was momentarily flustered. A smile warmed his dark eyes, crept into her veins and stole down her arteries like old cognac. She forced herself to keep on breathing as if it were an everyday experience for her to be teased by tall, dark, dangerous Greeks with beautiful, sexy mouths that curled up at the corners.

'I'd prefer it if you would drop the *Mr Stilakos* routine, and just call me Sam,' he added gently.

There was a pregnant silence while he waited for her to reply in kind. It was fortunate that just then a waiter materialised beside their table. She wasn't hungry, but she welcomed the lad as if he were her saviour, bathing him in her warmest smile. 'I'll have the salad, thanks,' she told him.

She was conscious of Sam leaning back in his chair, his long limbs idly disposed, his gaze flickering over her as he listened to the small exchange. When it was his turn he ordered the fish, and in a few brief words gave detailed instructions in exactly how it was to be prepared. After the waiter left, he moved his chair a little closer and said quietly, 'I'm wondering, Eleanor, if your friend will be able to spare you for a weekend, just over a month from now.'

A million unlikely scenarios raised their heads. 'Beth?' she said, taken off guard.

'Your friend. The *adventurer*.' Somehow he managed to invest the word with a subtle mockery.

'Oh, Mark?' She gave a small self-conscious laugh and mumbled, 'No, no. Well, he's not— He's not actually—' She folded her napkin carefully, folded it into smaller and smaller rectangles. She'd never intended to lie about Mark's presence in her life, only to divert suspicion. What if she had to produce him at some time? It would be so humiliating to be caught in a lie. Quickly she backed away from it. 'Why? What's happening?'

She felt his perceptive eyes home in on her nervous fingers, and forced them to stay still.

'So you'll be free?' There was a gleam in his eyes that suggested he hadn't been fooled by her little strategy.

Her heart lurched. Was he about to suggest a weekend rendezvous? For a wavering instant she allowed a shining mirage to float in her imagination—the two of them, making love in some decadent, luxurious hotel.

Despicable. Fatal. But such sweet poison. If the others hadn't resisted, how would she?

Breathlessly she replied, 'It depends what for.'

He hesitated. 'You met my mother this morning…'

She nodded, hypnotised by his mesmeric gaze.

'My mother has to go to a family wedding. Her heart isn't very strong and she finds she's nervous about having to go on her own. I wondered if I could impose on your good nature to ask if you would consider going with her?'

His *mother*! She nearly fell off the chair. This was nothing like she'd expected. Inviting her to a social function with his mother, his family—!

Her suspicions all fell in a heap. How could she have been so cynical? And foolish, suspecting him of seducing his PAs, even worrying about what he thought of her clothes when he'd probably never even noticed them. As for her fanciful dream of an afternoon of wild sex down at the Regis… She should have blushed with shame.

'Of course, I'll make sure you're handsomely reimbursed for your time and trouble.'

She pulled herself together. 'Why me?' she said. 'Why not you, or another family member, or a friend?'

He sat back. His lean, strong face hardened to become expressionless. 'It's a family affair. I don't know if you know anything about the Stilakos family—'

Only what everyone knew, that they owned a bank, half the media outlets in the country, and controlling interests in several trans-global corporations besides Sirius. She wasn't about to acknowledge what she knew of the personal stuff shooting along the office airways, and shook her head.

'It's my ex-wife, Natalie, who's getting married. You'll have met her this morning. She's marrying—another family member.' There'd been a hesitation, so slight as to be barely perceptible, but his dark eyes hardened to obsidian. 'On my mother's side.'

Ellie had a vague recollection of some scandal about Natalie a few years ago. While the star had been well known because of her television fame and wild-child reputation, at that time her husband's name had meant nothing to Ellie.

'As you might imagine, everyone in the family, all the *friends* of the family, are in some way involved with the bride and groom. You probably noticed this morning, Natalie can be temperamental…'

She gave a noncommittal shrug.

He laughed. 'Always the diplomat, Eleanor.'

A pleasant, unexpected glow irradiated her insides. Perhaps she should forgive him for forgetting her. After all, a man like him had serious things on his mind.

'Natalie can be—just a little volatile. Weddings are emotional affairs, and my mother is nervous of the possibilities. If she had some calm, sensible person with her, some neutral person, I think she might feel more confident.'

'You—haven't been invited ?' she hazarded.

His eyes darkened, and became so impenetrable she had the heart-gripping sensation she'd tripped a detonator wire set to blow her sky-high. For goodness' sake, why had she asked? Of course people didn't go to their ex's weddings.

'It's probably better you don't go,' she hastened to say. 'It would be sure to arouse painful memories.' His face remained tense, and she strove to lighten the tone with humour. 'I imagine the last thing anyone would want on their wedding day would be their ex turning up at the church. All their friends sitting on the edges of their pews… Everyone waiting for hell to break loose. I can see it all now—' she raised a solemn hand and intoned in a priestly voice '"—if any man here knows of any reason why this man should avoid marrying this woman…"'

To her relief his taut face relaxed and he broke into a laugh. 'It may surprise you to know I have been invited.

My ex-wife has infinite faith in my ability to keep my mouth shut. She begs me to come.' He added drily, 'That's what you were hearing this morning. Natalie persuading me.'

He smiled, but Ellie felt a little chill thrill down her spine. There were jagged depths beneath that brooding calm. She would hate to be the one who disturbed them.

'What do you think?' He scanned her face for a moment, then lowered his black lashes and said, 'This doesn't mean your job is on the line if you refuse, Eleanor. This is apart from your work. It's personal, and I'll understand and accept it immediately if you choose not to be involved.'

She'd been wrong. Absolutely wrong on all counts. The man wasn't a scoundrel in any way. He was a concerned, affectionate son willing to go out on a limb for his mother, even if it meant exposing his personal skeletons to a stranger. A mere employee!

The waiter arrived with the meals, and she took advantage of the distraction to think.

How she'd misjudged him. It was sobering to see how close she'd come to turning into a cynic in her old age. She looked up to meet his dark, velvet gaze and her heart warmed. What a relief to be able to think well of him. 'All right,' she said, smiling. 'I'll do it. If you're sure your mother will be comfortable with me.'

His eyes lit with satisfaction. 'Good.' He took up his knife and fork and added, 'I've phoned her and she thinks she will be. Now, eat up your salad. We'll need to see her and do some shopping. And we'll need to discuss the travel arrangements.'

Ellie raised her brows.

'Didn't I mention it? Natalie's parents live on the Gold

Coast. The wedding's at the Palazzo Versace. You'll be staying there.'

Ellie was dazzled. The Palazzo Versace was suppos-edly one of the glitziest resorts in the country. She tried to remember what she'd heard of it. Television ads she'd seen had left her with vague impressions of a glittering palace floating on a moonlit lagoon; beautiful languid people, lounging on luxurious chaises longues, sipping piña coladas. She could easily imagine Natalie there, but could Ellie O'Dea be one of those people?

'Great,' she said doubtfully.

'You might need to take your swimsuit,' he said, con-sidering her over the rim of his glass. 'Just because it's a wedding doesn't mean you have to suffer the whole time. There're bound to be things you can do to pass the time while my mother catches up with her family—beaches, sailing, wind-surfing—you know the sort of thing…' He made a careless gesture with one lean, bronzed hand, then paused, contemplating her with an intent shimmering gaze.

'I'm not much of a one for beaches,' she confessed. 'I have to avoid too much sun.'

His eyes flickered to her throat. 'Ah, yes. I can see that. You are very fair, aren't you? So you never go to the beach?'

Ellie felt herself grow warm. This was too reminiscent of a conversation she'd had with him before in quite a dif-ferent setting. Was it a coincidence that so many of the things he'd said to her since ten o'clock that morning in some way recalled the Night of Nights?

She gazed searchingly at him. 'Early mornings, or—or late afternoons are fine. I do like to swim. Sometimes I—' she waved her hand in a stiff gesture '—use the pool at the gym.'

'As I recall, there is quite a lovely pool at that resort. A spa, no less.'

'I'm not sure I can imagine myself at that sort of place.' She gave a small laugh.

'*I* can imagine it,' he said softly. A gleam lit his dark eyes. 'I can imagine it very well.' He looked silently at her for a long minute that grew longer and more deafening by the second as questions danced again in Ellie's brain. 'And there is always the night,' he murmured, still gazing at her.

She stared back at him in amazement. 'The night?' Her voice came out deeper than she expected; it sounded almost croaky. 'I don't think I'd feel safe on the beach at night.'

His eyebrows went up, then he laughed, a low, sexy laugh. 'Wouldn't you? But what if you were with someone?'

Her heart skipped a major beat while her lashes fluttered in shock. 'Who? You mean…someone I met at the wedding?'

His eyes chilled and his fork arrested in mid-air. 'I certainly didn't mean that.' He pinned her with a severe gaze. 'Try to remember this, Eleanor. You'll be there to keep my mother company, not for the sake of a hot weekend.' He must have seen her dismay because he added, his deep, smooth voice rich with charm, 'Though, of course, I know you aren't the type of person to ditch your responsibilities for a fling with some stranger.' He smiled at her, and turned his attention back to his meal while her head buzzed with indignant thoughts. *He* wasn't above a fling with a stranger. So why even mention it? Why, unless he was giving her some sort of signal?

She stared at her barely touched salad. All at once the uncertainty became too much. What sort of a pathetic coward was she to allow this cat-and-mouse game to continue?

If he sacked her, he sacked her.

'Look, Sam...' She took a deep breath and on a rush of bravado leaned forward and murmured in a voice just above a whisper, 'Are you—are you by any chance referring to the night of the masked ball?'

As soon as the words were out a blush the size of a tsunami swamped her. She clenched her entire body and held her breath.

Across the table Sam's bronzed hands stilled. She lifted her gaze and met his brilliant dark eyes. They were gleaming with a deeply unsettling intensity.

He spoke so quietly she had to strain to hear him above her madly thundering heartbeat. 'I'm not referring to it,' he said. 'I'm very carefully not. If you want me to discuss it, you'll have to release me from my promise, won't you, Eleanor?'

Relief washed through her. Impossibly, she felt the colour deepen in her cheeks. 'Oh. Well, of course, of course. I *do*... There's no point... I'm certainly not trying to...'

'Good. I'd hate to think we'd come this far for nothing.'

Her nerves jumped in shock. *We'd come this far...?* Towards...what?

Sam Stilakos laid down his knife and fork. When her glance fell on his hands she noticed that they weren't quite steady.

The waiter came with fresh water, creating such a welcome diversion she and Sam both hastened to chat warmly with him. After the boy had gone, Sam lounged back in his chair and said idly, 'So who is this boyfriend? What's-his-name—Tim?'

'Oh. You must be meaning—Mark.'

His thick black lashes screened his gaze while she

gathered herself to reply. She drained her glass and took her time refilling it from the carafe, then said with a careful lack of expression, 'Mark went to Antarctica.'

His brows lifted and he scanned her face. 'Antarctica! For a holiday—or…?'

She rearranged her salad. 'An expedition.'

His brows went up again. 'Ah. And do you—*when* do you—expect him back?'

She shrugged. 'Oh, some time,' with an airy wave of her hand. She didn't want to let on how long he'd been gone. And that he'd since been seen in Melbourne with a blonde whose idea of couture was to wear army boots with a denim skirt.

Samos Stilakos continued to study her face with a veiled gaze. After a long moment he remarked in a low, musing voice, 'Antarctica. That's a long way from here.'

CHAPTER THREE

'I THINK you've been in this car, Eleanor, haven't you?'

The lazy enquiry rocked Ellie on her heels just as she was about to get into Sam's Porsche. Of course she'd been in it. He'd driven her in it to Circular Quay, and kissed her long and lingeringly as the first rays of dawn had ignited Sydney Harbour in a sunburst of molten ecstasy. It had been the highlight of her life to date.

'Remind me again,' he said, flashing her a glance through his black lashes, 'which do you prefer? Roof open, or closed?'

Smiling, she indicated her hair. 'What do you think?'

He strode around to the driver's side and lowered his long frame into the seat next to hers. His hand moved to the gear stick, and she instinctively shifted her knees, although of course she knew he wouldn't have touched them. Not this time.

But it was far too reminiscent of the last time, when he'd driven her to the ferry terminal in the sweet haze of afterglow. Then, the city streets, the very air she'd breathed, had seemed intoxicating. It was intoxicating *now*, sitting beside him as he threaded a path through the traffic with breathtaking efficiency, his beautiful hands relaxed on the wheel.

No wonder Schanelle and the others had ogled him.

Scorchingly conscious of him in the confined space, she tried to restrain herself, but somehow her eyes were drawn to drink in his sexy mouth, so grave in repose. A suggestion of shadow on his firm, lean jaw evoked a stirring memory of his early-morning face, nuzzling a bristly imprint on her tender skin.

'Something wrong?' he said, turning his head suddenly and catching her.

'No, no,' she said, flushing a little. 'I was just—er—thinking about Schanelle.'

'Ah. Now there's a coincidence.'

Her heart plunged to the floor. Could she be going insane? Whatever had possessed her to remind him of poor Schanelle? But he made a sudden swift lane-change, executed a heart-stopping but brilliantly adroit U-turn in the face of oncoming traffic, and drew the car to a smooth standstill at the kerb.

She stared confusedly out, and saw they were parked in front of a boutique with elegant lettering across its large, black-framed windows. 'Oh, the *shop*.'

He cast her an amused glance. 'You know this shop, of course.'

'From the outside,' she admitted with a grin, surmising they were here so he could choose a wedding present for his ex-wife. 'I'll wait in the car.'

'No, you will not,' he asserted. He sprang out and strode around to open her door, forcing her out with a firm, expectant gaze.

She stood uncertainly on the pavement in front of the

entrance. How did he think she would be able to help? PAs with savings targets didn't shop in places like this.

'Come on.' He took her arm and manoeuvred her inside.

A severely smart shop assistant, with sleek blonde hair and emphatic eye-liner, registered his approach with an open mouth. Ellie wished a fly would buzz in, until she remembered her own first sighting and forgave her.

'We need things for a weekend wedding,' Sam told the woman, seemingly not put off by prolonged eye contact. 'Dresses, suits, shoes. Swimsuits. Size…' He turned a suave glance on Ellie. 'I'm guessing ten. Would that be right, Eleanor?'

Ellie dragged her eyes away from a shelf of fabulously high shoes with jewelled heels. 'What? *I* don't need anything.'

'Yes, you do,' he said. 'I can't plunge you into this without providing you with the necessary equipment. I've been through this kind of thing and I've learned the hard way about what's expected of women. You'll need dresses, shoes, handbags…' He began ticking a list off on his fingers. 'An outfit to be seen arriving in, casual things to lounge around in, things for daytime, evening, the church, and we mustn't forget the swimming.'

Ellie nearly tottered on her heels. She stared at him, then around at all the lovely creations poking from their racks. This attitude was absolutely the opposite of Mark's, who believed elegant clothes to be the trappings of empty vanity. It was religion with Mark that money should only be spent on functional items, like hiking boots and thermal underwear.

This was generosity on a scale she'd never encountered, but deep down she knew she couldn't accept it. She was a free and independent woman, and, whatever else Sam was, he was her boss.

She angled herself away from the interested stare of the saleswoman and mumbled, 'I have things I can wear.'

She felt the assistant's experienced eye assess her clumsy jacket and skirt, and tried to look cool and unconcerned, though she could feel her face turning pink.

'I know you do,' Sam said soothingly, 'but for this you'll need new things. Show us everything you've got,' he instructed the woman over Ellie's head.

Dollar signs danced in front of Ellie's eyes while the woman jumped to obey the command in his voice. Ellie watched helplessly as she reefed through the racks and pulled out hanger after hanger of gorgeous, to-die-for outfits, any of which would leave a massive hole in her savings.

'This is not the sort of thing I wear,' Ellie protested, waving away a purple suit with a short slim skirt. For the price on its label she could probably furnish a nursery and pay for five years of violin lessons.

Sam looked surprised. 'Isn't it? I think it'd look good on you. Try it on.'

She shook her head, 'This is very kind of you, but I don't *need* you to buy me anything, thanks.' She met his gaze steadily. 'I really can't accept this.'

Disconcerted, Sam stared at her, wondering if he was losing his grip. A delicate flush washed her flawless cheeks and disappeared into her hairline. There was a smile on her soft mouth, but her blue eyes were resolute. He felt a curious jolt, and was reminded of another time he'd come up against a brick wall with Ellie O'Dea. But surely none of the women he'd ever known would have refused clothes from this establishment.

He gestured to the saleswoman to turn her attention to other customers, and ushered Ellie to a quiet corner. It took him a moment to find the words. 'Let me explain, Eleanor.'

That deep, persuasive tone could melt steel, and Ellie braced herself for a major charm offensive, but the dark velvet eyes scanning hers were sincere.

'I don't wish to insult you,' he said carefully, 'but you don't know Natalie and her friends. You'll be competing in the most cutthroat market in the country. You'll need to wear something swish, or risk feeling uncomfortable. I can't just drop you in it. My mother would kill me.' He smiled and wrapped a reassuring arm around her, and every cell in her body surged. 'It isn't a big deal. Relax. I have to do this, believe it.'

The dark seductive resonance of his voice went straight to her head. Through the fabric of his suit she felt the heat of his large, lean body, and her blood went zinging on a dizzy dangerous course to her breasts and points south.

'You're—you're really very kind.' She quickly disengaged herself. Her ears felt as if they'd caught fire. She met the sensual awareness vibrant in his dark gaze, and knew he'd noticed her quick pull away, and understood the reason.

'Honestly, Sam,' she rushed to fill the awkward moment, 'this is too generous of you.' Her heart was racing, but she forced herself to keep her head. He was so persuasive. Beautiful things called to her from every direction, but to allow him to buy even one dress for her would be shameful, when she could very well buy something for herself. 'I don't need a whole new wardrobe just for one weekend. If I need a dress, I can buy it myself.' She made a small dismissive wave towards a shelf where shoes kept flashing in the corner of her eye like hot magnets. 'Or—or shoes, or whatever.'

His black brows knitted, and she could tell by the calculation in his gaze that he wasn't about to give in. 'Er…' He turned to glance around the shop in search of inspiration.

Suddenly he turned back to her, a gleam in his eyes. 'All right. Let's compromise. We don't want to offend these people, now, do we? You can't leave without at least trying something on. How about some of those shoes?'

Who was he, the devil? She glanced at them once, then averted her eyes. Somehow he'd homed straight in on her Achilles heel.

She shook her head and gave a small, reluctant laugh. 'You're very cunning.'

His eyes glinted. 'I *am* very cunning, and you'd do well to remember that, Eleanor. Go on. Try some.'

She looked over at the shoes. She could resist chocolate if she absolutely had to, for life-preserving reasons, but this was too much. She wasn't sure how it was a compromise, but with her blood churning like an excitable sea, she started with the shoes, and it wasn't long before two sales assistants were plying her with the clothes.

Obviously experienced with the ways of women in dress shops, Sam found an alcove with a pile of newspapers and dropped into a chair.

Ellie tried on the purple suit, and saw it accentuate her curves and turn her eyes to violet. The saleswoman brought her more suits, frothy skirts and evening dresses in rich colours with beads and sequins—jeans, swimsuits, even bikinis. Despite her initial reluctance, the fever for lovely things gripped her. There was a time for being frugal, she acknowledged to herself, and a high society wedding wasn't one of them. She had to accept that he knew what he was talking about. She did need at least one good dress. She would just have to make an adjustment to her IVF timeline.

Several times the woman dragged her to a large mirror outside the cubicle. Sam lounged across the room, buried in his newspaper, though once Ellie glanced towards him in the mirror and felt a small shock as she met his intent gaze.

'If madam would try these,' the saleswoman suggested, handing Ellie some extremely frivolous shoes with four-inch heels. She'd just finished zipping a short-sleeved dress, in a shade of pink so delicate it was nearly white. Cut to classic perfection, it moulded slinkily to her curves, emphasising the perky up-tilt of her breasts. The shade lent her pale skin a pearly glow, and her blue eyes sparkled like sea water. She examined herself in it with delight, feeling as if she could slither like a snake. She slid into the shoes, and her legs lengthened with the old fabulous miracle.

'I *love* this,' she admitted, twisting in the small cubicle to examine her derrière. 'It isn't too tight, is it?'

'No, no!' the woman cooed. 'It's made for you. Come outside and see.'

The saleswomen whisked her out to the big mirror and fluttered around her. One stood on tiptoes and tried to re-arrange her hair. 'How does it look out?'

She tried to explain that if it wasn't severely bound up it just fell straight, like a heavy curtain. She put her hands up to loosen it, knowing she was surrendering to more than letting her hair fall. For once she'd be breaking the embargo on her savings. But hadn't she been given a pay rise by the most generous boss a woman could ever…?

Her eyes slewed towards him in the mirror, and did a double take.

Far from being sprawled in his chair, he was sitting bolt upright, his big frame taut, his burning gaze riveted on her, as if on some vision. A thrill shocked through her at the concentrated wolfish expression of his lean, strong face. She felt his eyes sear her from head to toe, their electric message unmistakable.

Her mouth dried. Transfixed, she watched him drop the paper and rise to his feet.

'We'll take it,' he growled, striding purposefully across to her without shifting his gaze. 'And the shoes. Let me help you with that, Eleanor.'

The assistants fell back to give him space. He raised his hands to her hair, and she felt the sensual charge in his smooth fingers frisson in her skin as they coupled with hers to release the pins. Her nape, her scalp, the length of her spine tingled as his strong, lean fingers plunged into her hair. After a wild few moments in which her pulse roared through her veins like white-water rapids, he stood back to let the red silken mass fall free.

His hands gripped her shoulders and he held her to her reflection, a flame in his eyes. 'Look at you,' he said, gravel in his deep voice. 'You look perfect. Absolutely perfect.'

Her eyes glittered back at her from the mirror with a bluer intensity. His searing gaze locked with hers, their desire as seductive and compelling as it had been in that hotel room, and her breasts surged in a deep, responsive excitement. She felt a dizzy tide of unreality, as if she weren't in a shop with her boss, but with her lover in some private moment, on the verge of an explosive flare-up of passion.

But…he wasn't her lover. Not now and never again. Whatever images glowed in their memories were just that. Memories.

Restraining what felt like a natural compulsion to turn and embrace him, she lowered her lashes. 'I—I'd better take it off.' She made a move towards the fitting room.

'No,' he breathed. 'Leave it on.' His grip tightened for an instant before he released her. 'It's—ideal for where we're going next,' he said gruffly. A faint tinge of colour darkened his olive tan.

He swung abruptly away from her. She slipped back into the fitting room and took some deep, trembling breaths in an attempt to compose herself. One of the saleswomen came in to remove the labels from her dress, and took away the items she'd put on the possibles pile.

Ellie plunged into her bag for her hairbrush and did a quick tidy-up, her rapid heart thudding. She wasn't sure how she was going to face him when she came out. Something had happened between them, something irrevocable. Could they just pretend it hadn't?

She could hear the murmur of his deep voice in conversation with the saleswoman. 'We'll take them all,' she heard him say. 'And throw in all the matching shoes, et cetera.'

Though her poise was barely recovered, nonetheless her pride came roaring back.

'No! Wait.'

She burst from the fitting room, and hurried over to insert herself between Sam and the startled assistant. 'I'll take this dress and these shoes I'm wearing now,' she told the woman. She whipped her credit card from her purse, and pushed Sam's aside to lay hers on the counter. 'These are all I need,' she said with a firm glance at him, 'and *I* want to buy them. But thanks, anyway, for your most generous offer.' She smiled and added softly, 'I really do appreciate it.'

Something flickered in his intent dark gaze, and his brows knitted, but he must have seen the resolution in her face, because he stood back and allowed her to complete the transaction without argument. The assistant wrapped her work clothes and old shoes in tissue, and slipped them into stylish carrier bags.

She floated hazily beside him to the car in her chic little sexy dress and shoes, still in something of a turmoil. She'd expected a bigger fight over the matter of payment. Nonetheless, though she was still reeling at the price, it was a victory to have out-argued an autocrat who had an entire workforce quaking in its boots.

But there was the other thing. That moment in the shop.

He'd hardly spoken a word since, and, though he seemed as assured as ever, she had the feeling he was as burningly conscious of it as she was herself. It was hard to meet his eyes, but when she did they brimmed with satisfaction, and something more. Something very akin to the desire she'd seen in that mirror.

The trip in the car was surprisingly brief. She'd thought they were heading for the bridge, when, against all her expectations, he swung the Porsche into the driveway of a grand hotel. She craned her neck, trying to read the inscription over the portico. Wasn't this the—?

The doors were opened by uniformed valets. 'Welcome to the Crown Regis, Mr Stilakos.' And with a deep bow. 'Madam.'

CHAPTER FOUR

SAM ushered her into the marble lobby. The concierge, the porters—everyone greeted him by name.

'Wait here a moment,' he said, steering her towards a plush velvet sofa.

Ellie stood still, besieged by doubts. Hadn't he said he would take her to visit his mother? She watched him stride across to Reception, and lean over to murmur something to the receptionist, who picked up the phone, spoke briefly, then handed him something.

Ellie's pulse quickened. She thought she could guess what it was.

In a second he was back, his eyes glinting when they lighted on her like a wolf with his prey in sight. With a light touch on her arm he guided her to the lifts. This was the time to call a halt. But what mature, twenty-nine year old woman would refuse to allow the most thrilling lover she'd ever known to escort her to the Honeymoon Suite of Sydney's most salubrious hotel?

In the lift they stood slightly apart, watching the floor count on the display panel, Ellie's heart in a dilemma, rapids churning in her veins. What was she doing?

'She's expecting us,' he said as the floor count reached thirty-five.

'Who? Oh. Do you mean then—? Your mother is staying *here*?'

He glanced down at her, his devilish brows raised. 'Of course. Didn't I say? She always stays here when she comes up to town. Why else would we be here, Eleanor?'

The doors opened then, sparing her the impossibility of replying. Either she was a horribly confused woman, or her imagination had just taken her overboard. Or— Samos Stilakos was playing a game with her. A flirty, tantalising and very sexy game!

His mother opened her door to them and greeted them both warmly, although she regarded Ellie with faint surprise in her eyes.

'You've met Eleanor, Mother,' Sam said, with a glance at Ellie. 'I think she might be the person you're looking for.'

Ellie held out her hand. 'Hello, Mrs Stilakos.'

'Call me Irene,' the older woman said, taking her hand and looking her over with admiration. 'You look so nice. Is that how you were wearing your hair this morning?'

Ellie shook her head, conscious of Sam's eyes on her.

'Eleanor's hair was meant to flow free,' he stated.

She nearly gasped, wondering what Irene made of this, but the older woman merely beamed. 'And it does suit you. Come through, Eleanor.'

'*Ellie*, please.'

Sam's eyebrows twitched ironically at that, but he was silent as they followed his mother through to the suite's elegant sitting room. Irene showed them to winged chairs beside a large window, which overlooked the harbour and the Opera House. Other windows revealed different aspects of the city, sparkling in the afternoon haze. It might not have been the Honeymoon Suite, but it was certainly appealing.

Irene sat facing them on a crimson sofa. She'd changed from her chic morning suit to casual trousers and a dusty-pink top, and her hair was slightly flattened on one side, as if she'd recently woken from a midday snooze. With the light from the window on her face, Ellie could see lines of tiredness around her eyes and mouth.

'I'm so glad Sam had the brilliant idea of asking you, Ellie. Eleanor…' She tilted her head to one side. 'Is that a family name?'

Ellie could feel Sam's interested gaze on her face as she responded to Irene. 'My parents named us all after queens. One of my sisters is Cleopatra. There's an Isabella, and a Liz, of course, and I was called after Eleanor of Aquitane.'

'All very powerful women,' Irene nodded approvingly. 'Are your sisters married?'

Ellie found herself describing her family, including her father's work in the music department at Newcastle University, and her parents' rambling home on Lake Macquarie.

'Do all your sisters have children?'

Ellie nodded. 'Nearly all.'

'I bet you make a lovely auntie, Ellie.'

Ellie smiled. 'I do my best,' she admitted, although she didn't acknowledge her understanding of what this little fishing expedition was all about. Not with its unwary subject sitting right there in all his lazy drop-dead gorgeousness. She wondered if she would be like this with *her* sons? Always on the lookout for an eligible wife and mother for the grandchildren?

If she had sons, she thought with a small anxious pang. If there was an egg left by the time she could afford it!

Still, Irene's skills in helping her to relax, while extracting information from her about her family in the gentlest, least offensive way imaginable, were impressive.

There was so much one could learn from an older woman, she mused. Unless the older woman's son was sitting across from her, dripping with sexual charisma and soaking up every word.

'Mum! For God's sake,' he growled when Irene's curiosity threatened to go too far, and occasionally he rolled his eyes or exchanged an amused glance with Ellie, but she could feel his sharp intelligence weighing everything she said.

She had a slight respite when a knock came at the door, and Sam got up. A waiter wheeled in a table swathed in white linen, and set with Wedgwood china. Clever little warming drawers inserted underneath held a feast of toasted sandwiches, scones and a fluffy passionfruit sponge.

At Sam's insistence, Ellie accepted a toasted sandwich of baked ham and avocado. 'You don't know how long it will be before you get your dinner tonight, Eleanor,' he said. 'You'll need to keep your strength up.'

Tonight. She looked quickly at him. The dark eyes dwelling on her face were veiled, his sculpted mouth grave. She felt the heat rise in her cheeks. She took a small bite, but, delicious though it was, her appetite seemed to have deserted her.

Irene's bright gaze swung from one to the other of them, then she busied herself in pouring the tea. Ellie wondered how attuned the older woman was to picking up vibrations.

'I don't know how much Sam has told you about the wedding, Ellie,' she said. She inclined towards Ellie and confided, 'I'm afraid it might turn out to be quite dramatic.'

Sam's mouth curled wryly. 'Eleanor *has* met Natalie, Mum.'

'Well, I hope Ellie doesn't think I'm a coward.' Irene smiled at her. 'Milk?' She handed her a cup and saucer. 'Tea, Sam?' He waved a refusal, and she continued, 'I'm not really nervous. I love weddings, and I'm so looking forward to seeing my brother and his wife—the whole family! It's just that I like to have someone to talk to when I'm travelling.'

'Of course,' Ellie responded warmly. 'I understand exactly. No one likes travelling alone. Especially to weddings, where everything is about couples.'

Sam lounged back in his chair, his smooth, lean hands idle. Ellie could feel his dark gaze from beneath his sleepily lowered lashes scorching a pathway of sensual masculine interest from her Titian hair all the way down to her ankles.

Irene continued to give an excellent impersonation of a woman with energy to spare. 'That's true,' she agreed, her grey eyes sparkling behind her specs. 'And that's how you feel, don't you, dear?' she said earnestly to Sam, whose slumbrous gaze snapped into startled focus. 'A man without a woman is always twice as suspect at a wedding.'

Sam looked thunderstruck, but his mother ignored it, turning animatedly to Ellie. 'I knew you'd understand, Ellie. You and I'll get along perfectly.' She loaded a scone with cream. 'I'll let my brother know you're coming. And I'm sure you won't have any trouble with Natalie. She'll have so much on her mind she won't even notice you're there.'

'What?' Sam demanded, recovering. 'Why should Ellie—*Eleanor*—have trouble?'

Ellie's heart skipped an anxious beat for fear of what Irene might say, but she merely leaned over and patted her son's knee. 'No need to be alarmed, Sam. Ellie will be quite safe.' She gave Ellie a conspiratorial glance and said with a small, nervous laugh, 'If it comes to a showdown, Ellie and I can defend ourselves. We aren't scared, are we?'

'A showdown?' Sam's eyebrows shot up and he turned a sharp gaze from his mother to Ellie. 'What sort of a showdown? Why should anyone be scared?'

'Don't you worry at all, dear,' Irene said, her voice quavering a little. 'This is secret women's business. We don't need any men to protect us, do we, Ellie?'

Sam scoured their faces in such bemusement Ellie found it hard not to laugh.

As if in total innocence of the effect she was having on her son's peace of mind, Irene continued, 'Now, Ellie, you won't have to be stuck with me the whole time. I'll probably be gallivanting about with my relations for quite a lot of it.'

Sam shot his mother a quick frowning glance, but Irene went on, 'You're bound to meet up with someone your own age you can have fun with, isn't she, Sam? There's so much to do on the Coast.'

Ellie gave a noncommittal laugh. 'Either way is fine with me. I'm sure I'll find something to do if you're not around.'

She felt Sam's dark gaze searing a hole through her skull. His eyes were narrowed, and there was a sardonic little curve to his lips. 'What might you do, Eleanor? Planning on taking a good book?'

'Perhaps.' She gazed coolly back at him, refusing to let him mock her in front of his mother. 'Perhaps not.'

Irene glanced at each of them, and said brightly, 'Well, it won't worry you whatever Ellie does, will it, dear, because you won't be there.' She beamed at him and turned to Ellie. 'Michael—he's the groom—is a keen yachtsman, like Sam, and I believe some of his young friends from the yacht club are sailing up there in advance of the wedding. The Palazzo Versace has a marina, so you might have an opportunity to do some sailing.'

Sam frowned. 'Sailing would be a mistake for Eleanor,' he said, in cool, clipped tones, his gaze on Ellie's face. 'She can't afford to get sunburnt.'

'Nonsense, Sam,' Irene exclaimed. 'She doesn't have to be wearing a tiny little bikini like some of them do, but if she does want to there's always sunscreen. And I'm sure you'd look lovely in it,' she added with a warm glance at Ellie.

Ellie felt the blood rise in her cheeks as the vision of her bikini-clad self dangled in the air.

'The jury's still out on the efficacy of sunscreen,' Sam said, holding her pink face under the spotlight of his sensual dark gaze. 'Eleanor would be better to stay indoors.'

'Oh, well.' Irene shrugged. 'If she prefers to she can always stay in her room and order a massage from one of their health professionals. I've read that some of those fellows are artists with their hands. I think she'd find it very therapeutic.'

Uncontrollably, Ellie's gaze flew to Sam's. The image flooded her brain of his smooth, bronzed hands as she'd known them on that night. Massaging her wild, willing body, with such masterly expertise. Kneading and caressing her breasts to erotic ecstasy. Exploring her satin secrets, his beautiful sexy mouth rousing her to rapture.

'She wouldn't,' he said, his voice as smooth as silk. 'You wouldn't want some man coming to your room to rub you all over with essential oils, would you, Eleanor?'

Ellie was forced to lower her lashes. She felt an overwhelming rush of warmth to her breasts. 'I might,' she said, concealing her confusion behind an unfocused smile, her betraying voice overly husky. 'I'm not ruling anything out.' She felt his eyes on her hands, and saw they'd curled themselves up. Deliberately she made them unclench, and raised her gaze to his. His dark eyes were amused, but there was a hard sexual challenge in their depths that sent a fierce, responsive pang through her.

Irene gave a sigh of what sounded like contentment. She set down her cup and leaned her back against the sofa cushions. 'It's such a relief you're coming, Ellie. I had wanted Sam to come in the first place, but I think I'll have more fun with you. He never lets me have my head. I'll be able to try out the casino and the nightclubs, shop till I drop, do all the touristy things—'

Sam turned a thunderous gaze on his mother. 'I don't think so, Mum. You'll find it tiring enough just going to the wedding. Eleanor's job will be to keep you out of trouble.'

Irene looked solemn. 'I'll try to stay out of it, but you know how I am after champagne, dear. And knowing Jack and Rosemary, it'll be flowing from the moment we arrive.'

Ellie's lips twitched with the temptation to laugh, but she saw fatigue in Irene's face then, as if her store of energy for the day had suddenly been used up. Sam must have noticed it at the same time, because he got to his feet and ended the visit, with a peck on his mother's cheek and a quiet reminder to take her medication.

At the door Irene said, 'It's so kind of you to do this, Ellie. I hope Sam will be able to get along without you while you're away. But we won't be thinking about him, will we? We'll be too deeply immersed in the flesh pots of the Coast.'

Sam gave her an austere look and his lips thinned to a grim, straight line.

Ellie suppressed a laugh. She had to hand it to Irene. When it came to pressing buttons, she was a champ.

Sam was silent on the way down in the lift. He leaned against the wall, his hands in his pockets, his brooding dark gaze occasionally flicking to Ellie. When the doors opened on the ground floor the sound of a piano wafted their way. It was coming from the piano bar, set like an oasis in the vast lobby.

'I need a drink,' Sam said, taking her arm. 'This way, Ms O'Dea.'

The bar wasn't busy. The few customers chatting at nearby tables weren't audible above the notes dripping like honey from the fingers of the pianist. Ellie accepted the offer of a glass of red wine, and slid onto a bar-stool next to Sam's.

Her dress rode to mid-thigh, and she crossed her legs as the only possible safety measure. Sam swivelled his bar-stool round to face her, his dark-clad knee only centimetres from hers. 'You did very well then, Eleanor.' His gaze slid over her. 'My mother likes you.'

'I like her. She's funny.' She smiled at him, still cool, efficient Ms O'Dea on the surface, though her heart seemed to be in training for the Olympics.

'Funny, but deadly serious. She's a worry.'

She suffered one of those dangerous, weak melty moments she'd resolved to eliminate from her dealings with men. So he cared about his mother. Didn't they all?

She raised her wine to her lips. Sam continued to watch her while she took a tiny sip, his lashes half lowered. He murmured, 'Which queen was it whose skin was so transparent you could see the wine trickle down her throat?'

She met his shimmering dark gaze and felt her pulse hasten. 'Mary, Queen of Scots, I think. Though, you know, Sam, I suspect that story isn't true.'

'It might have been true, Eleanor,' he said gravely. 'If she was a Titian-haired beauty with skin like white satin.' He lapsed into a meditative silence while her head spun dizzily. Was this a compliment? Was he really saying that *she* was a…?

The wine radiated through her with a mellow warmth. It was so—pleasant being with him, not knowing what he might say next. She dangled on the edge of sweet suspense, waiting, in fact, *longing*, for him to make a move.

But he stared absently into his scotch. The bar's muted overhead light glanced off the chiselled planes and angles of his face from cheekbone to jaw. She had an overwhelming desire to touch his cheek and trace the lines with her fingers. Run her fingertips along that masculine mouth.

He held his glass loosely in his lean fingers, and gave the amber liquid an idle swirl, before connecting again with her eyes. 'It wouldn't be a good idea to let Mum do too much gallivanting, as she calls it.'

She nodded, uncrossing her legs. Funny how hard it was to keep four-inch heels on when perched on a barstool. Whichever way she disposed her legs, one of the shoes slipped halfway off to dangle, like some nightclub siren's. She wasn't intending to act seductively, but she couldn't help feeling it. It was the dress, and the look in his eyes whenever they lighted on her. She anchored one foot on the crossbar and let the other swing a little.

His heavy-lidded gaze scorched the length of her and back again. Her flesh rippled with fever, as if his lean, beautiful hands had actually touched her. Glances could burn, she mused, aware of that deep, sensual excitement she'd felt on the balcony at the masked ball. There could be the sensation of contact, even when people weren't touching.

His deep, dark voice seeped into her veins like an aphrodisiac. 'I'm depending on you to keep an eye on her.'

'Maybe you would be better to keep an eye on her yourself.'

He grimaced. 'No force on earth could get me to that wedding.' His gaze drifted to her mouth. 'All you have to do is to keep her from going overboard.'

'I'm sure she won't,' she rejoined, as steadily as possible for someone melting to the sexual pull of the most gorgeous man in Sydney. 'Irene doesn't strike me as someone who'd take unnecessary risks.'

His devil's eyebrows made a sardonic twitch. 'You don't know her. Once she gets with Aunt Rosemary there'll be no holding her.' He took a sip of his scotch. How could lashes so long and thick be so essentially masculine? 'It would be best if you could keep her in the suite.'

She roused herself from her voluptuous contemplation of him. 'In the suite!' she exclaimed. 'I'm going as her companion, not her gaoler.'

He put down his glass and leaned an arm along the bar, somehow enclosing her in a private little intimate enclave.

Her heart made an adrenaline leap. If body language was anything to go by, Samos Stilakos was feeling very open towards her.

'Try to see it my way, Eleanor.' His deep velvet voice swayed her senses into a giddy hypnotic state. 'If you insist on all this sailing and carousing on the beach with strange men at midnight, how much of a companion are you likely to be?'

She gasped, and waved her glass in protest. 'I'm not insisting on anything!' A few drops of wine sloshed over the rim onto her fingers.

He took the glass from her hand and set it on the bar. Before she could reach for a paper serviette, he produced a beautifully laundered handkerchief, took her hand in his firm, light grip, and wiped her fingers with patient thoroughness.

'There, now.' He continued to hold her hand, and she held her breath. Desire coursed through her, sweet and irresistible as nectar. A piercing sensual gleam lit Sam's dark gaze, and for an electrified instant she thought he was going to raise her fingers to his lips. He said softly, 'We don't want to spoil that amazing dress. Not when you have to do dinner in it.'

Her voice came out as a husky croak. 'Dinner? Who said anything about dinner?'

He laughed and his deep, dark eyes lit with delight, and something like triumph. What had she said that was so funny?

And what did he have to feel triumphant about? She hadn't actually agreed to go to dinner, although there was no reason why she shouldn't. She was wearing a sexy, elegant dress, she was with a sophisticated man who made her feel desirable and interesting, and all she had planned for the evening was a comparative survey of the donor options offered by the various IVF clinics around the city.

She slid off the bar-stool and accompanied him out to where the car waited. Outside, she was surprised to see the first glimmerings of dusk. Lights seemed to be coming on all over the city. Somehow, in that wine bar, she'd lost all track of time.

Once in the car he gave his jaw a thoughtful rub. 'Er—do you mind coming home with me and waiting while I change, Eleanor?'

She looked quickly at him, but his expression was innocent. Nothing like that of a man set on whisking his PA to the nearest secluded venue, so he could ravish her into total delirium.

'Of course not.' She smiled, with her usual calm acceptance of anything a boss could throw at her.

CHAPTER FIVE

APARTMENT towers of steel and glass were hardly Ellie's style, but she couldn't deny the heady magnificence of Sam's sensational views across the city to the horizon. If he'd wanted to train a high-powered telescope on Hornsby, he'd probably be able to see the front door of her flat.

He parked her in his living area—although she wasn't sure who could ever live in such clean, uncluttered surroundings—while he vanished through an archway. The all-white room she was in disappeared around a corner into the unknown. It was all soaring ceilings, white marble surfaces and spiral staircases. He'd lived here for three years, he'd told her casually. Which meant post-Natalie.

Not the home of a man who wanted children in his life, was her first thought.

She wandered out onto the terrace, thankful for its high balustrade. Vertigo wasn't her favourite sensation. There was an inviting pool and spa, with lights glowing in their blue-green depths. A man attending to the Babylonian-style hanging gardens around the pool nodded to her, before gathering his equipment and disappearing inside.

If a man had all this, she reflected, a Porsche Carrera and a bank, what did he have left to strive for?

Around her the city was a-glitter as dusk gave way to dark. Neon signs on neighbouring buildings pulsed with the same nervy rhythm the home territory of Samos Stilakos inspired in her heart.

However had she come to be in this place of all places? There was no way she should allow herself to succumb to another fling with him. Already she was struggling to maintain the barricades round her heart. She tried to remind herself of Mark's treachery, but found it hard to think of him here.

'It's too early in the evening for our balcony scene. You'd better come inside.'

The deep, mocking voice made her start. She turned and the breath seized in her throat. Sam stood at the terrace doors. He'd changed into casual trousers and a black, open-necked shirt. It deepened the velvet magnetism of his dark eyes and the olive tones in his skin, hung elegantly on his powerful frame, hinting at the muscled contours of his chest.

He looked relaxed and ready to play. Not the office Sam. The other one.

He strolled across to her. His hair was still damp from the shower, and he smelled of clean masculinity. He was her boss, she told herself giddily as an erotic mixture of tangy scents whooshed to her head.

Nothing was going to happen.

He reached out to touch her hair, further destabilising her. 'I can't wait to see you at the managers' meeting like this.' There was a glow in the depths of his dark eyes. 'I might have to make you do the presentation, so I can properly appreciate you from all angles.'

'Oh, but,' she replied, laughing, her pulse escalating,

'I can't just keep wearing this dress all the time. I've worn it today, and now tonight… It sounds as if you don't ever want me to take it off.'

He laughed wickedly and his arm snaked around her waist. 'Nothing could be further from the truth. Come inside and we'll talk about it.'

Inside the white room, a throaty female voice rendered a sexy old jazz ballad with a moody mellowness. Candles had been lit, adding warmth to the room, and some anti-pasto and champagne had been laid out on a buffet cabinet. If this wasn't a scene set for seduction, her wires were seriously in need of straightening.

Sam opened the wine with casual expertise. 'I told my housekeeper how much you've eaten today, and she's worried.'

'What?' She cast a quick glance about. 'You mean—you have a woman here, on the premises?' Her words conjured instant visions of a Hollywood-style maid in a frilled apron, stilettos and nothing else, and as soon as they were out she went scarlet. 'Oh! I'm sorry, Sam!' *Dying* with embarrassment. If only she could sink through at least twenty-seven floors. 'Truly! I didn't mean that as it sounded.'

He surveyed her, amusement in his gaze, and handed her a glass. 'I do have a woman. Not exactly on the premises, but close to the premises. She lives a couple of floors below with her husband. That was Martin. You might have seen him outside earlier. He doubles as my driver.'

'Oh. Of course.' She gave a foolish laugh. 'What else?' She sank down onto a white sofa with her wine, and nearly lost her balance as the deep, decadent cushioning dragged her down into its sumptuous embrace. She saw

Sam grin. What had happened to her legendary poise? Anyone would think she'd never been up in the stratosphere before with a sophisticated billionaire intent on having his way with her.

She laughed off her momentary disconcertion with graceful aplomb, but to be honest, faced with the old dilemma, her insides were churning. A massive risk was shaping up here. Her job, her plan, her foolish, stupid heart…

Looking too darkly sexy and nonchalant to be safe, Sam leaned against the buffet, sampling the occasional olive. He shot her a glance of lazy amusement. 'I'm sorry you find this room uncomfortable. If you like we can move somewhere else.' He tilted his dark head towards the archway.

What was through there? The master bedroom? 'No, no. It's not. It's—quite lovely here. Whatever makes you think I'm uncomfortable?'

'I've been studying your body language. I think I'm beginning to get the hang of it.'

A warning pang cut through her, but she saw the teasing light in his eyes and rose to the challenge, stretching her legs out in front of her and leaning back. 'You've got no chance,' she retorted with a careless laugh. 'I'm famous for my acting ability.'

'You're good, I admit that. *Yes, Mr Stilakos. No, Mr Stilakos*…as though we'd never been together.' He looked steadily at her and added softly, 'Never been lovers.'

Her heart made a wild leap and she quickly dropped her gaze, then, just as though his gleaming dark eyes weren't eating her up, and her pulse weren't madly racing, she said, 'What about you? You're very good yourself.' She put on a grim face and deepened her voice. 'So stern and dignified.'

His eyebrows twitched up in amusement. His gaze flickered to her legs, then met hers. 'Do you enjoy working?'

'Of course. I love it.'

'And you like the bank?'

She nodded.

'You've been there a long time,' he observed lazily. 'Have you ever considered exploring further afield?'

She shrugged. 'Not really. I've liked all the jobs I've had there.'

He picked up a small platter of the antipasto and strolled across to her with it. 'And you're very talented. Always cool, never ruffled. Always smiling and pleasant. Beautiful, efficient Ms O'Dea. But what goes on underneath?' He dropped down beside her and offered her the food. 'Who was the guy who taught you to play it safe?' His tone was casual, but no way was this a casual question, and his eyes pierced her with an alertness that threatened to penetrate her crucial internal fortifications. 'What do you think about when the lights go out, Eleanor?'

'Nothing.' She smiled and fluttered her lashes. 'You keep me working so hard, I just fall straight to sleep when the lights go out.' She accepted a caviare-laden cracker with the same calm smile, and forced herself to bite into it. But it was damnably hard to swallow. Her heart had started an uncomfortable pounding, and he was close. Far too close. This was hardly the seduction line she'd expected.

His long muscled leg was near enough to brush hers and light her up with fireworks. One part of her wanted it to happen, but another part wanted to run to the balcony and jump on the first passing jet to Hornsby. Was it fair for a boss to delve into the private personal heart of his PA?

Her aching cheeks needed a rest. She got off the sofa and strolled about, pretending to study the art works with interest, as conscious of the current between them as if it were tangible. In need of a breathing space, she stopped in front of a square of white canvas.

'What do you think?' he said, coming to stand next to her. The black hairs on his forearm lightly grazed her arm, with electric results. 'Inspiring? Uplifting?'

She put her head on one side as coolly as if her awareness of him weren't pulsing through her veins. The skin where his arm had brushed hers instantly craved it again, and she couldn't resist swaying imperceptibly closer for another touch. 'It's white,' she said, fleetingly closing her eyes to savour the brief tingling contact. 'Certainly a clean look.'

'Not empty and lifeless, like this place?'

'Don't you like it here?' She glanced wonderingly around at all the trappings of understated luxury that could only be available to the very, very rich, and risked turning to look at him.

His sensual dark gaze riveted her to the floor. 'I think I like it better this evening than I ever have before.' There was no easy smile with the words. His gorgeous, sexy mouth was as grave as if he were speaking from the heart.

With masterful ease he caught her in his arms. The dark desire in his eyes seared her like a flame. She'd play it cool this time, her wild thoughts flew. Hold back. Try not to expose herself as a weak, vulnerable fool.

But he held her head between his hands and kissed her, and her susceptible body surged to his remembered touch in rapturous welcome.

There was no playing it cool. At the first brush of his lips desire blazed in her blood like a bushfire. Just as he had the first time, he tasted her mouth with a tenderness so ravishing it turned her knees to water, and her breasts swelled in arousal as he slid his teeth across her lower lip with slow, sexy eroticism.

He pulled her hard into him and deepened the kiss, intensifying the intimacy by slipping his tongue inside and plundering her mouth with an artful teasing she was powerless to resist.

Helpless thrills quivered through her as his long fingers stroked the length of her spine and moulded her to his hard, vibrant body. She clung to him, her bones melting, a sweet urgency between her thighs, her breasts and straining nipples in delicious friction with his chest.

She kneaded his powerful shoulders and gave herself up to the voluptuous pleasure of his big, lean frame in contact with her soft curves. The taste and scent of him fuelled her potent memories of him, and fanned the flames of her secret longings.

He snatched the very air from her lungs. The kiss deepened to a molten pitch, her passion for more of him fighting with her need for oxygen. But he was in supreme control. In the very nick of time his sensual hands traversed her arms to her shoulders, and he ended it, breaking from her.

She swayed a little on her four-inch heels, light-headed for lack of oxygen, and he put a hand on her shoulder. 'Steady there,' he said with some amusement. But for all his cool, his deep voice sounded dark and gravelly, and through his dark lashes his eyes were black fire. 'That's how I remembered you tasting,' he said, exultation in his voice.

Knowing she was flushed and dishevelled, she angled away from him and made an effort to tidy her hair and smooth down her dress. 'How?' she said croakily, panting, shocked by the uncontrolled response he'd raised in her. With just a kiss!

'Sexy. Sweet. *Wild.*'

His eyes were smouldering, and her heart trembled at the intensity betrayed by his voice. Summoned by his mesmeric gaze, she felt overwhelmingly tempted to throw caution to the winds and melt back into his arms. Dimly her mind grappled with the awesome strength of the passion threatening to unleash itself in her. Had it always been there, or was it only when *he* touched her?

'I've thought of you so often since that night, dream girl,' he said thickly, reaching to twine a strand of her hair behind her ear. 'I've never met a woman like you.'

Dream girl! *Her?* But he was Samos Stilakos, and she was just… If he knew even the half of her ordinary old reality! No one had ever said anything so romantic to her, and, though he sounded sincere, how could he be believed? It was all happening too fast.

Unsure of how to respond, she backed a little away from him. 'Isn't it time for us to leave? For—for the restaurant?'

He blinked, but before he could make another move she excused herself as gracefully as she could, considering the strained breathlessness of her voice, swooped on her bag, and escaped to the guest bathroom.

Safe inside, she leaned back against the door and closed her eyes. *Dream girl.* The question had to be faced. Had he given her the job because she'd slept with him? And…because he wanted a repeat performance of that night? But he would have to remember her absolute rejection of an affair. He must.

Perhaps, though… An excitement there was no repressing uncoiled inside her. If there was a chance he was sincere, if that night was still as vivid to him as it was to her…

If he'd truly felt that deep connection, and craved *more*…

She hugged her arms tightly around her. There were reasons she mustn't succumb, she knew, but she needed time to recall them. Just a little time.

After a few moments of deep breathing, she recovered some semblance of sanity and came to a decision. If he did expect more she would have to remind him of her unshakeable stance on affairs, leave with stylish dignity and go straight home. Otherwise…well, otherwise, she'd just go with the flow and…go with the flow.

She washed and applied fresh make-up, and smeared her lips with moisturiser.

When she emerged Sam had slipped on a jacket, and held the car keys dangling from his lean fingers. The glance he gave her from beneath his dark brows was searching.

'Everything all right?' he enquired.

She smiled and arched her brows. 'Of course. Everything's fine.'

They didn't have far to drive to The Rocks. He parked the car in one of the small, private car parks converted from the old cellars of some adjoining buildings in the wharf area. As they climbed the stairs to the street he put a hand on her elbow to steady her, almost as a lover would, or a husband.

The restaurant he'd chosen was famous for its cuisine and glittering clientele. She made a covert survey of the room for famous faces, only to find numerous heads swivelling *their* way.

Their table was discreetly placed, perfect for a lover's tryst, or a quiet interrogation between boss and PA. 'Every man in this room envies me,' Sam murmured, with a gentle but possessive touch in the small of her back as the *maître d'* pulled out her chair.

She looked enquiringly at him, and her heart trembled at the warmth in his dark glance. 'Do you sweet-talk all your PAs so outrageously when you wine them and dine them?' she said, once they were settled and he'd ordered the wine.

Amusement glimmered in his eyes. 'I don't wine them and dine them.'

Questions clamoured in her brain. The evidence pointed another way. She needed to get things straight. Was she dining with him as a woman, or as his PA? 'But here you are,' she persevered, 'wining and dining *me*, sweet-talking me—'

'*Kissing* you.' His eyes darkened and he leaned forward, making her gasp as he traced her lower lip with a sensual fingertip. The bold desire in his eyes threatened to send her insides into meltdown all over again. 'How else am I to get to know you?'

Her heart bounded in her chest. Could she be hearing aright? Wasn't this the theme of her most extreme fantasy?

He sat back, a small frown creasing his brow. 'I know what's worrying you. It's tricky when office rules get tangled up with a genuine attraction. The important thing is not to let it get in the way.'

Her breath caught. 'The—the attraction?'

'No. The office.'

The words sank in. Samos Stilakos, worldly, sophisticated, gorgeous and elusive target for equally sophisticated, beautiful women, was spelling it out. To *her*.

'Do you believe in magic?' His warm, ardent gaze
thrilled her. 'It might sound like a cliché, but what else can
you call it when you meet someone—in the unlikeliest circumstances!—and instantly feel that rare connection?'

The breath caught in her throat. Hadn't this been her
own instinct at their first encounter?

'What do you think?' he added, seduction in his dark
eyes, in the smile playing on his sensuous mouth. 'Am I
telling it like it is? Do you feel it too?'

Her lashes fluttered uncontrollably, much like her
unsafe heart. Sweet talk had rarely been more convincing, or exciting. 'I think you're giving me the rush,' she
said huskily, almost needing to cling to the table edge. 'I
think you're making my head spin.'

'I hope so, Eleanor. I hope your head's spinning.
You're not convincing me with that oh, so cool and collected act. Not when I know how hot the little siren is
who's hiding behind that face.'

Visions rose in her mind of some of her unprecedented,
adventurous acts of passion on the Night of Nights, and
she couldn't prevent a fiery blush from rising up from her
toes and infusing her entire body.

He grinned, as if the scorching scenes flashing through
her mind were just as visible to him. Impossibly, she felt
her blush deepen. In an attempt to cool her confusion she
reached for her wine, took a much larger gulp than was
wise and nearly choked.

Sam laughed and his lashes descended in satisfaction.
'Paydirt! Come on, then. I want to know everything about

you. If you could have anything you wanted in the world, what would be your deepest, most fervent desire?'

She gazed at his lean, handsome face, smiling at her with such challenging warmth, and the truth resonated in her heart with a certainty that shook her to her soul.

Her chance to have a child, that was certain, but was that all? Didn't she want it the easy way? The old-fashioned, loving way? With someone she loved, who could love her?

Someone like…?

Her mind reared back from the unthinkable. Her lips parted, but no words came.

All her flippant protestations at Beth's warnings flashed before her now for the hollow bravado they had been. Who had she been kidding? She hadn't just taken the job for the money. She'd wanted to be close to him. How foolish and predictable. If she didn't fight it, the same old dreams would drive her to heartbreak now as inexorably as they had in the past. The next thing she knew, she'd be giving in to imagining floating down the aisle, visualising nights in the arms of her loving husband, dreaming of his beautiful, dark-eyed children…

'All right, let me guess,' he said. 'You'll never be happy until you're CEO of the bank. You want my job.' He spoke lightly, but all at once the question in his gaze was serious.

But if there was one certain thing her advanced years had taught her, it was how fast he'd vanish in a puff of smoke if she revealed the naked truth. So she deflected the query with an easy laugh. 'You're so right, Sam. How did you guess? And—and what would be your most fervent desire?'

His eyes veiled, and he lowered his black lashes. 'Ah…well…ordinary things. It's amazing how hard they are to come by, though, isn't it? You think you have them in your grasp, and then…' He shrugged and drained his glass.

What couldn't he come by easily? she wondered. A man as blessed as he'd been, with wealth, charm, genuine masculine beauty… Was he referring to Natalie?

'I often think now it would be good to live on an island,' he continued, 'without all the chaos, where life was simple.' He shrugged. 'There, that's probably my genes talking. My grandfather hailed from Samos, in the Aegean.' His eyes smiled into hers, and he reached across the table for her hand. 'I'll take you there one day, Eleanor, and show you.'

Such a beautiful promise. How many women had he made it to? But it enchanted her all the way down to her curled-up toes.

He told her other things, about his boyhood, his father, the mischief he and his cousin had got up to together. His words evoked a world of family life and good times, of beaches and bush picnics, far removed from the world he inhabited now. Despite her turmoil, she felt herself falling deeper under his spell. If only he wouldn't grin in that seriously weakening way. It was too easy to visualise the boy he must have been—the sweet, sexy, macho boy.

Perhaps she could risk one more time. Mightn't it be possible to have one more fling with him? One last fantastic night?

The waiter brought their meals, but she hardly noticed the food. She was too heavily in thrall to the most charming seducer in Sydney. But though he flattered her with his wicked words, there was sincerity in his gaze too, and warmth in his smile. His velvet eyes dwelled on her as if she were the most interesting and desirable woman in the world. She found herself telling him things about her life and her friends as if *he* were a friend. He flirted with her, mocked her and made her laugh, just as he had on that night.

All the time, though, it was clear where it was heading. The knowledge was in his every glance, in every brush of his fingers.

When they were offered the dessert menu, he said, 'Shall we stay here for dessert, or head somewhere else?' His mouth was grave, but the shimmer in his dark eyes was the colour of sin.

When had she ever resisted dessert?

CHAPTER SIX

WAS he drunk, Sam wondered, or was it the summer night that made him want to leap and spin about in some crazy dance? Strolling the uneven streets beside Ellie O'Dea, he pretended to catch his shoe, and lingered back a step to drink in the radiance of her heavy fall of hair, the subtle sway of her taut little edible behind.

The image of her moonlit shape on the hotel balcony rushed back to him with its erotic power, and his blood stirred with the old enchantment. She cast him back an enquiring smile, a sparkle in her eyes as if she guessed his small subterfuge. He grinned and caught her up again. The chemistry was magic, he thought with escalating excitement, but still he sensed a tension in her, a restraint.

How did she manage to remain so elusive? He could gaze into those clear, smiling eyes till he drowned, but why did it feel as if she were still wearing her mask? Since the first, every step he took with her was a tread on eggshells. Any false move, and she might vanish into the night as easily as she'd slipped through his fingers on that fateful dawn.

They reached the entrance to the car park and he used his security key to unlock the street door. Despite their renovation, the fishy harbour smell still permeated the dank walls of the old cellars, and rose to greet him as they descended to the lower floor. The few other cars parked there earlier had departed, and only the Porsche remained. Their steps echoed in the empty place.

They reached the shadowy alcove where the car was parked, and stopped to face each other. In the sudden silence and isolation, Sam felt an urgency to break through the constraints. They'd been lovers once. They would be again. Why pretend?

He scanned her face and said, his voice catching with the force of his desire, 'Do you know how much I want you?'

In the shadowy light uncertainty swirled in her eyes as she searched his face. After a heartbeat's hesitation she said, 'No—yes. Perhaps.'

'Do you ever tell the truth?' In mock frustration, he wound a swathe of her hair around his hand, held it to his face and inhaled its honeyed scent. The intoxication of it, the memories it evoked, flooded him with lust, and he groaned. In his urgent need to pin her down he took her smooth, satin arms in his hands. 'You do know. We both know. Tell the truth. You haven't forgotten what it was like that night! You still want me!'

His passionate conviction swept Ellie along on a giddy, irresistible tide. With her pulse thundering in her ears, she confessed tremulously, 'No, Sam, I haven't forgotten. I want you.'

He held her a little closer. His deep voice, his dark eyes, were compelling. 'And we'll always be honest with each other. Lovers without lies. Do you agree?'

Lovers. On his tongue the word had such thrilling con-notations she felt as if she'd been transported to some magic realm where everything was possible. Hope shivered down her spine.

'Hey.' Concern shone in his eyes. 'You're cold.' He slipped off his jacket and hung it around her shoulders.

The moment was so reminiscent of that first night, she was overwhelmed with the strongest sensation of *déjà vu*. He stood surveying her in it, his eyes growing more darkly intense and smoulderingly sexual, and her stomach coiled in excitement.

He pulled her against him and kissed her with hungry passion. His insistent lips demanded her equal response, and she surrendered to the sizzling assault and gave in, kissing him back with fervour as the ready fire ignited in her blood.

Her knees weakened, and she raised her arms around his neck, clutching at his thick black hair, heedless of the damp pungent smells of harbour and wet cement in the old converted cellar.

The element of risk in their dark corner reminded her of the forbidden flavour of their first embrace. She remembered how they'd urged each other on to greater and greater acts of abandonment, and it induced her to throw caution to the winds. She wanted him to do more than kiss her, and he seemed to know it.

He pushed her back against the car, his mouth on her throat and collar-bone, his lean, bronzed hands caressing her swollen breasts, seeking the taut nipples, inflaming them through her clothes.

He lowered his dark head, and through the light fabric took first one, then the other sensitive peak in his mouth to suck and tease. It brought her to such an intense pitch of wild, sweet pleasure that her desire roared through her like a firestorm and flamed between her thighs.

But their clothes were in the way. With feverish hands she tore at his shirt buttons and revealed his powerful, bronzed chest. Then, with hands and mouth, she explored the rippling satin skin with its whorls of black hair. She felt his flat nipples tauten under her tongue, relishing her power to send pleasure shuddering through his big, strong frame.

Panting, she stood back to enjoy the sight of him in disarray, his gorgeous chest gleaming from his open shirt, his breath tearing and catching like hers, his eyes dark and heavy-lidded in arousal.

She wanted more.

Instinctively, as though attuned to her hunger, he pushed up her dress and laid her thighs bare. 'Such charming thighs,' he murmured, his voice gravelled, eyes black as Lucifer's.

She waited, panting, for his next move. She felt as if she were on fire, her body a vessel of desire, his every light touch a match to the flame of her overheated flesh. He placed a caressing hand on her knee, then, with tantalising slowness, traced a wicked, purposeful finger up her leg, slipping it inside her inner thigh to tease the silken, sensitive skin there. With charged fingers he stroked closer, and ever deliciously closer, to the hot, urgent place concealed by her flimsy little panties.

She dug her fingers into his powerful shoulders, and held her breath, her heart's blood thundering in her ears, aching, aching for him to go the whole way. At the elastic's edge, his caressing hand paused for an electric, tingling instant, then, when suspense brought her nearly to breaking-point, crept on, to traverse the fabric across her vibrant mound. She clung to him, unbreathing, hypnotised by the dark magic of his touch.

He slipped his fingers underneath the fabric, and she quivered and gasped in delight. With sensual, knowing strokes he parted her sensitive folds while she leaned back against the car, half clinging to him in swooning ecstasy, on fire for him to find the pulsating pleasure spot at the centre. He made contact and she gave a small, wrenching cry. Tenderly, expertly he caressed her throbbing clitoris, then slipped a finger inside her slick, moist channel and stroked, rousing her with astonishing speed to a sweet, sobbing climax.

She sagged against him, supported in his arms, her face buried in his strong neck. He held her there for some heart-thundering moments, then tilted her back and brushed her face with quick little tender kisses. After a few seconds he let her go, and they contemplated each other in the pulsing silence.

Her heart thudded. Challenge gleamed in his fierily aroused eyes. Instinctively she understood the question. How far did she dare to go with him? In tacit response she ran her tongue-tip over her dry lips, then gasped with shock as in a quick, wicked movement he whipped down her pants.

His audacity exhilarated her. The element of danger pushed her passion and excitement to an even wilder pitch. Spurred to respond, she grasped his belt buckle and released it, and heard his sharp intake of breath as she slid her hand down to caress the promising virile bulge inside his trousers.

'Quickly, quickly,' she panted, and tried to help him to ease the zip down over his erection.

He gave a strangled laugh, and pushed her hands away to free himself unaided. With wide-eyed anticipation, she surveyed his impressive arousal, rock-hard and rampant.

He swept her onto his lap as he lowered himself onto the car's bonnet, and, with swift efficiency, positioned her so she was face to face with him.

She gave a sensual little wriggle, then levered herself to ease down on him, gasping with delight as his velvet hardness filled her. Then, holding her tight in his arms, his chest grazing her breasts, he rocked her, gazing into her eyes as he thrust repeatedly into her. In an escalating rhythm, he stroked her inner flesh, completely filling her sheath with such delicious, heavenly vigour, she could only cry out with each amazing plunge.

The sweetness and intensity of being held and gazed at and rocked with such thrilling intimacy rushed her up a wild, steep curve of gasping excitement, to an explosive, rippling climax.

After the last rapturous aftershock they stilled, gazes meshed in a primitive communion. At last the distant sound of voices from the street jolted them from their pleasure. Sam eased her onto her feet. Shakily, she scrambled to tidy her clothes, while he refastened his.

He stared at her, his breathing ragged as he surveyed her panting dishevelment. 'Let's go home,' he murmured, and opened the car door and ushered her inside.

He settled in beside her and bent to softly kiss her mouth. When he drew back she touched his face. She felt wrapped in a cocoon of blissful accord with him, knowing she was able to match his need for passion and excitement, as he matched hers.

'Not the place I would have chosen,' he murmured in his deep voice, his hand possessive on her thigh. 'We'll do better next time. Where do you live?'

'Hornsby.'

'Hornsby! My God,' he groaned, then fired the engine. After he nosed the car out into the street, he gave her an intense, glowing look. 'Has anyone ever told you what a beautiful and exciting, *sensual* woman you are?'

'You did,' she answered huskily. 'On the night of the masked ball.' He laughed a husky laugh, and, secure in the warmth of his admiration, she stayed enveloped in her dreamy, magical cocoon all the way to Hornsby.

It wasn't so far, now the night-time traffic had diminished a little. After a while her breathing calmed and she fell silent. The silence pulsed with the anticipation of more passion to come.

Sam occasionally glanced her way to make some observation, but she was barely aware of the Sydney nightscape. She was thinking about what would happen next. About making love with him again. In her bed.

Samos Stilakos. In her bedroom.

She made a mental review of the room, trying to visualise him in it. She hoped she'd made her bed. After the luxury of his sky-palace she wondered what he would think of rugs picked up cheap from the Taj Bazaar, and cushions embroidered by her mother's tapestry circle. It was hard to imagine him in her flat. She had the unpleasant realisation that it would declare, far more stridently than words ever could, the inequalities between the Boss and his PA.

What if one of her friends drove by and saw the Porsche? How would it look to them? The romantic cloud she was floating on lost a bit of height. A nasty little voice from her daily down-to-earth self piped up. What had he actually said to her that meant anything? Had she just allowed herself to be carried away?

'You'd better direct me from here,' he said in his deep, quiet voice.

She started, realising how close they were, and with a racing pulse gave him some directions that brought them into the entrance of her street. 'Along here, on the left.' She almost wished she could tell him to turn around and go in the opposite direction.

She swallowed. 'That's it there. The duplex.'

Her heart seized then as she was struck by the most horrible thought.

Hadn't she left all that stuff she'd downloaded about the IVF process on the kitchen table? *And* there were coloured brochures from the clinics.

She blenched at the thought of him seeing them. How much would it reveal about her? Her failure to find a partner in time. Her *desperation*…? A man with his razor-sharp intelligence would put two and two together and comprehend it all.

Perspiration broke out on her upper lip. She couldn't invite him in.

She dug her fingers into her palms. It would be too much to hope he'd had enough loving for one night. Even if he didn't want to make love again, he'd expect her to ask him in for coffee.

Her heart began to thump with the most ridiculous, erratic rhythm, and she uncurled her hands and surrepti-tiously put them to her cheeks. What had she done? She'd asked for this. She'd got herself into it, and now there was no graceful way out.

He drew up under the streetlamp in front of her gate and turned off the engine. The silence grew electric. She sat taut and still in her seat, tension gripping her throat.

He turned his head to examine her with a questioning gaze. She knew what he expected.

What she'd led him to expect.

He thought she would take him through her front door, lead him to her bedroom, take him into her bed. Or at least show him into her kitchen and sit him down at the table, with a coffee mug filled with instant.

He smiled and touched her cheek, his dark eyes warm. 'Is coffee on offer?'

Her eyelids lowered. How could she refuse? 'Of course.' She forced a smile.

His brows twitched curiously as he studied her face, but he sprang out and swiftly came around to open her door. She got out, and, with his arm around her, walked through the gate and up the path with him, every step a step closer to mortification, her brain teeming with desperate measures.

She would have to make him promise on his honour not to read anything. Or he'd have to promise not to go into the kitchen. But what if she'd left the literature on her bedside table? That was a real possibility. If she had, what were the chances he'd be able to avoid it?

There was only one solution.

No way, *no way* could she let him in, and she would have to find a compelling reason.

They arrived at her front door, and the security lamp switched itself on. She delved into her bag for the keys, but her shaking hands were ineffectual. After a hectic few moments, Sam took the bag from her hands, held it to his ear and gave it a shake. He plunged his hand in, and with a couple of deft movements produced the keys. 'Is this them?'

She nodded.

He handed them to her, murmuring, 'One of the few worthwhile things a man derives from a marriage. The ability to find a woman's keys.'

She slipped the key into the lock, then turned to face him, her back to the door. She cleared her throat. 'Look. About the coffee, Sam—' Her voice was embarrassingly strained.

He searched her face. 'You're out of coffee?' He smiled, desire smouldering in his eyes. 'What is it? You don't want to invite me in, is that it?'

She'd thought of a reason. Still, her heart pounded like a coward's to use it. 'I can't,' she said. 'Not—not tonight. Not like this.'

'Like what?'

She made an inarticulate gesture. 'Like—the way we are.'

His dark gaze scanned her face. 'How are we?'

'I like you very much, of course—'

He laughed, but his eyes were watchful. 'I'd hope so, after what just happened.'

She flushed, intensely conscious of her wanton compliance a bare half-hour before. 'Yes, yes, I know, but—' she steeled herself '—you're my boss.'

The silence missed a heavy beat. 'So?'

With trepidation she realised that a rejection now would go hard, but anything was better than risking him seeing those brochures. She took a deep breath, and asserted with only a slight tremor in her voice, 'I work for you. It's not exactly a free and open relationship, is it?'

Somewhere underneath her bravado her heart was still madly thumping. She studied him suspensefully, her hands clenched.

He shook his head and blinked in disbelief. 'Let me get this straight. You're bringing *this* down to office politics?'

The stunned question in his eyes, and the tone of his voice, made it sound as if he believed that what was happening between them was something very special and romantic. She was swayed with sudden doubt. There had been those moments, compelling moments, when she'd believed in his sincerity, those tiny glimpses into his real self.

Shame threatened her certainty. The word *betrayal* popped into her head.

'Oh, well,' she faltered confusedly, 'isn't it a matter of ethics?'

Samos Stilakos made a searing intake of breath. His eyebrows shot up and he stared at her. 'What? You're telling *me* about—?' He straightened up to his full height and reeled back a step, as if his very honour had suffered a mortal wound. His eyes turned to jet. For an instant his strong, handsome face was frozen in outrage.

Then he met her paralysed gaze and made a visible effort to recover his control.

Guilt began to flood through her, but after a few heart-stopping seconds he merely shook his head and shrugged. If he was enraged at such an insult, he summoned formidable restraint to conceal it.

Why did he have to be such a gentleman? It made her excuse all the weaker.

'So it's goodnight, then,' he said, back to being polite after the warmth and intimacy of the evening. He searched her face with a frown, then shrugged again and turned away from her, his eyes as chill and remote as the polar icecap.

She felt punished. It was as if the sun had gone out.

Irrationally then, she wished he could at least kiss her goodnight. 'I'm sorry, Sam,' she said nervously before he could walk down the path and leave her alone. 'No hard feelings. Won't you at least—shake hands?'

He turned. The glance he shot her from beneath his sardonic brows pierced her as if she were transparent, right through to her marshmallow spine. It was deeply discomfiting. 'Would this be about the *adventurer*, by any chance?' he said drily.

She gasped, momentarily struck speechless, and shook her head in utter, absolute rejection. 'Wh-what?' she stuttered. 'What are you talking about! No! As if *he*— As if *that*—' She took a deep breath. '*That* has nothing to do with *this*.' Anger made her unusually reckless, and she started to talk very rapidly, her words nearly falling over each other in her need to defend herself. 'If you must know I'm wondering about the others,' she blustered, with a defiant glare. 'You know—Schanelle, Vanessa, Sasha…' She waved her hand about agitatedly to indicate the dozens, probably thousands of women he'd seduced and forgotten, but when she saw his expression her heart shuddered to a halt. 'Everyone knows what happened with them,' she squeezed out.

His eyes had turned as hard as stone, his mouth a grim, straight line. She felt more than a bit frightened. For once she'd really lost her cool.

He said in a clipped, level voice, 'Sasha left because her fiancé was transferred to Brisbane. Schanelle got a better job offer in the Prime Minister's department in Canberra. Vanessa lost her position because she'd falsified her qualifications and wasn't up to the job.'

'Oh.' There was no mistaking the authority of the

words. She sagged back against the door, aghast at the fool she'd made of herself. 'Oh. Oh, I'm sorry. I shouldn't have said— Sam…'

'Forget it,' he said coldly. 'You were right. *This* would be wrong. My mistake, Ms O'Dea. I apologise for harassing you.' He swung sharply on his heel and walked away.

She didn't watch him leave. She turned her face to the door. As her key turned in the lock she heard the gate click shut. It cut through her with a lonely, final sound.

She nearly fell into the hall, tripping over a pile of rubbish just inside the door. She kicked it aside and hit the light switch. Numbly, she stumbled to the kitchen.

A jumble of indigestible emotions seized her, so intense she could have screamed. She noticed the muddle of papers and booklets scattered across the table, and swiped them to the floor. Then she thought better of it, picked them up, tore them into frantic little pieces and thrust them into the bin.

This was the time for alcohol. But she never kept the stuff in her flat, and had to resort to warming milk in the microwave. She drank a few sips, then made for the shower, taking care not to look at herself in any mirror along the way.

She felt as if something huge and jagged had lodged in her chest. It wasn't until she emerged from the bathroom clean, scrubbed and pyjamaed, her hair in a pony-tail, prepared for a final check of the locks, that she noticed the rubbish in the hall.

It had been a pile of bags and boxes delivered by courier, no doubt neatly stacked inside by her kindly next-door neighbour, who must have used the emergency key she held. Now it was a dishevelled mess, boxes with their lids off, tissue-swathed fabrics spilling out, shoes she could never have afforded, skewed across the floor.

She recognised them all, of course. They were the other things she'd tried on today that she'd liked. They amounted to a fortune's worth. How could a man so concerned with the bank's bottom line be so generous?

Then with sudden anger she thought, how dared he do this? How dared he not accept her refusal? What sort of man could not take *no* for an answer?

Long into the restless night, as she tossed in her empty bed her brain churned with the answers. *Arrogant, domineering, controlling, underhanded, cunning…*

She kept remembering that humiliating moment when he'd looked at her as if he could see right through to her very soul. The sheer, infuriating gall of it.

What could a man like *him* know about a woman like *her*?

CHAPTER SEVEN

SAM groaned and rolled over.

A minute later he was on his feet, dragging on gym shoes, shorts and singlet. A brisk run through the dawn streets of the old city was often the most pleasant start to the day, but not this day. This day required a punishing routine in the basement gym, followed by a stiff workout in the pool.

By the time he'd showered and shaved, donned an impeccably laundered shirt and tied his silk tie, he'd worked out a sane approach. He'd tell her succinctly that any personal association between them was in the past. He'd make it clear he had a bank to run and would not tolerate the distractions of feminine behaviour. He'd offer her a transfer...

Though what if she took it up?

No. He doubted she would. Where would she find conditions to equal what she had?

But as for the *personal* front...

In the Sirius basement he used his pass-key for the lift. As the lift drew closer to his floor the recollection of her astounding behaviour grew sharper and more stinging. Ellie O'Dea would learn he was not a man desperate for the company of beautiful women. The world was awash with redheads more beautiful.

More honest. More open, more straightforward.

More receptive. More compliant.

More *grateful* to have been offered the opportunity of enjoying an entire night with a virile and sensitive lover. If she only knew the desperate lengths some women had gone to to catch his eye. Actresses. *Models.*

Contrary to what he'd expected, and had carefully primed himself for, she wasn't at her desk, and there was no sign of her having arrived and gone off somewhere.

He frowned. Excellent. That gave him more time to concentrate on the important matters of the day. Although... She wouldn't have taken the day off, would she? Or...

A paralysing thought struck him. What if she'd decided against coming back at all?

Ellie woke late. She knew Sam would have been expecting her to be there before him, but after the heavy night she found it impossible to hurry.

Her hair took ages to dry, it wouldn't twirl neatly into its roll, and in the end, in desperation, she left it down. When it came to dressing she remembered that her better business suit was in Sam's car and the other at the cleaner's.

It was an emergency. She had her pride to consider. A woman in her situation couldn't, just couldn't, face the man again in nasty old clothes. There was only one thing for it.

On the way in to work she took a detour.

At David Jones it was early in the shoppers' day, and there were few others to contend with. Knowing instinctively this was not a battle that could be won with inferior weapons, she bypassed the floor of cheaper brands to head straight for the designer section.

Driven by the clock, she had to make her choice quickly. The first thing that called to her was a slim black dress. It was chic and feminine, with small cap sleeves in black embroidered tulle, and a price tag she'd have gasped at only a day earlier. With her rich red hair and white skin it looked stunning. She agonised over it for several uncertain minutes. No one had ever shown up at work in such a dress. She'd have to adjust her IVF timeline. Was a job worth so much sacrifice?

Yes! The answer rang in her head like a bell.

The saleswoman looked doubtful when Ellie said she'd prefer to keep it on and wear it to work, but she'd made her decision. It made a hole in her savings account, but she paid for it with barely a flinch.

It was only when she left the shop that she allowed herself to acknowledge the knot in her chest connected with Sam. Every step closer to the bank was an ordeal, but if she could just get past this one difficult day with him…

By the time she arrived the building was humming. People she passed stared and said, 'Ellie! *Amazing* dress,' and she smiled as though it were a normal day and everything was fine. Not that she was nervous. Not exactly. He would be as courteous as ever, she felt sure. That was the hard thing about him. He could be polite and freeze people to death, even when he wasn't sacking them.

It was past ten when she stepped out on her floor. Almost time for his coffee. She dropped her bag beside her desk, and hurried to put the milk she'd bought in the fridge.

Inside, at his executive rosewood desk, Sam heard the

sounds of arrival. He tensed, and glanced at his desk-clock with narrowed eyes.

Let her explain *this*.

He rose, adjusted belt and tie, and strolled to the door with the commanding, panther-like stride of Company Director and Chief Executive Officer.

She had her back to him, organising the espresso machine. Straight away he noticed she had her hair out again, hanging like a rich, silken waterfall. At the sound of the opening door she turned, and his insides were blown away.

Black. The dress was black. And above the lacy bodice the hint of her breasts glowed pearlescent white, like satin. And her legs. Her endless, endless legs. And surely her mouth was fuller and riper after last night's kissing? And her eyes, glittering like some— Dammit, he had to get a grip. Hadn't he learned? That glittering quality meant she was calculating something.

He said brusquely, 'You're late.'

Ellie heard the accusation in his tone and flushed. 'I know. I'm sorry. I was held up.' She saw his mouth thin, and hastened to placate him. 'I— Would you like some coffee?'

His expression froze. She realised the ghastliness of what she'd said and her heart plunged. For a horrified moment she hung there speechless, then pulled herself together to say faintly, 'Are you ready for—?'

He cut her off with a cool rejoinder. 'I've had coffee, thanks. Have you remembered the managers' meeting at ten-thirty?'

'Yes. Yes, of course.'

Damn. She'd forgotten it, but she still had ten minutes left in which to set up the boardroom. She'd already prepared illustrated take-home booklets for the managers, to support the presentation she'd helped Sam put together. At least she had no need to be ashamed of her work. She'd put a lot into it, and the booklet was a classy little production.

Sam strode away, and Ellie hurried to the boardroom. She placed the stack of booklets in a safe place for distribution at the end of the meeting, while she checked the audio-vis equipment, and set out the requisite stationery and mineral water on the oval table.

The managers began to trickle in, most of them greeting her with the easy familiarity of long acquaintance.

'What's this about a crèche in the building?'

With a jolt of alarm, Ellie saw that Trevor from Sales had spotted the booklets she'd prepared, and taken one to his place. 'Don't tell me we're doing an about-face and changing into a sensitive New Age bank,' he complained, idly flicking through it.

She was about to dive over and snatch it off him when Margot from Product Assessments, who still wore big eighties hair, leaned over to squint at it. 'Where'd you get this?' She perused the page, raising her Elizabeth Taylor eyebrows. 'Show me where it mentions the crèche.'

The manager on Trevor's left wanted to see as well, and in a short space of time several of them were loudly debating the pros and cons of having a childcare facility on the premises.

Ellie watched in apprehension, fearful of Sam arriving while they were talking about it. At any other time she'd have been delighted by their interest. She'd had a vague hope that, by including the research she'd gathered so the managers could take it away with them, the idea of a bank-funded nursery to support working mothers might grow, and have a trickle-up effect. It had been a momentary impulse to slip the page in. She'd half intended to slip it out again before the meeting, but yesterday's tumultuous events had completely wiped it from her mind.

The trouble was, Sam hadn't exactly approved her initiative. In fact, he wasn't aware of it.

'Well, it would have made all the difference to me in my day,' Margot told her colleagues. 'I could have kept coming to work. *I'd* have been the CEO by now. Instead, I had this dreadful struggle to keep going, and in the end it was easier to just stay at home with the twins and raise them poor. Good on you, Sam.'

Ellie looked around in alarm from where she was adjusting the screen. Sam had just walked in. Margot's rather penetrating voice immediately caught his attention, and to Ellie's horror he strolled over to her. He frowned and bent to look at the page they were all poring over. Ellie heard him say, 'A what? Where does it say that?'

With her heart in her throat, she watched Sam pick up the booklet. He leaned casually on a side table to scan it, then raised his eyes. From across the room his accusing gaze lasered to clash with hers. The enormity of what she'd done resounded in her head, and she felt the guilt rise to her cheeks in flaming neon. But pride wouldn't allow her to lower her eyes to a man who'd called her his dream girl and made frenzied love to her. Though blistered from head to toe, she held his gaze.

A cover story. For God's sake, why couldn't her fertile brain deliver? She was still racking her brains for one when her old ex-boss, Stephen Fletcher, swanned in.

'Hello all,' Fletcher said, dumping his briefcase,

somehow not noticing Sam at the other end of the room. Then, beaming and holding out his hands, 'Ellie, my love.' He made a big production of looking her over and whistling. 'Now, don't you look scrumptious?' He swung a portly arm around her and gave her a hug. 'Still running the bank? From the top now, eh?'

'*Fletcher.*'

The deep, brusque voice fractured the air like a whiplash. Fletcher started away from her as if he'd been shot, and conversations dribbled to a close. All heads turned.

Samos Stilakos had taken his power position at the front. In his elegant dark suit, his imposing height, powerful shoulders and strong masculine eyebrows emphasised his authority. 'If you wouldn't mind taking your hands off Ms O'Dea…' He spoke coolly, but his imperious eyes held dagger points. He pointed Fletcher to a vacant chair. 'Sit. Please.'

The *please* was an obvious afterthought.

Poor Fletcher's face crumpled. An embarrassed hush fell on the assembled group.

Sam nodded forbiddingly towards Ellie. 'Eleanor. The doors.'

She strolled to close them as casually as she could, sensing his gaze follow her every move from beneath his bristling brows. When she slipped into her own chair, she couldn't restrain herself from sending him a scathing glance for his treatment of her old boss.

Despite an icy look in return, Sam delivered his presentation in a relaxed style, like the professional he was. It went over well with the managers, who hadn't warmed to him when he'd first taken over the bank and cut so many of their perks. Now they applauded him, appreciating at last that they had a competent and dynamic leader at the helm.

He hardly looked her way, although a few times she had the definite sense he wanted to, but when he did flick her a glance his chiselled mouth was stern, his eyes coolly unreadable. He'd never looked more handsome. More smoulderingly sexy.

She kept her spine stiff, hyper-conscious of the things she'd said to him. Why should she feel so guilty? *He* should be guilty. It wasn't as if he'd said he loved her, was it? So why did she have to feel this huge, unswallowable lump in her chest?

What right did a man have to demand honesty from a woman anyway, just because he'd said a few romantic things?

He directed some occasional comments to her. They were smoothly polite, even considerate, on the surface. Only she could detect the biting under-edge. Once, when she reached for the water, several of the men sprang to assist her but Sam interrupted his talk to smoothly swoop on the carafe first. He poured her a glass and handed it to her with extreme courtesy, taking care not to touch her fingers.

Briefly their eyes clashed, his glinting, perhaps with some memory of a similar moment last night. Unless… Her unquiet blood stirred. Could he have been thinking of the car park? Was the potent scene still as raw in his senses as it was in hers—their greedy kisses, their avid lips and hands?

She fought the image off with a little shiver. It was ironic. The managers seemed more at ease with him than ever before, though that only made it worse. Before they broke up, to her horror someone felt confident enough to revive the discussion about the on-site crèche. Too clever not to recognise its value as an ice-breaker, Sam allowed the topic to continue, sitting seemingly relaxed, his lean, tanned hands lightly resting on the table.

Hands that had caressed her. Hands even now she wanted to reach out and touch.

The pros and cons of small babies in childcare were being robustly canvassed.

Sam listened to the debate with half an ear. His glance fell on *her*, a couple of simmering metres across from him, black lace at her breast, her long hair catching the light. She appeared to be listening attentively, but there was a rigidity in her posture. He grimaced. *Let* her be nervous. As though sensing his scrutiny, she angled her face away from him. The distinctive tilt of her head, the curve of her cheek, grabbed at something in his chest.

His jaw tightened. She was a mystery.

Ellie forced herself not to glance at him, though super-imposed on her brain was the recurring image of his stunned face at her front door. So she'd used a convenient lie. What else could she have done? Would he have enjoyed a heart-to-heart about her ovaries?

She made an effort to tune into the discussion. One of the firm's old dinosaurs was opposed to mothers working in any circumstances and had aroused a storm of debate.

'We need a younger woman's point of view,' Margot asserted, looking around. 'What do you think, Ellie? Could you imagine bringing your baby to work with you?'

Ellie's heart froze. All eyes turned on her, including Sam's. She had the sensation of her stomach dropping several storeys. This was the last thing—the *last* thing— she could discuss in his presence. In other circumstances she'd have loved to run this discussion, with these very same people, and knew she could do it well. But not in front of Sam. Not—for God's sake—after last night.

She avoided his eyes, in dread of seeing his lip curl, but still she felt his burning gaze sear her face like an oxy-acetylene torch. Oblivious to the undercurrents, the managers were fired up to persuade her to their points of view. Unknown to them, every word they said wounded her tender sensibility like napalm.

'Ellie won't want to work if she has a baby, will you, Ellie? She'll want to stay home and look after the kid properly, like any decent mother.'

'Rubbish, Gary,' Margot said testily. 'Women have the right to work. Ellie's a career girl through and through. She won't want to give it up for nappies and milky vomit. She'll go for having it all, won't you, Ellie? The job *and* the family.'

'Why can't her husband support her until the child goes to school?'

'He mightn't have a job. *She* might be the breadwinner.'

'It wouldn't work to bring a baby here,' someone growled. 'Too much distraction from the job. She'd be better off to put the kid in a nursery down the street.'

The arguments grew even more excruciating.

'But what if she wants to breast-feed?'

'Then she shouldn't have a baby unless she's in a position to do it.'

The discussion raged. All the way through it she could feel the weight of Sam's scrutiny burning a pathway into her quivering soul. Finally one of them stopped arguing long enough to notice her frozen silence. 'Look at poor Ellie. Here we are grilling her when she hasn't even begun to think of babies yet. Give the girl a break.'

The combined forces of all their eyes turned on her again.

Panic gripped her throat. She knew what they were all thinking. They were assessing her age, speculating about her love-life and her diminishing chances. Her ovaries were in the spotlight. In a moment some wit would mention the biological clock, and tell her to get a move on and find Mr Right.

It was the career girl's worst nightmare.

Normally, when public exposure or boss trouble threatened, she could summon a serene smile and handle it with aplomb. But right then she couldn't. For once she experienced performance failure. Her face felt stiff, and she knew her eyes were glassy.

She managed to push herself up on her high heels, and say with jerky dignity, 'If you'll all excuse me, there are some things I have to do.' With a bright, unfocused smile around at the assembly, she walked swiftly from the room, closed the door behind her and sprinted like an Olympic athlete for the Ladies.

After a few drastic minutes of hyperventilation—in lieu of a paper bag she had to bunch up a paper towel and pant into that—she dashed cold water on her face, and tried to pat it dry without disturbing her make-up. This was the worst day of her life so far, and she'd brought it all on herself. Her small effort to improve entitlements for the bank's workforce had blown up in her face.

She couldn't bear to imagine what Sam was thinking of her after she'd so seriously betrayed his trust. And how mortifying, how utterly humiliating, that he'd witnessed her crumble like that. How much had he guessed about her? Her soul screamed with embarrassment. She felt ready to burrow a hole in the tiles and bury herself there.

That a man, a sexual partner, a l—she shied from the L word—should see her in the light of a desperate spinster.

It took some heavy-duty slow, concentrated breathing to bring her pulse-rate back to a point approaching normal, so she could start to think.

She had to face it. She was definitely in the wrong over that booklet. The knowledge was unbearable, but how to right herself in his eyes? Her usual tactic of a sincere explanation with a lorryload of charm hardly seemed adequate this time. How would she justify *this*?

And after last night, the issue was so complicated. Shouldn't she apologise, just this once? Throw herself on his mercy, show him she had a conscience about insulting him and hurting his feelings? Crawl on her hands and knees to beg his forgiveness?

She left the sanctuary of the ladies' room with a half-formed plan of humbly admitting she was at fault, grovelling, and somehow appealing to his sense of fairness to leave the events of last night out of the equation.

As she approached the entrance to her office a burst of laughter reached her from the hall. With a jealous pang, she saw it was the group of managers, congregating in front of the lifts, exchanging what sounded like light-hearted banter with Sam. Judging by the approving glances they were giving him, rapport had been established. They were all basking in the sunshine of his smile. Even Fletcher looked to have been charmed into the fold.

She'd never felt so excluded in her life. She made the painful acknowledgement to herself that she'd do anything to have Sam smile at her like that again.

He caught sight of her and his face smoothed to become expressionless. 'Oh, there you are.' He detached himself from his worshippers and strode purposefully towards her. 'Come in here.' He opened his office door. 'We need to talk.'

She accompanied him tremulously, some weak part of her longing to abase herself, kiss his gorgeous bronzed feet and ankles and beg forgiveness, but another, stronger part knowing it was a mistake to ever acknowledge to a boss that he had the upper hand.

He halted in the middle of the room and confronted her, his lean, handsome face stern, his sensuous mouth compressed. He was quite close to her, as the crow flew, but somehow the small distance between them was sharply defined, like an unbridgeable chasm. Unfortunately, her body didn't understand what her mind knew, and surged with shameless longing for him to touch her.

'We need to get some things straight,' he said. 'Are you on the pill?'

She blenched. 'What?'

His sardonic brows lifted. 'Oh, it's the innocent maiden routine.'

She flinched as from a physical blow.

His dark eyes flickered over her in merciless condemnation as he said softly, 'Let me remind you, Eleanor, that you had unprotected sex last night. In a car park. I find it hard to believe that any woman, even a woman prone to screwing in such casual venues, wouldn't be alive to the risks.'

Her sensibilities felt savaged, but feminine honour demanded she defend herself. 'The possibilities of infection, do you mean?' she countered coldly. 'Yes, I am aware of it, and I intend to have a medical check at the first opportunity.'

A muscle tightened in his jaw and she knew she'd scored. 'I can take it, then, you are using a contraceptive?' His eyes were unfriendly. 'Considering that little discussion you took it upon yourself to engineer, it seemed reasonable to assume when you exited like that…a panicked gazelle springs to mind…that you might be fearful of being pregnant.'

She gave him a cold smile. 'I'm not fearful. There's no need to concern yourself.'

It was true. Pregnancy was probably the only thing left in life she wasn't concerned about. It was only two months since she'd given up using the pill, and with her ovaries, the chances of her conceiving so soon, if ever, were infinitesimal. Possibly non-existent.

'I can assure you,' she added sweetly, '*you* have nothing to worry about.'

She could tell by Sam's wintry expression the insinuation hadn't been lost on him. Anger flared in his eyes, and for a moment she thought he might seize her.

Goaded, Sam felt his hands twitch. He read the flash of uncertainty in her blue eyes, and clenched them to his sides. Touching her was now forbidden. With frustration he surveyed her slender form in the slim dress, her long legs fragilely balanced on the precarious shoes.

Her skin had never looked so meltingly soft and delicate as it did against the black lace trim. That white swell of breast just visible at the bodice was fatally desirable, or *would* have been if… He felt rising wrath. Where did a woman learn to be so unpredictable, so stubbornly intent on twisting things her way, so *difficult*?

Dammit, he was a man and he was in charge.

'My only concern is for your health and well-being,' he snapped. 'I wanted to assure you that, should a messy situation occur, you would be taken care of.'

Ellie wondered who would do the care-taking. Would he go with her himself, or send his chauffeur, or his housekeeper? 'I can imagine,' she said with heavy irony.

His eyes flashed, and he said very quietly, '*I* can only imagine what sort of men you've been with in the past, Eleanor, that you have such a low regard for them.'

She wanted to cover her face to protect herself from the shaming insults raining down on her. Instead she turned away from him. 'Is that all you wanted to say?'

'That's only the beginning.' He strolled right around her to plant his big, powerful frame in front of her and force her to look at him. 'I'd like to remind you that you aren't in control of this bank. What's more, this is a *bank*, not a testing ground for women's social agendas. Whatever your bosses tolerated from you in the past, for the pleasure of looking at you every day, won't be tolerated in this office. *I* am in control here.'

She gasped at the insult, but this was so much more the kind of fight she could handle. Her adrenaline surged and, along with it, her courage. Courage to justify, justify, justify!

'Of course I know you're in charge,' she said in a shocked, wounded tone, and added with quick sincerity, 'I can explain what happened, Sam. I knew how keen you were to find an issue that would bring the managers on-side. The crèche idea seemed ideal, being so controversial to their old-fashioned ways of thinking, without personally threatening any of them, and just the sort of thing you would choose yourself. I had intended to run it by you yesterday, but with all that happened—' Her voice grew huskier as an involuntary flashback to the car park nearly melted her defiance. 'It—it—I'm afraid it completely slipped my mind.'

She flashed a glance at him, but there was no softening in the severe lines of his chiselled, sexy mouth. She dropped her lashes and made a conciliatory gesture. 'Perhaps you're right. The idea might be just a bit too— *out* there for this bank.'

It was a subtle shot, and she could tell it registered by the way his eyes glinted. She followed it up with an appealing gaze through her lashes. 'You did say you liked PAs to show initiative. I suppose I must have misunderstood what that meant.'

His eyes chilled to ice. 'That is not the issue here.' He whisked the ball from her hands by stating with relentless accuracy, 'This is about a breach of trust, isn't it, Eleanor?'

The blood rushed to her face as if she'd been slapped.

'And there is the little matter of dress. Since when have you felt the need to come to work dressed like a tart?'

She gasped, but he went on inexorably. 'I may not know everything about fashion, but it's obvious to me that dress isn't appropriate for the workplace. It looks like something you should be wearing with a suspender belt and lace-topped stockings. Why aren't you wearing a suit?'

She said stiffly, 'My suit is in the Porsche.'

He paused. 'Oh. The Porsche.' For a moment the space between them simmered. She had visions of his hot hands on her thighs, her rapid panting breath, their urgent coupling in the pungent, salty air.

His eyes darkened and he turned abruptly away from her. 'It would be a mistake to try to capitalise on anything that happened between us out of working hours. I don't want a secretary who advertises her charms. I expect my PA to be a role-model of modesty and elegance to the remainder of the workforce.'

She bristled with indignation. Her beautiful dress *was* modest and elegant. She thought of the hole in her hard-won savings, what that meant now to her precious timeline, all the little deprivations ahead, the waiting, the sheer sacrifice, and rebellion boiled up in her. 'This,' she snapped, 'is an extremely expensive dress by a world-famous Australian designer. It's a work of art. It even has its own title.'

He turned to sweep her with a gaze of satiric amusement. 'Really. And what title would that be?'

Her blood pressure jumped a couple of notches, but she said coolly enough, 'It's called Flirty Noir.'

'Forgive me. A *French* tart.'

The insufferable mockery stung, but still she hung onto her temper. 'Other people like it.'

His eyes flared dangerously. '*Other* people. You mean Fletcher. And the rest of your fan club who couldn't keep their eyes off you. Ogling you at every chance they got. I'm sure they did like it. They don't have to work in close proximity to you.'

She felt a hot rush to her head that set her very scalp on fire. 'And that's what *you* want, isn't it?' she taunted in breathless anger. 'More proximity.'

He grabbed her and pushed her up against his desk. She felt a furious, excited thrill as he brought his mouth down on hers, and clung to him, relishing the ferocious hunger of his searing lips as her bones liquefied and passion instantly ignited her blood. She kissed him back, as fierce and fervent as he, her hands flying to undo his shirt buttons, his belt buckle, wriggling in frantic urgency to assist him to drag down her zip, unfasten her bra.

She positioned herself on the edge of the desk, her

knees parted for him, the breath coming in quick little pants as he pulled the dress from her shoulders and laid her straining breasts bare. For an intense, electric instant he stared down at her, lust in the black eyes feasting on her white nakedness. Drenched in desire, she quivered on the verge of the wild ride to rapture, her nipples taut and aching, fever between her thighs.

Through his open shirt, his broad bronzed chest with its smattering of black hairs tantalised her unbearably. In her impatience, she leaned forward and gave his nipple a long, languorous lick.

A shock roiled through his body. His hands tightened fiercely on her shoulders, then, with an almost superhuman effort, he thrust her from him and swerved away. She lost her balance and half fell backwards. He stood with his back to her, his hands bunched into fists, sinews straining in his powerful neck and shoulders.

'Dress yourself.' The words were as raw as if they'd been wrenched from him. Their disdain cut her to the quick.

A tidal wave of shame suffused her. She slid off the desk and reassembled her clothes with clumsy, trembling hands. How could her body have so betrayed her? How could she have shown herself so ready to surrender?

Sam fought for the strength to shut her from his consciousness, and waited for desire to subside. He struggled not to smell her fragrance, not to think of smooth breasts aching for a man's hands, of firm, slim thighs edged by black lace.

His father's stern, honest face flashed before him and he winced. Self-disgust rose in his throat like bile. He was no better than the series of greedy, lecherous executives who'd brought the bank close to ruin.

How had he, Samos Stilakos, come to this? When had a woman ever brought him so low?

He heard the door close, and felt overwhelmed by a guilty sensation of relief.

Shaky, disoriented, Ellie stood outside, her face in her hands, mind and body a painful, aching turmoil. She sat down at her desk and stared blindly at her keyboard. Despair would settle in soon enough, she thought. What man had ever treated her with such contempt?

She stayed outside until her hands stopped shaking, and the blood ceased pounding her temples, then forced herself to go in to face him.

He was helping himself to a drink from the water cooler, his clothes once more immaculate, every movement as controlled as if nothing had happened. He strolled to his desk, paper cup in hand, and flicked her a look. Just for an instant, she thought she caught uncertainty in his glittering black glance.

She lifted her chin, not wanting him to see how vulnerable she felt.

'This can't go on,' he rasped. 'It has to stop. I can't have this.'

'You don't have to worry.' Her own voice was equally emotionally charged. 'Because as of this moment, I quit.'

A muscle twitched in his lean cheek and he stood still, looking at her for a second with a fathomless gaze, then he coolly sat down. 'That might be the best solution all round.'

He picked up a pencil and twirled it idly between his lean fingers. It snapped. He straightened his cuffs, and, without looking at her again, pulled out his computer keyboard. 'You might as well clear out your desk.'

He became immersed in his screen.

Outside, she covered her face with her hands and suc-cumbed to a major shaking fit. Her legs gave way and she plumped down on her chair. She opened and shut her desk drawers a few times, then reached for an empty copy-paper carton. She stacked some useless things into it, tipped them out and started again.

After a few minutes the door opened and Sam came out. He took a few strides past her desk, then stopped as if he'd remembered something. 'Your contract requires you to give a month's notice,' he said in a cold voice.

She kept her gaze lowered. 'I'm leaving now.'

'If you do that you'll lose your severance entitlements.'

'Think of the profit to your bank,' she suggested.

He was silent for a moment, then said in a dry, steady voice, 'You will still have to come back to pick up your reference.'

She kept her head down. 'I won't be needing one from you, thanks. I have wonderful references from my previous bosses.'

His feet paused in front of her desk, then he strode back inside and shut the door with a snap.

When she'd piled as much as she could carry into the carton, she stood up with it in her arms and hoisted her bag onto her shoulder. The door burst open and Sam came out.

'Eleanor.' He stood directly in front of her so she was forced to meet his eyes.

Coldly, proudly, she faced her adversary.

'If you—if you did find yourself in a difficult situa-tion—a crisis, like a—an unplanned pregnancy, for example, what would you do?'

Despite her anger with him his eyes were serious, as if he was genuinely concerned, and confusion welled in her heart. Why did he have to remind her of how he'd been before he hated her? A multitude of the glib, savage things she could have said sprang to her tongue and died there. Whatever she was, she was a woman, and she had a heart.

With icy dignity she said, 'I would see it as a situation requiring a practical solution, and I would deal with it.'

The lines of his face tautened. 'How?' He added drily, 'Or can I guess?' With a grimace he half turned away. 'No, don't tell me.'

Her anger sparked back to life and she flung him a withering glance. 'Is it so obvious?' She slung her bag onto her shoulder and started for the exit. 'I'd find a job in a company that cares about its workforce and has an on-site crèche.'

He strode after her, grabbed her arm and pulled her about to face him. 'Understand this, darling,' he bit out through clenched teeth. 'No child of mine will ever be dragged up in a public facility.'

Darling. That caught her on the raw.

She arched her brows and flashed him a cruel smile. 'No child you know about, perhaps.'

CHAPTER EIGHT

ELLIE's state of shock lasted until she got home. Once the front door was closed behind her she peeled off her dress, collapsed on her bed and gave way to the huge black hole that had opened in her chest.

Afterwards, trying not to visualise Sam's cold eyes, she hauled herself up, changed into jeans, washed her blotchy face and tied her hair behind with a ribbon. She threw herself into some therapeutic house-cleaning, until she felt in enough control of her emotions to phone Beth to tell her the catastrophic news. Shocked, Beth promised to come over after work for a full report.

She drifted to the computer and half-heartedly keyed into a job-search site, but it was too painful. It only reminded her of how much she loved working at the bank. Surely she was a permanent fixture there. Wasn't she famous throughout the departments? So many of her friends were there.

He was there.

She still couldn't believe she'd thrown it all away. She stared miserably at the pile of things in the hall, then knelt to repack them in preparation for sending back to the shop.

How had she come to make such a mess of things? She

tried to think it all through with clear-headed logic, but Sam's furious face swam constantly before her eyes.

She couldn't imagine not seeing him every day. From the day he'd summoned her to the interview she'd been riding on a high. She closed her eyes and let herself dwell on her loss. The emotional impact of their first meeting each morning. Those charged moments at staff meetings when their gazes met. His deep, smooth tones on the intercom.

How flat her life would be now without it all.

If only she hadn't been forced to reject him last night.

But surely, all wasn't lost. Of course this morning she'd lost her temper, they'd both been carried away, but couldn't the situation be retrieved? It was obvious the passion between them was a living thing. Surely that must work to her advantage. And with her experience of talking bosses round, how hard could it be to persuade him she was worth another chance? If she went to see him in the morning and admitted her fault, apologised as she should have done today, instead of scoring points...

If only, if only she could have another chance...

She had a daydream that he would leave work and come in search of her. He'd beg her to come back, he'd apologise for the cruel things he'd said. Instead of being cool, clever Ms O'Dea she'd show him how she truly felt underneath. When he took her in his arms and kissed her she would...

Later, Beth brought over some chocolate éclairs to commiserate, and they sat in her little courtyard garden at the back while Ellie poured out the events of the last twenty-four hours.

True to form, Beth put her finger straight on the point at which things had gone bad. 'Couldn't you have just whisked all that IVF information out of sight?' Her green eyes were wide with incredulity. 'Stuffed it in a drawer or something?'

'It was too much of a risk. He might have seen it. He's very astute. He doesn't miss a thing. You don't know what he's like. He's—' Her throat thickened and she couldn't trust herself to go on.

Beth wanted to see the two dresses. 'They're both gorgeous, but this, *this*. Oh-h,' she moaned softly, fingering the black one. 'To *die* for. But it's far too good for work.' She examined Ellie with a rueful gaze. 'You didn't buy this just for the sake of your job, did you?'

Ellie shook her head without speaking, afraid of bursting into tears.

Beth stayed until after dark, then helped her clear up the coffee things, and left with sympathetic instructions to phone if she needed to talk more. After waving her off, Ellie was still standing at the front window, staring at the empty street, when a car nosed into the kerb in front of her gate.

It was sleek, dark and expensive-looking. Her heart gave a hopeful, joyous bound. She dashed to the bathroom to tidy her hair and met her anxious eyes in the mirror, huge and shadowy in her white face, their colour intensified by the deep blue of her tee shirt. When the bell rang her knees suddenly felt watery, and she had to discipline herself to walk to the door calmly.

Sam stood there with a carrier bag dangling from one hand. He was still in his office clothes and his lean face was serious and controlled, his severely sculpted mouth firm, black eyebrows slightly drawn. He looked the epitome of a powerful businessman. He flicked a veiled glance over her, taking in her jeans and shirt, then fastened his sharp gaze to her face. He made the slightest movement towards her. For a wild, fluttering moment she thought he was going to kiss her, but instead he just handed her the bag.

'Your things.'

'Thanks.' Her voice came out strangely, as if she'd been in a cave for twenty years without speaking. 'I— Would you—?' She cleared her throat. 'Please. Come in.'

She opened the door wide. His eyes glinted, and she knew he was thinking of last night. After a second's hesitation, he followed her down the hall and into her sitting room. For a tense, silent moment he stood facing her. His eyes were dark and sexual, and she felt an overwhelming desire to lace her arms around his neck and press herself into his big, hard body, but pride forced her to control it.

He sat down on her red sofa without touching her, his feet planted authoritatively apart in their hand-stitched Italian shoes, his intelligent eyes alert. She sank onto a chair facing him.

He glanced around at her bookshelves and pictures, the occasional photos she kept of family and friends, then switched his gaze back to her. His eyes travelled down her throat to the neck of her top, and she was overwhelmingly conscious of her bed, just visible through the half-open door to her bedroom, a few short metres away across the hall.

He wouldn't have come if he didn't want her. The knowledge drummed in her blood and swelled her breasts, and she had to force her hands still, to stop from reaching out to touch him. This was the moment to make her pitch, or lose everything.

'I'm so glad you came, Sam,' she said huskily. 'There are things I need to say.'

'There are things *I* need to say.'

'First I want to apologise—'

He raised imperious eyebrows, and she was silenced.

'No. I want to apologise.' He frowned down at his linked hands and drew a deep breath. 'I want to acknowledge that you were right in those things you said last night. I strongly regret the entire evening. What happened, and the way—the *place* it happened.' His hands lifted, eloquent of distaste. 'I blame myself. And—today. I should not have—exploited my working relationship with you in that way. You were my PA, and I should not have given in to… It was all my fault.' He looked up at her then lowered his black lashes and said quietly, 'You made the right decision.'

A shock wave roiled through her. She felt her life's blood drain from her heart.

'By—by quitting, do you mean? You're saying—it's a good thing I did?'

His eyes held hers with daunting firmness of purpose. 'I've written you a reference.' He nodded towards the carrier bag. 'It's in there with your things. In view of your long service with the bank, you will certainly receive all your severance and holiday pays.'

She was so stunned she could barely speak, but she couldn't just leave it at that. She gave a small, disbelieving laugh and made a weak gesture of appeal. 'I—I had thought—wondered, if you might try to talk me into changing my mind.'

'I'd like to.' His eyes on her face were grave. 'You're an excellent PA and I'll miss your input. You have skills and ability far in advance of PA work. In fact, I believe you can do better.' He dropped his gaze, and added quietly in his dark chocolate voice, 'And after what's developed between us on a personal level, Eleanor, I think you'll agree we can't work together any more.'

Her heart lurched. There was a buzzing in her head, as if all her worst-case scenarios had ganged up to confront her at the same time. 'So you—you don't want me back at the bank tomorrow?'

He looked gravely at her. 'Understand, I'd love to have you back. But it's not good for the bank when the CEO looks forward to seeing one face every day.' His voice softened. 'There is another of the Stilakos companies on the lookout for an executive PA, with opportunities for advancement to management. The salary is very attractive, better than what you were earning…'

Shock had sandbagged her brain to dullness, but her pride still had a vestige of life. She said with a stiff gesture, 'I can find my own position, thank you.'

He was silent for a moment, his dark eyes veiled. He examined her face, then lowered his gaze. 'Of course, of course. I know you can. You'll do well. With your talents and experience…'

Her mouth twisted. 'My pretty face…'

A flush tinged the olive skin covering his cheekbones. 'I—' He checked and made a stilted gesture. 'I shouldn't have said that. That was unfair. You're much, much more than…' With a stern effort he straightened his posture and met her eyes firmly. 'I take full responsibility for everything that has happened.'

Pain and disappointment closed around her heart like a vice, and she looked down at her hands. 'Tell me. Is this—is this really because of the crèche thing?'

'No.' His voice thickened. 'It's because of the passion thing.'

She turned her eyes away to hide them from him. Irrational, weak as it may have seemed, she longed for him to take her in his arms and comfort her for the hurt and desolation he was causing her. 'So, I'm just another statistic, after all,' she managed to say lightly, though the stranglehold on her heart made her voice hoarse.

Despite the cruelty of it, some treacherous part of her brain acknowledged the truth of what he was saying. There was no turning back the clock to the time when they hadn't made love. Everything between them now, every word, every gesture, was imbued with her almost tangible memory of his strong arms, his mouth and hands on her skin. Even now, while he was chopping her insides into little pieces, she craved for him to touch her.

But true to her feminine spirit, on the outside, at least, she kept her spine taut and her chin up, and stood up to signal him it was time to leave.

He rose with reluctance, as if racking his brains for what else he might say to help her swallow the bitter hemlock.

She gathered all the pride at her disposal and faced him coldly. 'You should know the passion thing was only ever a temporary aberration. It no longer exists. Thank you for calling.'

He shook his head and made a move to touch her, but she raised her hands to ward him off. 'Don't,' she said fiercely.

His eyes blazed. 'I'm sure, when you've had time to think, Eleanor, you'll realise this is the best way. How long do you think it would be before other people began to realise we couldn't keep our hands off each other?' He gesticulated passionately. 'Today I came close to having you on my desk. How long before we're taking afternoons off, missing meetings, locking my door to keep other people out while we make love? Everything is noticed and discussed at the bank; you said so yourself. This is not what I want for *us*.' His brilliant black eyes glittered and his deep voice took on a sharp, stern edge. Light glanced from his proud cheekbones, his firm jaw. His Greek heritage had never been more clearly defined. 'I am not a man who conducts affairs in his office. And you are not the kind of woman to enjoy being gossiped about.' He looked like the severe, uncompromising Samos Stilakos who'd commanded the workforce's respect. *Her* respect.

'You're assuming an awful lot,' she said in a low, trembling voice. 'You're assuming I'd be a willing participant.'

Sensuality stirred the depths of the dark eyes fixed on her face. 'I am, yes,' he said softly. 'I am assuming that.'

The naked desire in his gaze pierced her and she weakened. Longing for him rose in her to war with her embattled pride. He was only a metre's distance from her. She could reach out to him, press her mouth to the strong bronzed column of his neck. He would seize her and the dark flame would flare and consume both of them. She felt the dangerous erotic surge, and knew if he touched her she would surrender to the blaze, even as he was destroying her.

But how easily a man discarded a woman, even one he desired. And what foolish arrogance had ever deluded her into dreaming she could have the upper hand with Samos Stilakos? The bitter realisations clamoured in her brain. Her breasts rose and fell with the intensity of her struggle, and with her voice hoarse and trembling, she said, 'Whatever it was that happened between us is over, Sam. Thank you for returning my things.'

His lean dark face was focused and intense, his eyes

ardent. 'It's not over. We have hardly begun. You're upset now, understandably, but when you cool down you'll see. We both know the passion between us. If I touch you… even now, if I touch you, if we…' He took her arms in his firm, warm hands. 'We're meant to be lovers. I want you with me every night.'

She cried, 'You must be joking.' She gave a violent twist and tore herself from his grasp. Angry tears sprang to her eyes. 'The bank has been like my second home all the years I've worked there. Do you think this is nothing to me, losing my job? My *life*? And can you seriously believe I would want to carry on as your—toy? Can you imagine that after today I would ever want to see you again?' She brushed back her hair with impatient, shaking hands. 'You can have no idea—*no idea!*—of how much I have put into my work there. Of how much—over—over the years—I have *done*—' Emotion took control of her voice and she was forced to stop to take a series of breaths.

She caught a fleeting, almost unrecognisable glimpse of herself in the hall mirror, her face dead white, her eyes glittering with blue fire, and turned from the unbearable sight.

Sam said, harsh bitterness in his deep voice, 'Oh, I assure you, I am well aware of the sacrifices some women are prepared to make for their careers.'

'Just—just look at what has happened here,' she carried on in her distress as if he hadn't spoken. 'How are you different from all those big-time executives who ran the bank into the ground? And *I*—I know I've been just as stupid as all those secretaries. How could I? How could I have allowed myself to—?' She dashed away a tear with the back of her hand. More tears choked her throat.

The lines of his lean strong face clenched. Fire blazed

in his eyes. He breathed harshly. 'What has happened between us has nothing to do with other people. It is unique to you and me. If you can't see that I am different from those men…I don't have woman after woman. I only want…'

He drew a long simmering breath. After a moment he said, his deep voice uneven despite his effort of control, 'We need to talk about this rationally. You need to grow used to the idea of changing your employment, then we can talk about the kind of relationship we want. It doesn't have to be difficult for you to find a new place. I want to help you.'

Such cynical promises, while all she'd striven to achieve lay in smoking ruins, swept away the last vestiges of her self-possession.

'Oh, please.' She wiped her brow with a trembling hand. 'You don't have to pretend this is anything but what it is. A sordid office affair you want out of. Don't worry. I want nothing more to do with you in my life.'

His handsome face tautened. He gave a cool shrug, then swung stiffly for the door.

At the front door he paused with his hand on the knob, his shoulders rigidly set, then turned to scan her face. 'You'll find another position without trouble, I promise.'

'I'm sure I can rely on that.'

He lowered his thick black lashes, but not before she saw his eyes flash. He said through gritted teeth, 'Believe it or not, I *do* honour promises if I can.'

Her glance fell on the boxes of vain, frivolous clothes still awaiting the courier, and she nudged them with the toe of her shoe. 'I hope you know I'm sending these things back to the shop.'

'Why? Keep them. I want you to have them.'

Her voice trembled. 'I'd rather not feel like some rich man's mistress.'

He tensed and paused on her doorstep, his eyes chill and stern, and said quietly, 'I hope any woman fortunate enough to be my mistress, Eleanor, would also be gracious enough to know how to accept a gift in the spirit in which it is given.'

He spun on his heel and walked away.

Out of her life.

CHAPTER NINE

TILL hell freezes over, Sam thought.

Still, he kept his cool. He opened his car door, slid into his seat, snapped on the seat belt, every movement measured. He inserted the key and fired the ignition, not a tremor in his fingers. With controlled precision he drove to the end of the street, slowed at the lights.

A tidal wave of black emotion rose up to engulf him. His hands clenched the wheel.

Women didn't reject him. Not twice. He winced. Not *once*. The lights turned green and he slammed his foot to the floor.

He would have her. He would have his fill of her and she would be grateful. She'd crawl to him for more. She'd be on her knees, sobbing for an affair with him.

He sped through a small local shopping precinct and screamed the car to a halt at a street-crossing. A lone female pedestrian, paralysed in the middle of the crossing, turned an outraged glare into his headlights.

He yanked at his tie and loosened his shirt collar. He had done the only possible thing. So why did he feel like such a bastard?

Of course she was upset. It was only natural. She'd lost

her job. If he was guilty of anything it was of having underestimated just how upset she would be. He thought back to the moment when she'd first opened the door to him, the joyous expectation in her sapphire eyes, and his heart twisted.

For a moment he longed to do anything, *anything* to wipe away the pain he'd caused her. Drive back there, give her the job, set it all straight, turn back the clock…

Bleak dismay swept through him at the vision of her once-tranquil face, twisted in outrage and despair.

How would he ever retrieve himself in her eyes?

CHAPTER TEN

IT WAS shattering to find how soon she could be forgotten by friends, people she'd worked with for years.

In the days following the crisis they phoned, dying to know what was behind her departure. Ellie sensed the avidness in some of the enquiries. People fishing for gossip, hoping to hear some juicy scandal about her and Sam. It was humiliating, but she put on a bright performance, and pretended to have decided on a change in career.

All too soon, though, the calls began to drop off.

With frightening speed her bank world started to recede, and she guessed the reverse would also be true. Even the most popular staff member could leave, with barely a ripple to disturb the daily functioning of the big machine.

Sam didn't recede. Not in her mind, at least. Night after night she agonised over her last scene with him, raw with pain that he'd put his personal honour and reputation ahead of her happiness and security.

She didn't care who was right. Or that she was the one who'd resigned, she was the one who'd insisted on bringing in ethics, and she had been an equal and willing sexual partner. What she needed was for him to suffer as she was suffering. And to care, and feel sorry. And to crawl on his knees to beg her forgiveness, while she ground him into the earth with her heel.

But he didn't contact her. He didn't call to see how she was, or to check if she had anything to tell him about work, or to enquire about meetings and appointments.

It was cruelly frustrating, because she wanted to punish him properly. Shout and scream at him, shake him and show him how it felt to be cut to ribbons. And she wanted him to give her her job back, and make the terrifying pain better, as though it had never happened.

As two weeks turned to three his implacable silence slammed home the finality of his goodbye, and her anger turned to herself. How could she have allowed herself to fall into the same old trap? Once again she'd been beguiled by a man's charm, only this time the consequences had wiped her out. She'd wasted her savings, and it had been her own fault. She'd had a goal, she'd made sacrifices for it, and she'd allowed herself to be tempted from it.

She'd never fallen in so deep. Her passion for him was like a madness.

She knew she had to fight it, but she was weak. At every turn the shock of her loss asserted itself. Like an addict deprived of the fatal poppy, the touch and feel and taste of him were on her hands and skin as if he were a part of her very fibre.

She tried to fight the constant longing, but couldn't stop willing the phone to ring, running to the window to check every car that drew up in the street. She checked her message bank a dozen times a day; even, in some shame-fully low moments, considered texting him, begging him to forgive the terrible things she'd said to him.

But of course he wouldn't. A man like Samos Stilakos

would never forgive such a blow to his pride, and she steeled herself to the daunting necessity of rebuilding her life and starting afresh.

Her practical side fastened to the task of getting back on course.

With a mental gritting of teeth, she set her sights on her next job and travelled daily to the city on the round of job interviews. Too proud at first to use it, her reference from Sam, when she eventually relented, opened doors to her that would certainly have been otherwise closed, despite her qualifications.

Weeks after her last conversation with him, she was plunged into a dilemma when a friend from the bank phoned to invite her to a farewell lunch in her honour. Ironically, it had been given the nod of approval from the top.

What did it mean? Her first instinct was to avoid the torture, but her friends didn't deserve such cold treatment. Besides, she would already be in town that day for her second interview with a firm of management consultants. Going back to the place she'd loved would be hard, but how much harder would be the possibility of seeing Sam?

She couldn't quell the pathetic hope that he'd arranged it so he could see her. That should have warned her. Her struggle to put him out of her mind and heart was still too new to be safe. Although, she argued with herself, he might not be there. Why would he be, when she'd told him she never wanted to see him again in her life?

Though if he didn't, if he took her at her word and she missed seeing him, what new vistas of pain would open before her then?

The day was overcast. A storm gathered on the horizon, giving the sultry sky a bruised, brooding quality. After a rocky start, in which anxiety made her feel almost nauseous, she dressed as neatly as she could in her best suit and steeled herself for another Oscar-winning performance.

It must have gone over well with the consultants, for she was scarcely out of the building and into the street before they phoned her to tell her she had the job. That was cheering, at least. Of her friends at the bank only Beth knew the truth behind her departure, and at least now she could honestly tell people she had another job.

Still, as she braced herself to pass through the familiar glass doors into the bank's marble lobby, and smelled the familiar smells of floor polish and copy paper, regret for the world she'd loved welled in her heart.

Her hand hovered over the lift button for Sam's floor. But the certainty of seeing some new lovely queening it at her desk, melting to Sam's velvet tones on her intercom, was too cruel to contemplate. She bypassed it and rode straight to the top.

Determinedly working at his desk, Sam tried not to glance at his screen-clock. Neverthless, in the corner of his eye the hour flashed, then another minute, and another.

What if she didn't come?

The black void that occupied his chest swelled and threatened to engulf the world. It was everywhere—his apartment. This desolate bank...

She'd been true to her word not to contact him. There'd been nothing for weeks. Just a phone call from the boutique to inform him of the return of his gifts. The finality of the rebuff had cut him to the quick. It had been another sign of his clumsiness with her. Everything he'd done, it seemed, had offended her sensibilities. Everything he'd said.

He needed to find the right words. What were the words?

He thought of Natalie, the women he'd known before his marriage, and their greedy passion for expensive fripperies. Things he thought he knew about women had been turned upside down.

The desk phone rang. His insides clenched, but he forced himself to reach for it coolly. 'Yes?'

The party in the restaurant was quite lavish for the new regime. They'd arranged a cake, and achieved a festive air with flowers and gifts. The first thing that struck Ellie's notice was Sam's absence. Her disappointment was cruel, but she concealed it before her friends, who welcomed her with hugs and cheerful enquiries about her new job.

Amazingly though, a few minutes of listening to their small exchanges about current events in the bank already made her feel like an outsider. They toasted her and made speeches, and she forced herself to pretend with all her heart that a career change was what she'd wanted most in the world.

Towards the end a slight hush fell, and people sat straighter in their chairs. Her insides lurched, and she looked up to see the tall, autocratic figure of Sam at the entrance. Her heart swelled with its bitter-sweet knowledge.

His dark eyes skimmed the assembly until they lighted on her. From across the room she saw his lean, strong face tense, then smooth to become expressionless.

He strolled over and greeted her with quiet courtesy.

She tried to respond normally, but her burning awareness of him dominated her every small action. Her heart thudded with stress and she could hardly meet his eyes, she was so conscious of the insulting things she'd said to him at their last meeting. But as always before his work-force, he remained cool and composed. The last time she'd seen him he'd been all steel and fire. Now he was back to steel and velvet. In his elegant suit and crisp white shirt, he'd never looked more handsome, more remote and inaccessible, more achingly desirable.

He'd written a speech, and stood to deliver it in an easy, friendly style, as if he'd often done this sort of thing, and knew exactly the right tone to take.

She listened to all the flattering things he said about her with downcast eyes and a smile to cover her wounds. He must have gone to great trouble to prepare the speech, because he'd unearthed amusing anecdotes about her from years past at the bank that her friends recognised and laughed at uproariously.

Despite her turbulent heart she laughed too. At the end she stood to receive the customary bank gift. As usual it was a watch, and this one had the quiet elegance that signalled expense. Someone had chosen it with care.

Sam held out his hand and she gave him hers. For a brief instant their palms met. At the familiar leap of her untrustworthy pulse she couldn't prevent the quick rush of emotion, and had to lower her gaze to hide the shimmer of tears. He bent to brush her cheek with his lips. The faint masculine roughness of his jaw grazed her skin in a potent reminder of pleasures lost.

She made a pretence of linking the watch around her wrist. Sam saw her difficulty with the clasp and helped her. Her skin surged to his quick, deft fingers and she had to discipline herself to meet his eyes. After the small applause had died down, she didn't trust herself to give a speech of her own, beyond thanking everyone for their thoughtfulness.

Mindful of not overstaying their permitted hour in the boss's presence, people began to make moves back to their work. When the last noisy group had gone, the restaurant staff swarmed in to clear the tables.

She gathered up her gifts and flowers. Unlike everyone else, Sam hadn't yet made the move to leave. She eyed him uncertainly, and he tilted his head to indicate an alcove by the window, out of the way of the waiters. After a second's hesitation she joined him.

The moment grew tense, and they both spoke at the same time. 'Have you—?'

'Do you—?'

They each gave a strained laugh, then Sam started again. 'There's something I need to ask you. Have you remembered your promise to accompany my mother to the wedding?'

'Oh! The wedding.' She had forgotten. With the events of the past weeks it had been pushed to the back of her mind. 'Are you sure you still want me to go? Wouldn't you rather find someone else?' She made a tremulous effort at a smile but her voice caught. 'Sever all undesirable connections?'

Something flickered in his dark eyes. 'There isn't anyone else. My mother is counting on you. She's—fixed now on having you with her.'

'I see. Oh, well, of course, then.' She shrugged in acquiescence. 'I did—I did promise.' She felt her insides knot then as she remembered the cutting things she'd said to him on her doorstep about his promises, and she flushed and turned from his perceptive gaze.

'Look, Sam. I'm sorry I said those things to you the last time we—talked. I was upset at the time… About my job, you understand. But I shouldn't have been so rude.'

'You have nothing to apologise for.'

There was a short, constrained silence. She became conscious of the muted sounds of rattling crockery and bustle from the restaurant kitchen.

He touched her cheek lightly with his knuckle. 'You will settle into your new firm and be happy, Eleanor. I'm sorry it had to be this way.' His voice deepened. 'I'm sorry you've been hurt. That I've—hurt you.'

She felt her throat thicken and said huskily, 'Nice watch. Who chose it?'

'Oh, er—' he made a vague gesture '—a—a man—a jeweller brought some trays up for me—'

'Could those be actual sapphires?'

His hands shot out and he took her arms in his strong grasp. 'This wasn't what you think it was. You know one of us had to leave.' His sardonic brows were drawn, his eyes fierce with concern.

Emotion swelled in her heart. Everything in her yearned to step into his arms and sink into his hard body, let him comfort her and kiss her. But she daredn't risk it.

'I do know.' With a sharp twist she disengaged herself. 'I even know why it had to be me. Don't concern yourself with it. I'm fine, my life is fine, I have a new job and I'll like it just as much as I did the last one.' She forced a smile. 'I couldn't feel more—positive about the future.'

She hoped he hadn't guessed what a lie that was. Her croaky old voice might have told him that all she had in her was pain. She could feel his frowning gaze scouring her face.

'Is that true? Have you really come to terms with everything?'

What did he want from her? Blood? Did he really want to know the anguish she'd suffered when he'd discarded her, the agonies of fear and hope the possibility of seeing him today had put her through?

She knew with sudden certainty she didn't want him to feel guilty. She was to blame as much as he. It was time to walk away with her head high, no hard feelings. It took a supreme effort, even after all her experience. As usual, her voice was the hardest to control.

'I don't deny it's been hard.' Bright, sincere smile, airy shrug, if a bit jerky. 'A change always is. But in the long run it'll do me good. One thing I realised coming here today was that I've been in the one place too long. You were right about that. I needed to climb to higher ground.' Her emotions threatened but she crushed them down. 'It was a—a shame it had to happen that way. But I'm a big girl, I know the score…I always did, and I have no regrets.'

The words seemed somehow to clang in the hushed atmosphere of the restaurant. 'You know the score,' he murmured in echo, with a frown. He glanced at his watch. 'Look, let's go somewhere where we can talk.'

He flicked open his mobile and made a couple of quick calls, then took her arm and ushered her out to the lift. On the drive to his apartment the silence was charged. She glanced at him a couple of times, but his expression was grim, his mouth unsmiling.

The apartment was bathed in a dim hush, in waiting for its master. Sam opened some blinds and windows to let in the sultry afternoon, then turned to her. 'Drink?'

She shook her head, but he poured one for himself, half raised it, then put it down again, and loosened his tie.

'Come this way. Please. Through here.'

She followed him uncertainly through the archway,

into a suite of rooms. He showed her to a sitting room, which opened into a light, spacious bedroom with furnishings that were essentially masculine, including an opulent bed. A glass ceiling dome above it gave a thrilling glimpse of stormy sky. Light glanced off mirrors and discreet touches of gilt filigree set in the wall panelling. It reminded her of some exotic sultan's palace.

He turned to face her, his lean, stern face taut and strained, his dark eyes intense. 'I had decided not to see you again,' he said abruptly.

Her heart pained, and she folded her arms over her breasts to protect herself from more wounds. Why put herself through this? 'Then why—?' She made an inarticulate gesture. Her voice came out in a dry croak. 'Why are we here?'

'You know why.' The words were wrenched from him, as if he'd had a bitter struggle with his pride, and lost. He strode across and his hands lifted as though to touch her, but he controlled them sharply and let them fall. 'Seeing you again… You know what I want. What we both want.' His deep voice was harsh.

The fire in his eyes fuelled the old yearning in her, and played on her weakness. In a confusion of emotion and resolve, she clenched her hands against her to prevent herself from throwing herself into his arms.

As though he read the conflict in her face, a flush darkened the taut, bronzed skin across his proud cheekbones, and he swung stiffly away from her, and continued his impassioned words, pacing about with a fierce, relentless dignity.

'I am—deeply remorseful to have hurt you.' He cast her a searing look from beneath his lashes. 'I'm not *al-*

together heartless. I admit I didn't understand how much working at the bank meant to you. I hoped you would see that another job, in another place, would make it easy for us to—' He made an abrupt, wordless gesture and with simmering restraint, 'From your long silence, Eleanor, I gathered that with you the job was everything.' His shoulders were rigidly set, his hands bunched into fists while he waited for her reply.

Passionate, truthful words of her love and longing for him rose to her tongue, but her courage to express them failed her. Even so, as if he'd read them in her face, triumph lit the ardent gaze, and he added very softly, 'But seeing you now, I just can't believe that.'

He moved swiftly to her, his chest just a centimetre from hers. Her resolve to resist him warred with his formidable sexual power. His deep, seductive voice pulled at her with its smouldering intensity. 'You have to acknowledge that at least now there are no more barriers between us. I'm not your employer. You're not my PA. Now, we're just a man and a woman.'

The words stirred her to her depths, but her battles of the past weeks were too fresh to be dismissed. 'Sam,' she said unsteadily, shaking her head, 'it's not so easy.'

The dark flame flared in his eyes. 'Yes, it is. Don't try to deny this.' He curved his fingers under her chin and tilted up her face. His voice thickened. 'This isn't the time for us to lie to each other to save face, sweetheart. Passion isn't something you can hide.'

The endearment touched that deep inner spring she was fighting so hard to quell. Desire unfurled in her belly, and she felt the immediate, swelling heat to her breasts. She gazed into the dark eyes glinting in his proud, strong face, his mouth twisted with emotion, and the irresistible force of her love overwhelmed her.

She kissed him, and, as though it was the spark to the bonfire, he crushed her to him, and took charge, possessing her lips with scorching authority. Her body blazed like a torch, and she threw every atom of herself into his embrace with willing abandonment.

With wild, panting urgency they tore at each other's clothes, their hands barely steady in their haste to remove the constricting barriers to skin on skin. For a second he stood naked before her, in all his bronzed, muscled magnificence, feasting on her nude body with his aroused black eyes. Then he lifted her in his arms as though she were weightless, and tossed her onto his bed. He came down beside her, triumph mingling with the fire in his dark, devouring gaze.

In the first ferocious urgency, they made hot, clumsy love, rushing to a shattering climax in almost unbelievable concert. Then, long into the afternoon, while the storm raged over Sydney, with sizzling deliberation, Sam slowed passion to an infinitely more languorous pace, relishing every curve and hollow of her nude body, teasing the sweet strawberry nipples, tasting the honeyed secrets beneath her soft tangle of curls. With fierce, erotic tenderness, he roused Ellie to the wildest fever-pitch she'd ever known, until she begged for him to take her.

When he judged the moment right, he plunged into her, burying his hard shaft in her to the hilt, and pleasured her with slow, sinuous strokes, increasing the tempo into a virile, athletic rhythm that transported her beyond the pinnacle of ecstasy.

Much later, past satiety and exhaustion, she lay beside him in the huge bed, her head resting on his ribs, gazing drowsily through the domed ceiling at the midnight sky. Her body felt supple and replete.

'Tomorrow…' His deep murmur sounded sonorous against her ear. 'We'll send the car over to pick up your things.'

Ellie tensed. 'What things?'

'Everything you need. Your clothes, your books. Your music.'

She lay still for a moment, tilted her head around to look at him, then stirred herself to sit up. She pushed aside the red mass of hair tumbling over her shoulders. 'Why would we do that?'

'So you can be comfortable.' He surveyed her white nakedness with slumbrous satisfaction, then bent his dark head to graze her bare shoulder with his lips. His mouth curved in a grin. 'I think you would miss your shoes.'

She caught her breath. 'But—I don't need them here. I live there.'

With studied casualness he said, 'I think it's better if you live here. Hornsby's too far.'

She felt stunned. For a few moments she let the dream dazzle her. Belonging to him. Sleeping in his arms every night. The intimacy of it. Everything she'd hardly dared to wish. Well, nearly everything. Pleasure, romance and…

'For—for how long does this invitation extend?' she said lightly.

His black lashes flickered down, and he hesitated. His dark eyes connected with hers for an unreadable instant, then slid away. 'Who knows?' He shrugged, and a warning pang shot through her. 'A week, a year. Until we've had our fill of each other.'

He kissed her, stroked her hair back behind her ear, and said gruffly, 'That might take a while.' He pulled her down beside him, and gathered her against his broad, warm chest. 'We'll work out the details in the morning.'

She closed her eyes, but her mind wouldn't stop spinning. He could be hers. For a while.

A week, or a year…

A year of heavenly delights.

But after the year—what?

She had to face it, be honest with herself. He'd already shown her how ruthless he could be. How long before she was back on the scrap heap, another precious year of her life wasted, left with an incurable heartbreak?

But it was tempting. Could she do it, live the glamorous life? She would have to put aside thoughts of a child for another year or so. Then a year or two to get over him and save up again. Although after that, at thirty-three or thereabouts…

She fell off her cloud with a crash. Thirty-three was too late. Already she was in the danger zone.

She worried and churned while the moon sank low in the sky, and the starlight grew faint, then extinguished altogether. At last, in the first grey light, she carefully disentangled herself from Sam's strong, warm limbs, and slipped from the bed.

A few minutes later, a small sound impinged on his consciousness, and Sam stirred himself from his dream to a vague sense of bliss. The smile swelled in his heart in sleepy recollection. Eleanor. He reached for her.

Nothing.

He half opened his eyes. Her place was still warm. His eyes drifted shut and he drowsed, waiting for her. After a hazy time he resurfaced, and forced himself to lift his head.

Blearily he scanned the room. The shadows were shrinking into the corners, but there was no sign of her. With a sudden foreboding in his bones he got up, pulled jeans from a drawer and dragged them on.

He found her in the living room. She was fully dressed in her suit and heels, handbag slung on her shoulder, her glorious hair tamed into a neat coil in the nape of her neck. She was leaning over a table, frowning at a sheet of paper, her pen poised while she considered. She started, and straightened up when he walked in. 'Oh,' she said, her eyes widening.

Her eyelashes gave a nervous flicker, and with a lurch Sam knew. He nodded towards the paper. 'For me?'

She looked pale and drawn, her blue eyes bruised and shadowy in the pale light. Her dismay at being caught was almost tangible. 'I didn't want to wake you.'

He kept his expression under control, though he could feel an unpleasant blood-beat in his temples. 'Isn't it…?' He forced his lungs on. 'Isn't it early to be going out?'

'I'm…' She hesitated, then said, in her low voice, 'I need to go home.'

A coldness began to seep through his insides. To stall her, he tried the only thing he knew: drew her to him, kissed her cheek and the corner of her mouth. Generous girl that she was, she complied, put her arms around his neck. He crushed her to him, felt her precious heartbeat against his chest, then as the inevitable desire rose between them felt her pull back. In the empty space in his arms he felt the desolate chill of goodbye.

'But you are coming back,' he said, still careful, in the face of defeat, not to pressure her.

Her gaze wavered over him, down to his bare feet, took in his jeans and chest. Her soft mouth, still red from his kisses, made a telling little tremor. He considered seducing her back into his bed, but there was a certain nervy resolution in her posture, as of a decision reached, and he had his pride.

She brushed his bristly cheek with a gentle hand. 'Sam, I love—love being with you. But I'm afraid I'm not really mistress material.'

Mistress material. A blade sliced through him, but he kept severe control.

Her face was working with distress. 'Last night was wonderful,' she said, regret in her warm, husky voice, blue eyes swirling with some dark tragedy. 'It would be gorgeous being here with you, but I—have goals of my own.'

'Goals.' It was difficult to smile. His heart was slamming so hard he could barely breathe, and a hoarseness entered his voice. He didn't want to sound as if he was begging, but it was necessary to point out the obvious. 'I have no intention of making your career suffer, Eleanor. I know how important it is to you. I can be of great help to you.'

She shook her head, her slim hands fluttering, as if what he'd said had somehow proven how hopeless he was.

'Look—' He felt himself flush to hear the note of desperation in his voice. 'I should have made myself clear.' As happened on the rare occasions he felt powerless, his hands flew around like some old Greek's. 'I—I fully recognise how independent you are. We'll get the lawyers to draw up a contract to protect your interests. You won't be worse off financially, far from it.'

She covered her ears in a small, defensive gesture. 'Please, Sam.' The words came out almost as a strangled cry, and she turned her face away from him.

Humiliation flooded his soul like blood.

She started for the foyer. Dimly he knew he'd said all the wrong things, but what were the right ones? With women, a man never knew.

'I'll drive you,' he said quickly, catching up with her, thinking of the long drive there. Plenty of time to talk her round.

'No. No, please,' she said, stepping into the lift. 'I've phoned for a taxi.' She turned to face him. 'It's better this way.' That fragile pulse was beating in her throat. He stared, unbelieving, as tears filled her eyes. 'Goodbye, Sam.'

A crippling pain inhabited his being. For a crazed instant he teetered on the verge of spilling his guts. Pleading, like some love-struck teenager.

Instead, he controlled himself in time and stood back with the dignity of a man. His face felt stiff, and when the words came he knew they sounded cold and formal. 'I wish you well on your climb to the top, Eleanor.'

CHAPTER ELEVEN

How the rich lived.

There was no need to phone for a taxi. Irene said she would pick Ellie up on the way to the airport, and at the appointed time a limo drew up at her door. A uniformed chauffeur sprang out to help her with her bag, and she was ushered to join Irene in its plush interior like Princess Mary.

It was clear now why Irene had seemed vague about reservations. The Stilakos family didn't make reservations. They had their own private jet.

She might have enjoyed it all more if she hadn't felt like such an imposter. Irene had wanted her on the basis of her being connected to her son, and now the connection was broken. Should she explain, or did Irene know? she wondered, eyeing the bright-eyed older woman after they'd greeted each other with a warm hug.

It didn't take long for the sore point to come up. They were in the sky, with Sydney passing beneath them like a sequinned cloth.

'What will Sam do without you?' Irene said. A gleam of satisfaction lit the older woman's eyes every time they settled on her. 'It will do him so much good to miss you.'

Ellie felt the heat in her cheeks. The choking pain

threatened to burst through her chest. 'Well, no. Actually I don't work for Sam now. I've got another job.' The words sounded so suspect, even to her own ears, she wasn't surprised when Irene arched her brows and looked keenly at her through her specs.

'I felt I needed to extend myself,' she explained. 'It's time to set my goals in place and carve my path to the top. I'm a career girl, you know, Irene. Through and through.'

Irene looked doubtful, and Ellie felt a spurt of exasperation. What would it take to convince this old woman?

'Oh, sure I liked my job at the bank,' she went on breezily. 'I'd been there a long time. Personal connections are all very well, but, between you and me, nothing can measure up to the thrill of discovering what you're capable of in the world of big business and testing your abilities to the limit. That's the real adrenaline rush.' The scepticism in the shrewd grey eyes only increased, and she added firmly, 'I've joined a team of management consultants.'

Irene's musing, 'Oh-h-h. Is that right?' was unsettling. Ellie could practically see her well-exercised brain-cells ticking into calculation.

Lunch was served by a uniformed flight attendant, but Ellie couldn't eat a thing. People who'd ruined their own lives had no need of sustenance. They lived on their regrets. She hadn't even been able to raise a laugh at the postcard she'd received from Tierra del Fuego. 'On my way home to you, babe. Sorry the team was held up. Love, Mark.'

Love. Ironic that. It was a word he'd carefully avoided in the past. That blonde in Melbourne must have taught him a thing or two.

The sight of sea and long white sandy beaches should

have lifted her spirits. As the plane circled Coolangatta Airport before coming in to land, the famous strip of high-rises shimmered in the sun with the old promise of holidays and pleasure.

Funny how the idea of pleasure could be so depressing.

An elderly couple wearing expensive-looking casuals and anxious expressions stood waiting in the arrivals lounge. When she and Irene walked in, there was a moment of mutual hesitation, then the couple and Irene surged forward to fall on each other's necks with teary sobs. In a storm of questions and protestations and more hugs, all three of them talked so fast no one could possibly make sense of anything anyone else said.

After they'd mopped up, Irene introduced them to Ellie as her brother Jack, and his wife Rosemary, explaining they were the groom's parents. 'And this is Ellie,' Irene said with a warm look at Ellie, 'a friend of Sam's.'

Jack's and Rosemary's brows shot up and they looked Ellie over with surmise. Ellie fired a questioning frown at Irene and was met with an innocent smile. Was there the faintest tinge of smugness in that smile? Ellie wondered.

The flight crew appeared with their baggage, then handed it over to a waiting chauffeur. With a minimum of fuss they were soon in another limo, cutting a swathe through the Gold Coast traffic.

'How are the preparations coming?' Irene enquired.

The couple looked at each other and Jack rolled his eyes. Rosemary inclined her head. Scarcely moving her mouth, she said, 'They've been problems.' She gave Irene a speaking look. 'I think you can guess.'

'Ah.' Irene narrowed her eyes and nodded. 'Yes, I think I can.' She slanted Ellie a meaningful glance.

'Luckily our villa is away from all the goings-on.' Rosemary's lips thinned. 'I hope you two won't mind being in the thick of it. We're hosting the groom's dinner tonight at the Palazzo, so fingers crossed.'

The Palazzo Versace was as elegant as its brochures promised. The resort was lapped by the ocean Broadwater. From where Ellie stood in the white-and-gold marbled vestibule, her view across its green lagoon seemed faintly reminiscent of Venice, but a gleaming, sprucified Venice, a Venice that was still gracious, but re-assuringly solid.

Theirs was not the only limo to draw up to its charming entrance. As Ellie smoothed down her slim dress more cars arrived, disgorging more glittering guests. Some she recognised from the television world, while others bore the faintly bored, relaxed demeanour of the very rich.

A noisy group were in occupation of the bar at one end of the lobby. Ellie's experienced eye could tell they were already into party mode. They kept shouting with laughter, and welcoming every new arrival with theatrical embraces and much witty repartee.

While Irene dealt with Reception, Rosemary and Jack made beckoning motions to someone in the bar crowd. A slight, intense-looking man detached himself from the group he was with, and tried to snag the attention of a vivacious young woman in the throes of relating some story to her friends. She was telling her story with gusto, throwing her arms about and screaming with laughter.

Natalie Stilakos.

Who else would flaunt hectares of her naked midriff between a couple of scraps of floaty gauze to her fiancé's family?

The black-rooted blonde spun about, and as her glance homed in on her in-laws, past and future, the laughter died on her face, to be reconstituted into a nervous, unconvincing smirk. She clutched her fiancé's arm, and it seemed to Ellie that the couple braced themselves. They started across the foyer, Natalie clinging tight to her lover's arm.

Michael composed his rather sallow face into a smile, and greeted his aunt with a few stilted, though friendly, words and a quick kiss, and Natalie was forced to follow suit, though her lips made no actual skin contact.

'It's so nice to see you, Natalie,' Irene said warmly. 'Welcome again to the family, dear. I'm sure you'll make Michael a lovely wife.'

Natalie's smile faded. Her black eyes glowered through the heavy kohl smudging their rims. 'What's that supposed to mean?'

Rosemary and Jack made nervous shuffling movements and pretended to look out at the lagoon. Michael quickly took his fiancée's wrist and gave it a little shake. 'Chill, darling,' he said, winking and giving everyone a grin. 'Wedding nerves. It'll all be over soon.' Everyone joined in the false hearty laugh.

Rosemary quickly eased the moment on, announcing, to Ellie's intense chagrin, 'And this is Ellie, Sam's girlfriend.'

Ellie would have denied it but for a sudden steel clamp on her elbow. No wonder Sam had such a strong grip.

She managed a smile and accepted Michael's hand. He examined her with frank curiosity, then leaned forward to peck her cheek as if she were family. Still with her smile in place, she turned to Natalie. After an awkward second, the blonde stuck out a hand for a brief brushing of fingers, her eyes guarded. 'But aren't you Sam's receptionist?'

'Oh, no, no,' Irene intervened before Ellie had a chance to speak. 'Ellie's a management consultant.' She gave a fond laugh. 'Sam gets all the benefit of her advice at home.'

Ellie swivelled an outraged look at Irene, who bestowed such an affectionate beam on her it was all she could do not to gasp.

A porter stood patiently by waiting to escort them to the condominium owned by the Stilakos family. Rosemary and Jack made moves to leave, with an arrangement to meet later, and to Ellie's relief the group broke up. Michael called after Ellie with an invitation to come back down once she was settled. The glance the bride flung Ellie over her shoulder was puzzled.

The Principessa Suite was spacious and filled with light, its gleaming marble floors exquisitely tiled with a mosaic design. Broad balcony windows opened to views of the Broadwater. Ellie barely gave herself a chance to take in the fabulous Versace furnishings, before advancing on Sam's mother, who was narrowly inspecting the master suite.

'What are you up to, Irene?' Ellie's hands were on her hips. 'What's the idea of telling people I'm Sam's girlfriend?'

'Oh-h-h…' Irene shuddered '…wasn't it harrowing?' Kicking off her shoes, she flopped onto a sumptuous king-sized bed, draped in the rich deep colours of the Renaissance, and gave a throaty chuckle. 'Did you see Natalie's face?'

'I could hardly miss. Why did you do it?'

Irene sat back up, all wide-eyed innocence. '*I* didn't say you were his girlfriend. It was Rosemary who said that.' She gave her head a despairing shake at Rosemary's chronic hopelessness. 'Trust her to leap to conclusions.' With a sigh she sank back on the assortment of tasselled cushions and pillows adorning the bed.

Ellie checked her retort and drew a deep, calming breath. 'You could have corrected her impression, though, couldn't you? You didn't have to encourage it.'

Irene arranged herself more comfortably, and cast Ellie an amused glance. 'Oh, don't give me that stern face. I get enough of that from Sam. Why can't you go along with it for a couple of days? It will serve that little piece right for letting people think Sam can't get over her. ' She leaned up on a gold and purple embroidered cushion and her eyes glistened. 'It would be better if he was here with you, of course. Why don't I give him a call and tell him you've broken your ankle?'

Ellie shook her head in bemusement. 'What are you talking about? Sam wouldn't... Don't, please, for heaven's *sake*!' She flushed. Her feelings about Sam and the things that had happened between them were raw. Too raw to be used in some game. With difficulty she said, 'I don't think you realise, Irene, how—how painful and embarrassing this would be for me if Sam found out. He was my boss, you know.'

'But he isn't now, is he? *Is* he, Ellie? It's a whole new ball game.'

Ellie's body suddenly felt twitchy and in need of fast, furious exercise. She walked out into the sitting room and back again, her hands as restless as her feet.

'Anyway,' she said, ignoring Irene's sly riposte, 'why should Natalie care what Sam does? They're divorced, aren't they? She doesn't have any hold on Sam. She's marrying someone else, for goodness' sake. She and Sam are—over.' She stopped to gaze out at the Broadwater, but all she could see was what she couldn't stop seeing. Sam's dark eyes, aflame for *her*. She turned to Irene and said in a choked voice, 'Aren't they?'

Irene was watching her from her room with a shrewd little smile. 'Of course they are. They've been over practically since the first.'

'Really?'

Irene gave her a long look and heaved a sigh. 'Yes, yes, yes. The whole thing was a mistake. I doubt if he'd have stayed married to her for as long as he did if it hadn't been for the baby.'

Ellie's eyes sprang wide with shock. 'They have a child?'

Irene compressed her lips. 'No, but I'm pretty sure there was one. I can usually tell when a girl's in the family way.' Her eyes clouded and she shook her head. 'I'm afraid the baby didn't eventuate. Goodness knows what happened. Whatever it was, things went very wrong between them. Sam would never breathe a word about it, of course. Then five minutes after the wedding Natalie was flaunting her affair with Michael, and the marriage was doomed.' She sighed and patted her cushion. 'To give the girl her due, she's tried everything she could think of to persuade Sam and Michael to patch things up. If Sam would only get over it and come to the wedding…' She lay back and lapsed into gloomy thought.

Ellie stood very still and forced herself to say coolly, 'I suppose it would be hard for Sam to watch his wife marry someone else.'

'Oh…!' Irene roused herself to make a dismissive sweep of her hand. 'The spoilt hussy barely was his wife. But Sam's an old-fashioned Greek man at heart. He's too much like his father. If he believes his honour has been insulted he can be very proud.' She rolled her eyes. '*Men*. Who knows how the creatures think?' With another hefty sigh, she rolled back on her pillows and stared at the ornate baroque ceiling.

Ellie went to her own room, which was as richly furnished as Irene's. Mirrors and sparkling Italian mosaics reflected the watery light from the lagoon, but it was hard to appreciate it all when her heart knew only darkness.

Would rejecting a Greek man three times constitute an insult to his honour? she wondered. Of course it would. It would sting any man like fury. He'd never want to lay eyes on her again.

But there was no use giving in to this dreadful, tearing ache. Wishing she'd taken a chance. Tears swelled her throat. Hoping...*pretending* love had happened to her too, the way she had with Mark. It was ironic really, how she'd thought she'd come to terms with all this ages ago. But the same old conditions still seemed to apply. For Ellie O'Dea, no love at all was better than half-love. So even if she loved Sam enough for ten people...

'Ellie?'

She pulled herself together. Irene had resettled herself on a chaise longue in the sitting room and was riffling through her handbag. When she saw Ellie she pushed the bag aside and threw up her hands. 'Oh, all right. I give in. Tell them all the truth about you and Sam if you have to. I'm sorry if you were embarrassed. I suppose I hoped you might be a woman after my own heart.' She placed a be-ringed hand over her breast and gazed at Ellie, her grey eyes sparkling with reproach. 'I had the impression you might enjoy a little graceful subterfuge. It never occurred to me you might actually *be* a goody-two-shoes.'

Ellie gasped and let out a shocked laugh. 'Irene. You are the limit!'

The older woman grinned. 'I sincerely hope so. Now be a dear, will you, and phone for some tea? And ask them to send up a butler.'

'A butler?'

She elevated her brows. 'Well, dear, we need to unpack. Someone has to locate my pills.'

Remorse snapped Ellie from her gloom. What could she be thinking of, ticking off an old woman with a heart problem? 'Yes, yes, of course,' she said, moving across to pick up the phone. 'And why don't you have a little rest afterwards so you'll feel nice and fresh to meet Rosemary and Jack?'

'Good idea.' Irene's eyes twinkled. 'I think I might need to be fresh. What about you?'

Ellie shook her head. She was restless, and she wasn't especially hungry. No, Ellie O'Dea, for all her faults, was an action woman. It was time to brave the bride.

Once the butler was ensconced and Irene was settled with some delicious pastries from the Palazzo kitchen and a fat romance novel, Ellie slipped into her room to change.

The party had dispersed a little in the time she'd been away. People had drifted out to the lagoon terrace. Natalie was still near the bar, hunched in an armchair, scowling morosely into space. Michael was engaged in urgent conversation with an actressy-looking brunette who kept glaring around him at Natalie, in between bouts of furious hissing and ferocious gestures with her fist.

Not a good time, Ellie's antennae suggested.

She paused for a moment to decide where best to head, and a waiter materialised beside her. She ordered a squash and sauntered through the glass doors to the terrace. At once she was assailed with the holiday smells of swimming pools, sunscreen and salt sea air.

An umbrella table was vacant at the edge of the party set, and in no time a tall glass garnished with lemon was misting with condensation in front of her. She paid and smiled her thanks, then settled in to watch the human drama.

Across the lagoon on the beach side, people—couples mainly—lolled side by side on loungers, reading or dozing in casual intimacy. Occasionally they'd disturb themselves to apply lotion to each other's glistening bodies, or drink from each other's glasses. They'd murmur things into each other's ears, and writhe with sexy laughter at their private little secrets.

Other people romped with their children in the turquoise waters. Happy people. People with love in their lives.

A shadow blocked out the sun, and she looked up. Natalie hovered there, a couple of splotches on her pretty make-up job that looked suspiciously as if she'd been having a weep.

'Are you and Sam really together?' She remained standing for a second, then pulled over a chair and sat down. Like a genie, the waiter appeared from nowhere and she ordered a margarita.

'No,' Ellie admitted.

'Oh, right.' Natalie's gaze clouded. 'I thought Irene must have been winding me up. I lived with Sam long enough to know that much about him. He'd never sleep with his office girl, unless he's changed a whole lot. As soon as any of them showed they thought he was hot…'

She grimaced and made a slashing motion across her throat. 'You're his receptionist, aren't you?'

'I was his Personal Assistant.'

'Was!' Her dark eyes widened. 'You don't mean he got rid of you, too?'

The raw spot must have grown its first delicate protective layer, for Ellie found herself able to say quite calmly, 'Yes, I'm afraid he did.' She took a long, sustained sip of her squash.

The bottle-blonde studied her, unexpected sympathy infusing her smudgy gaze. 'Oh. Oh, that's a shame.' She ran a pensive finger around the rim of her glass. 'But you must be still in there with a chance, or why has Irene brought you?'

Ellie shrugged. 'Oh, well, this arrangement was made a while ago. You know…before…' She echoed Natalie's throat-cutting gesture.

Natalie nodded her understanding, resting her head in her hands and staring gloomily at the table-top while she toyed with a coaster. 'I was hoping there might still be a chance of him turning up,' she said casually. 'If you two *had* been together, I thought you might've been able to talk him into it. I know he has all these really old-fashioned *ideas*, and he never forgives a person for *anything*, but it would mean so much to Michael if he would just get over it and—move on.' She shook her ragged head and chewed her lip.

Ellie stirred her ice cubes with the straw, wondering how long it took the average man to get over a divorce. Four years should have been long enough, surely. When would Sam get over it? What was wrong with him?

Natalie had lapsed into a frowning reverie, and in an

effort to distract her Ellie hazarded, 'You aren't having a hen-party? You've already had it?'

She looked up, then her dark eyes shifted to evade Ellie's. 'Oh, look, who needs one? I can do without people who have to turn every little thing a person says or does into a major Cecil B De Mille production. What do I care? All I want is to marry the love of my life on that beach tomorrow and forget about the world. I don't need anyone to hold up my train.' She flung out her hands. 'It's a beach, for God's sake.'

Ellie wondered if the brunette in the bar had been a bridesmaid.

Natalie finished her drink and rose. She made a move to leave, then turned back and bent towards Ellie. 'You know,' she said abruptly, 'Sam is really an old-fashioned Greek man, at heart, like his dad. And like mine. He doesn't understand that a woman might want to have a *life*. He thinks a woman should be *this*, or should be *that*, but she can't be both. What he wants is someone who's happy to be a good little wife and mother.' She turned away again, lifting a casual hand in farewell. 'See you.'

Ellie smiled, though an amusing irony was crushing her heart. Maybe that *was* what he'd wanted. At least, that was what he'd wanted with Natalie. He wanted a whole different ball game with his ex-PA.

The blonde sashayed away. Just what was it that made some women so desirable as wives that men would fight over them and move heaven and earth to win them, while others could only ever aspire to being mistresses or live-in housekeepers?

Was it their clothes, their hair, their beauty? Their wit?

Their senses of humour? And if Irene had been right about the baby, what was the tragedy that had driven the newly-weds apart instead of drawing them closer? She could just imagine Sam with a baby.

Suddenly the smell of sunscreen and swimming pool was too festive for Ellie's mood. She dragged herself up and headed inside for the lifts. Why had she agreed to come to a wedding, of all things? Weddings were only enjoyable to people who'd successfully had one, or people who had every chance of pulling one off.

A lift arrived almost immediately. The doors slid open to reveal it chock-a-block with Irene, the butler and all her baggage.

'Oh, Ellie. Good, good,' she said, bustling out. 'I'm glad I've caught you.'

'What's happening?' Ellie said, surprised. 'Are we leaving?'

'No.' Irene explained that Rosemary and Jack simply wanted her to stay over in their villa so they could catch up properly. 'You come if you want to, Ellie.'

'I think I might stay here,' she said, sensing she would be an intruder in the family reunion. 'I'll see you all at the dinner.'

She noticed that Irene didn't try to insist. In fact, she looked quite excited, as if she had some elderly mischief up her sleeve.

Ellie followed the small entourage to the hotel entrance, and watched the butler and Jack's chauffeur bundle Irene and her belongings into the limo. She felt a twinge of misgiving. Wasn't she supposed to keep her eye on Irene?

A tinted window slid down in the rear and Irene put

her head out. 'Mind you have a good time, now,' she warned before she was swept away.

How? Ellie thought with a flat feeling. What was there for a single woman to do, alone at the Palazzo Versace?

CHAPTER TWELVE

THERE were changes in the Principessa. The bed in the master suite looked as if it had been stripped and remade with fresh linen, and Ellie's clothes had been hung there, her toiletries arrayed in the bathroom.

Someone—Irene's butler, she presumed—had been busy.

Should she indulge herself by wallowing in that enormous spa bath before it was time to change for dinner?

While the tub filled she undressed in the steamy atmosphere, then caught up her hair in a clip. Over the gushing water, she heard what could have been a knock. Probably another maid with towels. She turned off the taps and slipped on a luxurious Versace bathrobe. The knock came again, strong and unequivocal. Hang on, she frowned, tying the belt around her as she padded across the marble floors in her bare feet.

She opened the door and her heart jolted in shock and an immediate deep, wild joy there was no repressing. Sam stood there, tall, dark and solidly real, his dark eyes glinting in instant connection with hers.

His lean, powerful form was encased in close-fitting jeans and a black tee shirt that outlined the contours of his chest, and clung to his arms and shoulders. The sheer sexual impact of seeing his bare arms again, bronzed, muscular and so close, trapped the breath in her throat.

His brilliant dark gaze ran over her state of dishabille as though her robe were transparent. Overwhelmingly reminded of the hungry, panting creature he'd reduced her to in those sinewy arms with such ease only a couple of days before, she had to restrain herself from stepping into his embrace.

Then the painful knowledge of the wounds they'd inflicted on each other reasserted itself, and she drew back. The gulf between them loomed deeper than the Tasman.

'Am I allowed in?' There was a dark shadow of beard on his jaw and upper lip. The lines around his mouth were grim, and seemed more deeply etched.

She flushed. 'Of course. Please. Please do come in.' She fell back to allow him past, and her glance fell on the suitcase he was towing.

He parked it inside the door, strolled through into the sitting room and turned to appraise her. Their last goodbye hung heavy on the air, though his eyes were cool and steady.

Her hand strayed to her hair. She saw his glance and knew the nervous gesture had betrayed her. 'I—I wasn't expecting you.'

'I can see that. I'm sorry if I've arrived at an inconvenient time. I don't mean to upset you.' The quiet, dry tones of his voice wrung her insides.

'I'm not upset,' she retorted quickly.

He searched her face with a veiled gaze, then glanced about, through the open door to the bedroom where her undergarments were laid out on the bed. 'Are we alone here?'

She nodded. As though more layers of clothing could hide her vulnerable feelings, she wished fervently she had the underwear *on*. Her hand crept to draw the lapels of her robe together at the neck.

His sharp glance caught the movement, and her feeling of being at a disadvantage deepened. His brows edged up. 'Mind if I ask what you've done with my mother?'

She explained about Irene's departure, adding, 'I'm meeting them all a little later at the groom's dinner.'

The space between them throbbed with her aching awareness of her love for him. He was so straight and tall and handsome, so intelligent and honest and stirringly sexy. If he took her in his arms now…

Indecision flooded her heart. What if she changed her mind? He was here. Might there be a chance he'd come because he still wanted her? If she agreed to be with him on his terms, it would ease this cruel yearning, at least in the short term. The more she thought of it, the more it seemed obvious that he *was* here for her. Who else?

She swallowed. 'Are you—? Do you…? Have—have you come to see Irene?'

He met her eyes coolly. 'Why else but to pay my respects to the bride and groom?' There was no softening of his expression, and her small hope died.

He strolled over to pick up his suitcase, then paused. 'Would it embarrass you if we were to go to this thing together?'

Her heart gave a wild flutter. 'Oh. No. Not at all. Where—where are you staying?'

'I'll take a room in the hotel.'

Regret washed through her for the constraint between

them now. 'Oh, Sam. Is that really necessary? This *is* your apartment. There's plenty of room.'

He looked down, then raised his glinting gaze to her. A grim little smile twisted his mouth. 'It is necessary, believe me.' He strolled to the door with his athletic, long-limbed stride, and every one of his steps tore at her with their finality. He paused with his hand on the doorknob. 'I'll call for you. At seven?'

She nodded, unable to speak because of the tide of disappointment rising to engulf her. The door clicked shut behind him. Nothing could have stated more clearly the impossibility of reneging on a rejection delivered three times to a proud man.

It was too late to change her mind.

She hauled herself miserably back to the bathroom and sank into the bubbles. At least she would have this one last evening with him. She made the stern resolve to conquer her grief and savour every precious last moment of his company.

Her wardrobe hadn't offered much choice, so for the dinner she'd decided to resort to Flirty Noir. In truth, she'd gone off it since that last fateful day at work, remembering how Sam had criticised it as inappropriate. She had an anxious moment wondering if he would remember it, then persuaded herself he wouldn't. What man ever remembered what a woman wore?

Still, with the most desirable man in Australia as her date, it did feel like an occasion worth some trouble. She rose from the bubbles and towelled herself dry. Despite everything, she did feel the tiniest glow of anticipation. Perhaps Sam would thaw out as the evening progressed. Perhaps they could recover some sort of ease with each other.

When she had the dress on, it still had the old magic. Her breasts were as full and perky, their swell just as defined through the embroidered black tulle. It was pleasing, she thought, turning sideways in front of the mirror. Perhaps even a little cheering.

She applied her make-up with special care, and didn't spare the eye-shadow.

She heard Sam arrive, and called out to him to let himself in and help himself to a drink. When she'd brushed her hair into a gleaming river, she squirted a cloud of perfume into the air, walked through it, and on a deep, quivering breath opened the bedroom doors.

Faint masculine scents of soap and sandalwood reached her. Sam was seated on a sofa, one arm resting on his thigh in the classic masculine pose as he frowningly perused some papers. He looked elegant, in a black evening suit and open-necked white shirt. His blue-black hair was still damp, his lean, tanned jaw smooth-shaven. He was so darkly gorgeous her heart surged with longing.

At the sound of the doors he glanced up. His black eyes flared into riveted focus, then made a slow, scorchingly sensual sweep of her from head to toe. For a few thundering moments the tempestuous passions of her last day in his office were potently present.

All at once she felt breathless, overwhelmingly conscious of the simmering desire snapping the air between them like an electric arc. Desire, she recalled now with a sudden lurch, that had been tinged with disdain. She felt an agonised doubt about her appearance. Did he think she looked like a tart now? What if he was embarrassed by her before his entire family? Red-hot humiliation threatened to surface, and she said stiffly, 'Do I—does it look all right? Do you think it's—suitable?'

He rose to his feet. Something flickered in his dark, impenetrable gaze as he looked at her. 'It's perfect,' he said softly. 'You've never looked more beautiful.'

Such unexpected generosity after the jagged emotions of their last goodbye pierced her heart, and her throat thickened.

His brows drew together and he looked keenly at her, and held out his hand for hers. 'Come on, then. Let's go and surprise them.' She made a constrained movement, but their fingers didn't quite touch.

Though thronging with billionaires and celebrities, the dinner was an informal affair.

There was a reception area outside the silk-panelled ballroom where Jack and Rosemary greeted their guests. The large crowd of family and friends were being served drinks and hors d'oeuvres. Some of the guests had wandered inside, where tables had been set around a sumptuous buffet, laden with delicacies. A few of the younger people were already on the dance floor.

When Ellie walked in with Sam, the first person she spotted was his mother. Irene appeared to be in sparkling spirits. She was holding a glass and laughing about something with Jack, while next to them Rosemary stood, deep in conversation with a middle-aged Greek couple. Natalie's parents? Ellie wondered.

Rosemary glanced their way and her eyes slid back in a double take. She leaned over to Jack and murmured something out of the corner of her mouth. Jack's head snapped back, and his bristly grey eyebrows swooped up in astonishment. 'Sam!'

At least ninety heads turned, in varying degrees of surprise and curiosity. After an uncertain pause, in which urgent, meaningful glances were telegraphed from woman to woman across the room, Jack surged forward with his arms outstretched. '*Sam*, my boy.'

It was the signal.

'Sam.'

'*Sam!*'

People came from all corners to welcome Sam. Ellie stood back while he was embraced, exclaimed over and had his back warmly slapped by relatives and friends, past and present. After the initial excited flurry, Sam turned his dark, inscrutable gaze on her, and with every appearance of pride drew her forward.

To her horror Rosemary burbled, 'Oh, yes, Sam, dear. We mustn't forget your lovely new fiancée.'

Mortification shocked through Ellie in a crimson tide. As though oblivious of the bombshell, Sam continued introducing her with suave aplomb. How would she explain? It would look as though she'd told people they were engaged. How did a woman inform a man that his mother was a mischief-maker?

Her frantic inner turmoil of possible explanations was interrupted when she felt someone's gaze burning a hole through her skull. She turned her head. Irene stood to one side, her hands demurely folded, the picture of a sweet elderly lady, but her eyes were dancing, pure wickedness pouring from her every blood vessel. Ellie glared at her, and the old she-devil responded with a gleeful wink.

Natalie's parents had retreated, stiff-faced, into a corner, but Sam strolled to greet them with the smooth courtesy he was master of. Natalie's father rose to the occasion with a formal, dignified, very Greek embrace, while her mother murmured some wary, indecipherable words. Ellie was just exchanging greetings with them herself when Natalie bowled in from the ballroom, Michael in tow. She stopped short, shrieked, 'Sam!' then covered her mouth with her hand.

The entire room held its breath. Incredibly, Natalie pulled herself together, seized her fiancé's hand and walked across to them with queenly dignity.

Ellie had to hand it to her. That soap Natalie was contracted to was way beneath her capabilities. Her award-winning performance enabled the greetings on both sides to go smoothly, Sam shaking his cousin Michael's hand with cool civility, even if it was tight-lipped and a little stiff.

The families then seemed to heave a sigh of relief. People started moving into the dining room and seating themselves. Irene murmured a few words to her son and went to join the oldies, while Sam steered Ellie to a table where some of his well-heeled yachting cronies were ensconced with their wives and girlfriends.

Champagne was poured, but Ellie felt it best to keep a clear head. In her dangerously emotional state, who knew what she might do to disgrace herself? The crowd converged on the buffet, and she and Sam followed, and allowed their plates to be piled with lobster and exotic salads.

Natalie came up behind Ellie at the buffet and whispered, 'You lied.'

'No, I didn't,' Ellie murmured from the corner of her mouth. 'It's a mistake. Honestly.'

'Be careful,' the blonde warned.

'What was that about?' Sam asked, frowning, when Natalie had darted away and they were back in their seats.

'Oh.' Ellie blushed, weighing up how to broach the excruciating subject. She met his questioning gaze, took a deep breath and plunged in. 'Er—she was enquiring about that vicious rumour. You know, the idea your aunt seems to have.' Sam's eyes sharpened on her face in just the way they used to when she was justifying something she'd done at work. 'I don't know how Rosemary came to think it. I'm so embarrassed, Sam. Honestly. I was mortified when I heard her say that.'

'Were you?' He studied her face with a narrow, meditative gaze.

She suffered the most frightful suspicion that Sam thought she'd done it on purpose to plant the suggestion in his head. 'Well, yes,' she said urgently, imploring him with her eyes to understand that *this* time she was speaking nothing but the unvarnished truth. 'I honestly was. I hope you don't think *I* had anything to do with it. It wasn't my doing. I've no idea where it came from, only Rosemary and Jack seemed to get the idea, and now everyone…'

Sam's thick black brows made an ominous merger. 'Is the idea *so* distasteful to you? Would you like me to make a public announcement?'

She stared at him in confusion. 'Well, no, no. It's not distasteful to *me*! I thought it would be to you.'

He sighed, and glanced irritably about at the other guests at their table. 'Look, haven't you had enough of all this yet? Can't we leave?'

They'd barely embarked on their meals. 'What, *now*?' She gave him an incredulous look, then around the brilliant room at all the people. If they left now her last evening with him would be over. He'd go off somewhere, she'd be all alone in her room… 'We can't leave yet,' she whispered.

Was he so desperate to escape? She'd been so thrilled to have him with her. Couldn't he put up with the party if she was with him? A lump rose in her throat. She stared blindly at her poor dismembered lobster for a while, then, in need of a sanctuary to compose herself, excused herself at the first opportunity and made for the bathroom.

Natalie was in there, nervily dragging quick heavy puffs from a cigarette. Judging by the density of the fumes it wasn't the first. The toxic smell made Ellie feel sick and she backed outside again and stood in the corridor, fanning herself with her hand and trying to fill her lungs with oxygen to dispel the clammy feeling.

The door opened and Natalie came out. For a woman about to walk down Paradise Beach with the love of her life, she looked strung out, her dark eyes stormy and intense.

'I don't know how you got him here, 'she said urgently to Ellie, 'but thanks.'

'It wasn't me.' Ellie shrugged. 'I don't know what inspired him to come.'

Natalie looked sceptical. 'Oh, come off it, Ellie.' She glanced about and edged a little closer. 'See if you can get him to talk to Michael.' She grabbed Ellie's arm in a desperate appeal. *'Please.'* To Ellie's horror she burst into tears.

'Oh, God.' Ellie gave a swift look around, then put her arm around Natalie's heaving shoulders and bundled her back into the Ladies. 'Here.' She shoved her a handful of tissues, and patted her back until the storm subsided.

When Natalie had blown her nose and had more of a grip, Ellie went to the door and waved it back and forth to help the fumes diminish. Thank heavens the bathroom had a super-efficient exhaust system.

'Weddings are supposed to be stressful,' Ellie said sympathetically. 'Is there anything I can do to help?'

'It's all going wrong,' Natalie squawked in her high-pitched wail. '*Again.*'

The floodgates reopened. Ellie thoughtfully closed the door and clicked the lock.

The bride dabbed at her nose with a tissue. 'Jen was supposed to be the Matron of Honour and Mad was the bridesmaid. Mad's gone off in a huff, Jen's gone home sick and Michael and I have had a fight. And I thought it was bad the *first* time.'

She gave Ellie an anguished glance through her wet mascara, and Ellie felt a wave of compassion. 'We've got all these people coming from all over.' She made vague sweeping motions. 'Athens, Italy, LA.' She put her face in her hands and rocked back and forwards on her heels. 'It was m-meant to be so beautiful. Now there won't even be a wedding party. There'll hardly be a *wedding.*'

'Don't you have a cousin or someone who can stand in for the bridesmaid?'

'Too fat,' she wept. 'All too fat.' Her nose started to run and Ellie swiftly thrust her more tissues.

Ellie sighed, and sat down on the nearest toilet seat. 'Does it matter so much if your bridesmaid is a little overweight?'

'It's the dress,' Natalie replied when the flow had stemmed a little. 'Mad's really skinny. The theme is Pisces, because that's both mine and Michael's star sign, so it has to be tight.' She glanced earnestly at Ellie. 'You know, fish scales.' Her voice veered up into her upper register. 'And now Michael will think that's my fault too.'

'The fish scales?'

'That I can't even get anyone to be my bridesmaid.' The tears started again. 'That's how it'll *look*.'

'Unless you find someone,' Ellie suggested. 'What about Michael's family?'

'They hate me. They *all* hate me. They all blame me for Sam and Michael being enemies now and…' She buried her face in her hands and sobbed. After a minute she lifted her head. Her reddened eyes slewed over Ellie and brightened a little. 'You could probably wear it if it weren't for your bust. I could get someone to work on it.'

'Oh,' Ellie said, alarmed. 'I don't think so. I don't think Sam would—'

'Sam, Sam. Always *Sam*.' As if driven stark raving mad, Natalie grabbed a couple of fistfuls of her blonde hair and made savage wrenching motions. Ellie noticed, though, that she was quite careful not to cause it any lasting disruptions. 'As soon as Sam appears everyone forgets Michael even exists. It's just Sam, Sam, Sam. He ruined my first wedding, and now he's ruining this one.'

'But you wanted him to come,' Ellie pointed out gently.

She rolled her eyes. 'Are you insane? Do you ever listen? Not for *me*. For Michael. Please, Ellie, *tell* me, will you look at the dress?'

Ellie heaved a sigh and got up. 'All right. I'll look at it. But I'd have to try it on. You can show me later.' She added firmly, 'No promises, now.'

Natalie was so pathetically grateful, Ellie felt remorse for her reluctance. But fish scales? Did a woman want to be seen by the love of her life, for what was probably the last time ever, dressed as a fish? Inevitably, her eyes misted over. She had hoped they could leave each other at the end with dignity, at least.

Outside in the corridor she was surprised to see Michael, leaning against the wall with his arms folded across his chest, scowling. He looked up anxiously, and she smiled and reassured him that Natalie was just coming. The brief exchange was interrupted by Sam, who strode up to them wearing the stern, inscrutable expression that terrified people at the bank. He directed a cold glance at his cousin, then examined her closely and muttered, 'Are you all right?'

She looked curiously from him to Michael. 'Fine. I've just been talking to Natalie. I haven't been gone that long, have I?' She gave him a searching glance. 'Were you worried?'

'Why would I be worried, Eleanor?' He turned his back on his cousin, took her arm and smoothly hustled her away from the infected zone. 'I don't think you should allow yourself to get too friendly with people like that.'

'Oh, Sam. They aren't so bad. I know Natalie's your ex, and no one likes their ex, but...' She met his chilly glance and bit her lip. 'Sorry.'

In fact, an idea had occurred to her inside that toilet cubicle while Natalie was going through meltdown. For all her drama, there was something quite vulnerable and endearing about the shaggy-haired blonde. Was this why Sam had fallen in love with her? Why he'd wanted to *marry* her?

A horrifying possibility began to unfurl its poisonous tentacles. She'd shied away from imagining him with Natalie because it cut her like hot knives. But now she couldn't stop imagining it. What if he was still in love with her? Was this the answer?

She supposed bitterly that he needed a woman who could bring out his protective instincts. Underneath all that smooth, sophisticated intelligence, he was still just a macho male animal. A together woman like herself, renowned for her independence and efficiency, could never have filled the bill.

'What's wrong?' Sam halted her to scrutinise her face. 'You're looking a bit peaky. I've noticed you've hardly eaten anything yet. I think you should finish your dinner, then go back upstairs and lie down.'

'Oh, thanks.' She knew he was raw over her not agreeing to be his mistress, but did he have to be so unflattering? It was as though he couldn't wait now to unload her. She decided to put an end to her misery, and know the worst, once and for all. 'As a matter of fact,' she said casually, 'I was just thinking…I can see why you fell in love with Natalie.'

His brows shot up, then he gazed at her for a long time, a frown gathering in his brilliant black eyes. 'Who said I was in love with her?'

'Well, you're so angry with her.'

Her heart was pumping like a marathon runner's, but she forced herself to continue on lightly, though her hands were curled into tight balls. 'I thought it must be because it's so painful for you to see her marrying someone else.'

'I'm delighted to see her marrying someone else,' he bit out. 'Only not *that* bastard.'

'Oh. Good.'

He wasn't very convincing. She realised the ice she was on was wafer-thin, but, having gone this far, she drew another tentative breath and met his gaze squarely, hoping her desperation and panic didn't swirl in her eyes. 'But you did marry her, Sam. You must have loved her at one stage.'

He stared at her for seconds, his mouth grim, his eyes

glinting in speculation, then took her arm firmly and urged her towards their table. 'It's not Natalie I'm angry with, it's myself. This is not the time and place to discuss it. The sooner we finish our meals, the sooner we can escape.'

He held her chair for her and resumed his own. It was hard to think of eating when the full heart-shattering impact of her insignificance in Sam's scheme of things had only just dawned. Strangely, apart from Irene, who wasn't likely to admit it anyway, she seemed to be the only person in Sam's life who'd never considered, until this weekend, that he might still be in love with his ex. She recalled the first time she'd ever seen Natalie at the office, and the things the peroxide blonde had been screeching.

The signs had been there all along. How could she have missed them?

Thankfully the remains of her meal had been taken away, and she was able to get off lightly with some thin vegetable soup Sam found for her at the buffet. During the lull, a dauntingly groomed billionaire's wife across the table from them leaned forward and said, 'Excuse me, Eleanor…'

'Ellie, please.'

The woman smiled, then indicated Ellie's dress. 'Do you mind if I ask? Is your dress a Dinnigan?'

'Yes.'

'Not Flirty Noir, by any chance?'

She nodded, and the woman sighed, 'How I envy you.'

Even while trawling the depths of despair, there were a few pleasures left to a woman. Sam would probably have forgotten the foul aspersions he'd cast on her dress and her spirited defence of it. Nevertheless, she couldn't resist a subtle sideways glance at him to see if he'd heard.

Amazingly, his eyes meshed instantly with hers, brimming with amused comprehension.

Smiling, he set down his glass. 'Excuse me,' he said to their neighbours. 'I have to dance with my fiancée.'

His use of the word cut deep, but she didn't protest. She let him lead her to the dance floor and draw her into his arms. Other dancers were jerking about as single, separate entities, but Sam, being the old-fashioned guy he was, liked to hold a woman close. His long thighs brushed hers, and she inhaled the familiar, masculine scent of him and gave herself up to the impossible torture of being held against the man she loved.

As if to add to her bitter-sweet joy, the band eased into a poignant old love song. Sam steered her through the open doors onto a small circular terrace that had been designed to vaguely resemble a small Venetian temple, and was open to the starry sky. The warm, scented Queensland night, meant for lovers, tormented her senses unbearably.

'Alone at last,' Sam said with a shuddering sigh. His hand slipped under her hair and stroked down her spine, moulding her close to his big, hard body. 'Do you know what torture this is for me?' he murmured, brushing her temple with his jaw. 'Do you have any idea what a living hell I'm in tonight?'

Hot needles of pain lanced her heart. She closed her eyes. 'I think I do.'

There was a hoarseness in his voice, as if he spoke from the very depths of his being. 'Imagine, Eleanor… Imagine knowing you could have been happy with the one person you belong to, who should belong to you, but, like a fool, you ruined all your chances.'

Misery choked her throat. 'I *can* imagine.' The song spilling from the ballroom swelled into its plaintive refrain of tragedy and heartbreak.

His deep voice grew laboured and emotional. 'If you knew…what it means to me to—smell the fragrance of your hair, to feel your soft breasts against my chest…'

She looked up blindly at him. '*My* hair? But I thought you… You know… Natalie.'

'Natalie?' Sam stood stock-still and stared at her, gripping her shoulders. Then he said, very softly and distinctly, 'I married Natalie because she was pregnant. For no other reason. It was my mistake. Then two months after the wedding she was offered the part she longed for in that soap. She chose to get rid of our baby rather than lose her big break.' As he gazed at her his stern, sensuous mouth twisted. 'And most of it was my fault.'

Shock, and the rock-bottom despair so eloquently expressed in Sam's wry unemotional tone, welled in Ellie's heart to join all her own grief and pain and disappointment, and flooded through her in a huge rolling wave. The tears rushed to her eyes and spilled over before she could stop them.

'Don't, *don't*.' Sam's voice was suddenly strained and urgent. He folded her in his arms and pressed her tenderly to him as if she were some piece of rare fragile china, stroking her hair. She could feel the tense emotion racking his big lean body as he murmured passionate endearments. 'Please, please Ellie, my sweetheart. Don't cry.'

For a while she couldn't even speak to deny the charge, and she was grateful when he hustled her back through the hotel, past the glimmering lagoon and up to the Principessa.

The lamps were on, warming the sitting room with their glow. Ellie mopped abjectly at her eyes with a handful of tissues. 'I'm so sorry, Sam,' she said, turning away from him to spare him the ghastly sight. 'I can't imagine what got into me. I'm not usually a weeper. It must have been the—the lobster, or...' She caught sight of her face in a mirror and saw to her horror that her mascara had started to drip.

Sam turned her around to face him and wiped under her eyes with his handkerchief. Sighing, he said, 'I thought—*hoped*—you might be feeling sad about breaking my heart.'

She looked to see if he was joking, but his eyes were darkly serious, intent on her face, the lines around his chiselled mouth taut. She gasped and her wet eyelids fluttered in shock. 'Your—your *heart*, Sam.'

He said hoarsely, 'We both know I'm not good at saying the right words to you, Eleanor. God knows, I've made mistakes. But I have to try one more time to...to somehow *show* you...what's in my heart, what's been in my heart since the first time I saw you on that balcony.' He kept gesturing very emotionally. 'I know I-I've hurt you. I upset your life, plunging you into an affair like a selfish bloody fool. Expecting you to forgive me when...' His hand made a passionate reefing motion through his hair. 'I thought you seemed to—I *hoped* you felt the same way.' He half turned away and said wryly, 'But then I understood it was your career you loved. I felt...'

Her eyes started to swim. 'Oh, no, Sam. No.'

He was gazing at her with the most earnest, and fiercely tender expression in his gorgeous dark eyes. 'You see, my darling Eleanor...'

All at once she had the most thrilling sensation that, against all the odds, the grand and magical moment she'd dreamed of in her wildest fantasies might have arrived. She touched his lean, tanned hand, and, to encourage him, said, 'Ellie, please, Sam.'

His eyebrows lifted and he broke into a laugh. 'Thank God, at last. *Ellie*.'

On his tongue her name sounded so romantic, almost haunting in fact, it was music to her ears.

He took her hands in his firm, warm grip, and grew serious again. 'You need to understand something. It's taken me a while to realise all this myself.' He let go of her hands and gestured his remorse. 'Looking back now, I have to accept most of the responsibility for the disaster with Natalie. When she discovered she was pregnant, I was horrified, to say the least, but I gritted my teeth and pressured her into marriage.' His expression grew very grave. 'In our families, you know, we don't deny our children. I suppose I knew vaguely how serious she was about being an actress, but I was intolerant.' He evaded her eyes and stared down at the floor, shaking his head. 'And as you can imagine, we didn't get on from the start.' He glanced up at her, a wry smile lighting his dark eyes. '*You* should have been there. You could have poured your magic oil. Every day was World War Three.'

Ellie could well imagine it. Volatile Natalie, with an icy cool, controlled Sam. Not a marriage made in heaven.

'Then,' he continued with an apologetic grimace, 'I'm afraid I made it clear that I expected her to give up acting when the child was born, and for several years after. In that industry, as she was always insisting, the opportunities have to be seized when they arise. I suppose she felt trapped.' He sprang up and started to pace restlessly about the room. 'I can never, ever excuse what she did. But lately I can't help wondering if things would have been different if we hadn't married. She'd probably have been happy to be a single working mum, given the chance. But I didn't really give her the chance.' He halted his pacing and stood with his face averted from her, his breathing heavy and painful, his powerful shoulders rigid. With a tortured sideways glance at her he said, very quietly, 'I was gutted when I found out, Ellie. I hadn't realised how much I'd looked forward to it.' He lifted his hand in a sharp, constrained gesture. 'The child.'

A hot, fierce surge of compassion flooded Ellie's heart, and she jumped up from the sofa. 'Oh, Sam,' she said, rushing across to throw her arms around him. 'You did what you thought was right.'

He held her against his chest, then put her a little away from him to frown intently down at her. 'I did, of course, but do you see? When you came home with me that last night I so wanted you to stay, Ellie. But I was afraid that if I put pressure on *you* to—to change your direction so drastically when you love your life the way it is, you would run like the wind.' The rueful grimace he gave tore her heart. 'But then you did, anyway.'

'Oh.' She shook her head in dismayed remorse. 'But I thought… You know, you said you only wanted me for a week, or—or a year…' Her voice started to wobble with the memory of the devastation it had caused her, and Sam drew her back into his strong arms and dragged her against him.

'Shh, shh,' he said, stroking her hair and tenderly kissing her neck. 'Don't cry any more, my love.' Pressed with such passionate tenderness against his warm chest, she felt his deep voice resonate through her. 'I was such a fool. I was so afraid of losing you, I said all the wrong things.'

She drew back to smile at him through the mist. 'What was that you called me? Your *love*?'

'Well, you are my love!' He looked wonderingly at her, and his voice deepened with raw emotion. 'You must know I love you, Ellie. I fell in love with you on that very first night, and then like a fool I let you disappear. But I couldn't forget you. I was crazy to find you. For God's sake, I bought a bloody *bank* to find you! You're the love of my life!'

Fireworks and starbursts were exploding in her heart, but Sam held her from him, a sudden uncertainty dawning in his eyes. 'And you? Do *you*…?'

She said softly, 'I do, Sam. I do love you. I adore you.'

With his dark velvet eyes glowing, he said very solemnly, 'So then, Ellie O'Dea, will you marry me?'

She hesitated. Her heart began to quake with a suffocating fear that caught her entire body in a cold, vicious clench. In a voice toneless with dread she said, 'Sam, there is something I need to tell you.'

He frowned. The shining light in his eyes was doused.

'It's possible—' She braced herself with a deep trembling breath. A blush rose inside her and flooded her all the way to her roots, but for all her faults she had her own code of honour. She met Sam's anxious, uncertain gaze, and forced her chin and voice to stay steady. 'It's quite possible, Sam, that although I would *love* to have your children, it may be difficult for me to conceive. This being the case, you might want to reconsider the idea of marriage to me.'

He let out a long breath and his eyes lit with the most fervent relief. 'Oh, Ellie. My darling Ellie. As if that could make me not want to marry you.' He gazed tenderly at her, his eyes ablaze with concern. 'There are alternatives, you know. There're…clinics…adoption—' He waved his hands expressively and said very firmly, 'There are options. Let's talk about all that later. You still haven't answered my question.' He captured her hands again in his warm, sure grip. 'Well, my love? Will you?'

An exquisite joy filled her heart to overflowing. 'Yes, Sam. Oh, yes.'

CHAPTER THIRTEEN

Beds at the Palazzo Versace were exceptionally springy and comfortable. Just supposing a person had time to sleep and was in need of a pillow, there were seven varieties to choose from, each softer and more cushioning than the last.

After her night of sheer heavenly bliss with the most tender and virile lover a woman could ever expect to know, Ellie faced the dawn feeling energised right through to her soul, with her every muscle supple and relaxed.

She felt dreamily ready to embrace the day and take charge of her commitments. The first was the little matter of Natalie's and Michael's disagreement.

When she informed Sam of Natalie's wedding being in doubt, his first response was to yawn. 'Oh, for God's sake. Seriously?'

'I'm afraid so,' she said, lounging beside him in the sumptuous bed, enjoying the warmth and support of his gorgeous bronzed chest. 'Poor Natalie. After everyone's gone to so much trouble. What a shame if, at the end of all this, she's still Natalie Stilakos.'

She slanted a glance up at him, and noted, with some satisfaction, horror dawning on his stubbly morning face.

'Bloody hell,' he exclaimed with heartfelt fervour. 'What's it all about, anyway?'

She snuggled up to him. 'Oh, I don't know. Something about Michael wanting someone to forgive him for something he's done in the past. He's all depressed about it. You know how these things can fester.'

There was a heavy impenetrable silence, then he bit out softly, 'Some things are unforgivable.'

'Yes.' She sighed. 'I know.'

After a small lapse he said, 'What do you know?'

'I agree with you. Some things can't be forgiven.'

He enquired with what sounded like difficulty, 'Are you referring to the way I hurt you—the things that happened about your job? Or the other things. The things I told you about with Natalie.'

She arched her brows and said airily, 'No, no, no. I was merely making the point that while *things* can't always be forgiven, people can. Especially when you're happy.'

He smiled down at her for a moment, and whispered, 'I'm happy.' Then the smile grew sinful and his eyes lascivious, and he planted a greedy kiss on her bare shoulder.

Eventually she was free to deal with Natalie and the dress, which turned out to be a magnificently beaded sheath, with a fish tail to the ground, shimmering with sequins in blue, silver and pinky mauve. She managed to squeeze into most of it, although, as Natalie had predicted, the bust was a little in need of letting out. Fortunately her parents could summon seamstresses from afar at will, and did so without hesitation.

While the fitting was going on, she happened to glance out of Natalie's window, and with a pleased little glow saw Sam, strolling towards a table beside the lagoon, deep in conversation with his cousin. Michael seemed to be doing lots of fast talking, while Sam had that stern, listening demeanour she'd experienced on a few occasions herself.

After the fitting, and satisfied she wouldn't look any worse than the average rainbow trout, she allowed Natalie to sweep her off to the Palazzo beauty parlour, where she was pampered, manicured, waxed, painted and perfumed like a sultan's courtesan. Inspired by the fish frock, she opted for a return to her pale strawberry hair, ensuring it was more on the blonde side this time than the pink. She submitted to it all with enjoyment, thinking with a deep, joyous excitement of the magic night to come.

All the magic nights. Sam would appreciate it as thoroughly as any sultan.

Natalie's wedding was a romantic, twilit event. A Persian carpet, scattered with frangipani and flanked by hundreds of lights, was laid on the sand for the wedding party. An enormous marquee spread with more exotic carpets and big soft cushions, was provided for the guests to lounge upon like Arabian potentates. Dozens of security guards had been employed to hold back the sea of media cameras.

The bride looked beautiful in a diamond-and-pearl encrusted dress, with a veil and train worth millions, that was reminiscent of hanging seaweed. Michael wore a long white embroidered shirt-frock affair over his trousers. Ellie couldn't see that it was very fishy, but it was dignified, at least.

Ellie did her part gravely, walking barefoot behind Natalie along the Persian, in her beautiful fish frock and mermaid's hair. Though most people's attention was on the bride and groom, whenever Ellie looked at Sam, he was smiling at her.

When it came time to kiss the bride, Sam strode over to swing Ellie off the ground and kiss her, then a beaming Irene dashed over to kiss and violently hug her as well. While the wedding barbecues and bonfires were lit, and people plunged into the party, Sam held Ellie's hand and walked with her along the beach. And while the festivities raged on into the night, Sam took her up to the Principessa and made passionate love with her till dawn.

'Is Ellie always this cool, calm and collected, Sam?' a friend queried the next day, when Ellie and Sam were lazing by the lagoon, wrapped in blissful contemplation of each other.

'Not always,' Sam said, pausing in taking a sip from Ellie's straw to gaze meditatively at her. ' I think I may have seen her get a little frayed around the edges, once or twice.'

Their smiling eyes met.

EPILOGUE

Samos, Greece.

Dear Beth,

So lovely to hear your fabulous news. I know you'll be thrilled to hear that Sam and I have some too, at long, long last! Our darling Lilli-pilli was born last Thursday, almost two years to the day of starting the programme. So far she looks to have all Sam's gorgeous colouring, although it's hard to say how her eyes will go. (Though Irene says she knows.) Right now they're as blue as sapphires, like the sea around this wondrous isle.

We won't be home till autumn, so we want you here with us soon to join the family celebrations. Tickets are on their way.

Love…Ellie

MILLS & BOON®

MEDICAL™

Proudly presents

Brides of Penhally Bay

A pulse-raising collection of emotional, tempting romances and heart-warming stories by bestselling Mills & Boon Medical™ authors.

January 2008
The Italian's New-Year Marriage Wish
by Sarah Morgan

Enjoy some much-needed winter warmth with gorgeous Italian doctor Marcus Avanti.

February 2008
The Doctor's Bride By Sunrise
by Josie Metcalfe

Then join Adam and Maggie on a 24-hour rescue mission where romance begins to blossom as the sun starts to set.

March 2008
The Surgeon's Fatherhood Surprise
by Jennifer Taylor

Single dad Jack Tremayne finds a mother for his little boy – and a bride for himself.

Let us whisk you away to an idyllic Cornish town – a place where hearts are made whole

COLLECT ALL 12 BOOKS!

MILLS & BOON®
MEDICAL™
proudly presents

Brides of Penhally Bay

Featuring Dr Nick Tremayne

*A pulse-raising collection of emotional, tempting romances and
heart-warming stories – devoted doctors, single fathers,
Mediterranean heroes, a Sheikh and his guarded heart,
royal scandals and miracle babies…*

THE ITALIAN'S NEW YEAR MARRIAGE WISH
Sarah Morgan

Brides of Penhally Bay

MEDICAL

Book Two

THE ITALIAN'S NEW YEAR MARRIAGE WISH

by Sarah Morgan

On sale 5th January 2008

A COLLECTION TO TREASURE FOREVER!
One book available every month

MILLS & BOON

100 YEARS

of pure reading pleasure

100 Reasons to Celebrate

2008 is a very special year as we celebrate Mills and Boon's Centenary.

Each month throughout the year there will be something new and exciting to mark the centenary, so watch for your favourite authors, captivating new stories, special limited edition collections…and more!

www.millsandboon.co.uk